Complex Analysis: a Self-Study Guide

by Terrence P. Murphy

ISBN No: **978-0-9961671-5-4**

Library of Congress Control Number: **2022904752**

Publisher:
Paramount Ridge Press
Bellevue, WA 98008
terry@riemann1859.com

The formatting/layout of this book was produced using MiKTEX (with the LuaTEX compiler), which is a software front-end for the TEX / LATEX typesetting and document preparation system.

The fonts used in this book are:

Serif font (primary document font): **TeX Gyre Termes**
Math font: **TeX Gyre Termes Math**
Sans Serif font: **Latin Modern Sans**
All fonts: © Bogusław Jackowski and Janusz M. Nowacki
Licensed under version 1.0 of the GUST Font License: http://www.gust.org.pl/projects/e-foundry/licenses

Front cover by Terrence P. Murphy
Book design by Terrence P. Murphy

Contents

Preface   **ix**

Notation   **xi**

1   The Complex Plane   **1**
   1.1   Points in The Complex Plane   1
   1.2   Absolute Value   2
   1.3   Complex Conjugate   2
   1.4   Basic Operations on Complex Numbers   3
   1.5   Triangle Inequality   3
   1.6   The Exponential Function   4
   1.7   Polar Representation   6
   1.8   The Complex Logarithm   7
   1.9   Complex Exponentials   8
   1.10 The Extended Complex Plane   9
   1.11 Supplemental Material   10
       1.11.1   Exercises   10
       1.11.2   Cauchy–Schwarz Inequality   11

2   Topology of the Complex Plane   **13**
   2.1   Sets – Basic Definitions and the Language of Sets   13
       2.1.1   Definition of Sets   13
       2.1.2   Functions/Mapping of Sets   14
       2.1.3   The Cardinality of Sets   14
       2.1.4   The Union and Intersection of Sets   14
       2.1.5   Classification of Points in a Set   15
       2.1.6   Classification of Sets – Open and Closed Sets   15
       2.1.7   Open and Closed Disks   16
   2.2   Countable Sets   16
       2.2.1   Countable Sets - Some Simple Properties   16
       2.2.2   Countable Union of Countable Sets is Countable   17
   2.3   Sets Using Rational Numbers   19
   2.4   Bounded Sets and the Bolzano-Weierstrass Theorem   20
   2.5   Compact Sets   21
       2.5.1   Closed and Bounded   21
       2.5.2   Convergent Subsequence   22
       2.5.3   Open Covering and the Heine-Borel Theorem   22

	2.5.4	Nested Compact Sets	23
2.6		Supplemental Material	24

3 **Paths, Connected Sets and Polygons** **25**

3.1		Paths and Contours	25
	3.1.1	Reverse Path	26
	3.1.2	Reparameterization	26
	3.1.3	Contour	27
3.2		Connected Sets	27
3.3		Regions and Domains	28
3.4		Polygons	29
3.5		Supplemental Material	33

4 **Derivatives and the Cauchy-Riemann Equations** **35**

4.1		Some Preliminary Definitions	35
	4.1.1	Continuity	35
	4.1.2	Continuity on a Boundary	35
	4.1.3	Uniform Continuity	36
	4.1.4	Differentiable / Derivative	36
	4.1.5	Holomorphic Functions	37
4.2		Component Parts of Complex Functions	37
4.3		Basics of Complex Derivatives	38
4.4		The Cauchy-Riemann Equations	40
4.5		Harmonic Functions	43
4.6		Holomorphy of the Complex Logarithm	44
4.7		Supplemental Material	45
	4.7.1	Exercises	45
	4.7.2	Continuous on Compact Set	46

5 **Complex Integration** **47**

5.1		Introduction	47
5.2		The Contour Integral	48
	5.2.1	The Complex-Valued Riemann Sum	48
	5.2.2	The Parameterization Function	48
	5.2.3	The Contour Integral - Final Form	49
	5.2.4	Parts of the Contour Integral	49
5.3		Properties of the Contour Integral	50
	5.3.1	The Basic Rules	50
	5.3.2	Change of Parameterization	51
	5.3.3	Length of the Path	51
	5.3.4	The Inequality and Estimation Lemmas	52
5.4		Fundamental Theorem of Calculus for Contour Integrals	53
5.5		Supplemental Material	56
	5.5.1	Exercises	56

| | 5.5.2 | Examples . . . . | 56 |
| | 5.5.3 | Another Look at the Complex Logarithm . . . . | 58 |

6 Infinite Sequences, Series and Products   **61**
6.1	Convergent Sequences	61
	6.1.1	Convergent Sequences – The Cauchy Criterion	61
6.2	Infinite Sums	63
	6.2.1	Infinite Sums – The Cauchy Criterion	63
6.3	Infinite Products	64
	6.3.1	Infinite Products – Three Simple Lemmas	65
	6.3.2	Infinite Products – The Cauchy Criterion	66
	6.3.3	Infinite Products – Convergence and the Logarithm . . .	67
6.4	Absolute Convergence	67
6.5	Function Series – Infinite Series of Functions	70
6.6	The Geometric Series	72
6.7	Supplemental Material	73
	6.7.1	The Zeta Function	73
	6.7.2	Exercises	75
	6.7.3	More on Cauchy Sequences	75

7 Cauchy's Integral Theorem   **77**
7.1	Cauchy's Integral Theorem for Triangles	77
7.2	Cauchy's Integral Theorem for Rectangles	80
7.3	Cauchy's Integral Theorem for Polygons	81
7.4	Cauchy's Integral Theorem for Closed Contours	81
7.5	Principle of Deformation of Paths	83
7.6	Supplemental Material	85

8 Cauchy's Integral Formula   **87**
8.1	Cauchy's Integral Formula	87
8.2	Cauchy's Integral Formula for Derivatives	89
8.3	Supplemental Material	93
	8.3.1	Cauchy's Inequality and Liouville's Theorem	93
	8.3.2	The Maximum (and Minimum) Modulus Principle	94
	8.3.3	Restating Cauchy's Integral Theorem	96

9 Power Series   **97**
9.1	Power Series	97
9.2	Holomorphic Functions and Power Series	102
9.3	Supplemental Material	104
	9.3.1	Exercises	104
	9.3.2	Boundary of Radius of Convergence	104

10 Zeros and the Identity Theorem   **105**
| 10.1 | Zeros of Analytic Functions . . . . | 105 |

10.2   Identity Theorem 107
10.3   Analytic Continuance 108
    10.3.1   Example – Intersecting Sets 108
    10.3.2   Example – Subset 109
    10.3.3   The Exponential and Trigonometric Functions 110
10.4   Supplemental Material 111
    10.4.1   Exercises 111

11   Laurent Series   **113**
11.1   Laurent Series 113
    11.1.1   The Foundational Idea 113
    11.1.2   Deriving the Laurent Series 114
11.2   Supplemental Material 118
    11.2.1   Exercises 118

12   Isolated Singularities   **119**
12.1   The Punctured Disk 119
12.2   Classification of Isolated Singularities 119
    12.2.1   Removable Singularities 120
    12.2.2   Poles 122
    12.2.3   Essential Singularities 124
12.3   Analytic Functions at Infinity 125
12.4   Supplemental Material 126
    12.4.1   Exercises 126

13   The Residue Calculus   **127**
13.1   Winding Number 127
13.2   The Residue Theorem - Simple Closed Contour 130
13.3   The Residue Theorem - Any Closed Contour 132
13.4   Calculating Residues 133
13.5   Using Residues to Evaluate Real Integrals 135
    13.5.1   Cauchy Principal Value 135
    13.5.2   A Bounding Condition Allowing Use of the Residue Theorem . . . 137
    13.5.3   A Singularity on the Real Axis 138
13.6   Supplemental Material 140
    13.6.1   Exercises 140

14   The Argument Principle   **141**
14.1   The Logarithmic Derivative 141
14.2   The Argument Principle 142

A   Exercise Answers   **145**
A.1   Chapter 1 - Answers to Exercises 1.1 145
A.2   Chapter 4 - Answers to Exercises 4.1 146
A.3   Chapter 5 - Answers to Exercises 5.1 148

A.4   Chapter 6 - Answers to Exercises 6.1 148
A.5   Chapter 9 - Answers to Exercises 9.1 151
A.6   Chapter 10 - Answers to Exercises 10.1   152
A.7   Chapter 11 - Answers to Exercises 11.1   153
A.8   Chapter 12 - Answers to Exercises 12.1   154
A.9   Chapter 13 - Answers to Exercises 13.1   154

Notes   **157**

Bibliography   **159**

Index   **161**

Preface

You're thinking: "Just what we need. Yet another college textbook on complex analysis." Right? Fortunately, this is *not* a college textbook.

With a college textbook and a college course, you are expected to develop the skills to independently prove a medium-difficult complex analysis theorem. Our goal here is more modest. After studying this book, you should have the skills to read, follow, and understand *someone else's proof* of a complex analysis theorem.

Motivation for This Book

My first published book is *A Study of Bernhard Riemann's 1859 Paper* [10]. Riemann's 8-page paper makes several important advances in mathematics and, famously, speculates (the "Riemann Hypothesis") about the location of the zeros of the Zeta function. My Riemann book is intended to bring an understanding of Riemann's paper to a wider audience by bridging the gap between John Derbyshire's excellent but less technical book, *Prime Obsession* [5] and Harold Edwards's also excellent but highly technical book, *Riemann's Zeta Function* [7].

To advance your knowledge substantially beyond Derbyshire's book, you must have a good understanding of the field of complex analysis (call it knowledge at the "hobbyist" level). Several people told me they want to get to the "hobbyist" level so they can better understand my Riemann book. However, when they look at Ahlfors and other well-known (400+ page) textbooks on complex analysis, it feels like a mountain just a little too high to climb. This book is intended to help you advance to the "hobbyist" level.

Who is This Book For?

Let's first assume that you have an interest in the Riemann Hypothesis and would like to read my Riemann book. This book may be suitable for you if:

- It's been a while since you took a college-level course in complex analysis. You need a refresher course, but you don't want to slog through one of the 400+ page textbooks.
- You have no prior exposure to complex analysis, but you meet the requirements below in "background knowledge assumed". With no skimming and careful study, you should rise to the "hobbyist" level.

Another possibility. You are currently a student and have just finished a course in real analysis. Your course in complex analysis is coming up soon. You really want to ace the course and are looking for a leg up. If you invest some time studying this book (some skimming allowed), your efforts will be rewarded.

Background Knowledge Assumed

We assume you have a good understanding of the following topics:

- Sets, including point sets in two-dimensional spaces and their Euclidean distances.
- Differential and integral calculus, including Riemann sums.
- Functions of a real variable, including key properties of the elementary functions (that is, the exponential, logarithm and trigonometric functions).
- Continuous functions (continuity and limits); sequences and series.

The above list essentially describes knowledge obtained from a course in real analysis or advanced calculus. More than anything, you must be familiar with epsilon-delta proofs.

What is in This Book?

In this book, we develop much of the central theory of complex analysis, using standard/classic proofs. In our version of those proofs, we provide enough detail so the reader can follow the proofs (without outside help) from beginning to end. At the end of each chapter, we demonstrate what was learned, either with proofs of supplemental theorems or with exercises for the reader. We provide answers to all exercises in the book Appendix.

Chapters 1 through 6 are the warm-up, with important definitions and with a review of familiar concepts (and an extension of those concepts to the complex plane). Chapters 7 through 13 are the heart of the book, where we study the central theorems of complex function theory, from Cauchy's Integral Theorem through the Residue Theorem. We end with a chapter on the Argument Principle, which Riemann used to determine the number of zeros of the Zeta function inside a region of height T in the critical strip.

Spot any Errors?

If you find any typographical or other errors in this book, we would very much appreciate hearing from you. Drop a note to terry@riemann1859.com. Other feedback (e.g., some proof/concept is not very well explained) is also appreciated. Our plan is to list *errata* at www.riemann1859.com.

Notation

The standard meaning of typical symbols and functions is assumed and not separately defined. The table below lists various notations used in this book.

$\mathbb{N}$	The set of positive integers: $1, 2, 3, \ldots$
$\mathbb{N}_{\geq 0}$	The set of non-negative integers: $0, 1, 2, 3, \ldots$
$\mathbb{Z}$	The set of all integers: $\ldots, -3, -2, -1, 0, 1, 2, 3, \ldots$
$\mathbb{R}$	The set of real numbers.
$\mathbb{Q}$	The set of rational numbers.
$\mathbb{C}$	The set of complex numbers (the complex plane).
$\mathbb{C}^*$	The extended complex plane $\mathbb{C} \cup \{\infty\}$ (Definition 1.5).
$Re(z)$	The real part of the complex number z.
$Im(z)$	The imaginary part of the complex number z.
$[x]$	The integral part of the real number x (largest integer no larger than x).
$\{x\}$	The fractional part of the real number x (so that $\{x\} = x - [x]$).
$\log(z)$	The natural logarithm $\log_e(z) = \ln(z)$.
$\text{Arg}(z)$	The principal value of $\arg(z)$ (Definition 1.2).
$\text{Log}(z)$	The principal value of $\log(z)$ (Definition 1.3).
$A \backslash B$	The set includes all points in A minus all points in B.
$\partial \Omega$	The boundary of the set Ω.
Ω°	The interior of the set Ω.
$z \in \Omega$	The point z is an element of the set Ω.
$\Lambda \subset \Omega$	The set Λ is a subset of (or possibly equal to) the set Ω.
$\mathbf{C}_r(z)$	The circle of radius r centered at z.
$\mathbf{D}_r(z)$	The open disk of radius r centered at z.
$\overline{\mathbf{D}}_r(z)$	The closed disk of radius r centered at z.
$\mathbf{D}_r^\circ(z)$	The *punctured disk* of radius r centered at z, excluding the point z.
$\mathbf{W}(\boldsymbol{\gamma}, z)$	The *winding number* of the contour $\boldsymbol{\gamma}$ around z (Definition 13.1).
$\mathbf{Res}\,(f(z), w)$	The *residue* of the function $f(z)$ at w (Definition 13.2).
$L(\gamma)$	The length of the path (or contour) γ (Definition 5.1).
LHS or RHS	The left-hand side (or right-hand side) of a given equation.
s, w, z	The variables s, w, z are complex numbers.
x, y	The variables x, y are real numbers; typically the coordinates of $z = x + iy$.
i, j, k, n, m	The variables i, j, k, n, m are non-negative integers.
ϵ, δ	The variables ϵ, δ are small, positive real numbers.
$|z|$	The absolute value of z (Section 1.2).
$\bar{z}$	The complex conjugate z (Section 1.3).

Chapter 1

The Complex Plane

1.1 Points in The Complex Plane

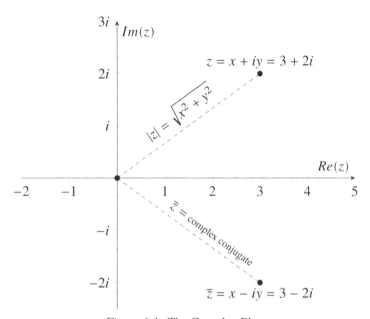

Figure 1.1: The Complex Plane

We assume the reader is familiar with the 2-dimensional Euclidean plane $\mathbb{R}^2$, including the (x, y) coordinate system, as well as basic Euclidean geometry and Euclidean distance.

The complex plane, denoted $\mathbb{C}$, is very similar to $\mathbb{R}^2$. Both are 2-dimensional, with a horizontal x-coordinate and a vertical y-coordinate. If you plotted a given point (x, y) in either plane it would appear in the same location. Both use the real number 1 as the base unit for the x-coordinate. The key difference is that, instead of the real number 1, $\mathbb{C}$ uses i as the base unit for the y-coordinate, where $i = \sqrt{-1}$.

Thus, points in the complex plane are of the form $z = x + iy$, where z is a **complex number** and x and y (real numbers) are the x- and y-coordinates of the complex number z. We also call $x = Re(z)$ the **real part** of z and $y = Im(z)$ the **imaginary part** of z.

1.2 Absolute Value

Let $z = x + iy$ be a complex number. We use $|z|$ to mean the **absolute value** of z, which is the distance (in the complex plane) between the point $(0, 0)$ and the point (x, y). For this purpose, we apply the Euclidean distance rule of $\mathbb{R}^2$ and have

$$|z| = \sqrt{x^2 + y^2}.$$

Of course, the resulting value is a real number. One important use of absolute value is to allow a comparison of complex numbers. The statement $z_1 < z_2$ is meaningless for complex numbers, but the statement $|z_1| < |z_2|$ has its normal meaning as the comparison of two real numbers. Comparison of two complex numbers by use of absolute value often involves the *triangle inequality*, discussed in Section 1.5 below.

Note also that

$$-|z| \le Re(z) \le |Re(z)| = |x| \le |z| \quad \text{and}$$
$$-|z| \le Im(z) \le |Im(z)| = |y| \le |z|.$$

1.3 Complex Conjugate

Let $z = x + iy$ be a complex number. We use $\bar{z}$ to mean the **complex conjugate** of z, which is simply $\bar{z} = x - iy$. Thus, the complex conjugate of z is a mirror reflection of z on the other side of the real axis. The following properties of complex conjugates are easily shown:

$$\bar{\bar{z}} = z \tag{1.1}$$
$$\overline{z + w} = \bar{z} + \bar{w} \tag{1.2}$$
$$\overline{z \cdot w} = \bar{z} \cdot \bar{w} \tag{1.3}$$
$$|z| = |\bar{z}| \tag{1.4}$$
$$|z|^2 = z \cdot \bar{z} \tag{1.5}$$

Using the last formula, we also have:

$$\frac{1}{z} = \frac{\bar{z}}{|z|^2} \quad z \ne 0. \tag{1.6}$$

For the real and imaginary parts of z:

$$Re(z) = (z + \bar{z})/2 \tag{1.7}$$
$$Im(z) = (z - \bar{z})/2i. \tag{1.8}$$

Using $|zw|^2 = (zw)(\overline{zw}) = |z|^2|w|^2$, we have:

$$|zw| = |z||w|. \tag{1.9}$$

> **Remark**
>
> Using the definitions of complex conjugate and absolute value, prove some of the properties given above.

1.4 Basic Operations on Complex Numbers

Let $z_1 = x_1 + iy_1$ and $z_2 = x_2 + iy_2$ be any two complex numbers. The basic operations on those complex numbers work as follows:

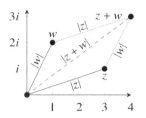

Figure 1.2: Addition of $z + w$

- **Addition** $z_1 + z_2 = (x_1 + x_2) + i(y_1 + y_2)$.
- **Subtraction** $z_1 - z_2 = (x_1 - x_2) + i(y_1 - y_2)$.
- **Multiplication** Here we use the fact that $i^2 = -1$:

$$z_1 \cdot z_2 = (x_1 + iy_1) \cdot (x_2 + iy_2)$$
$$= [x_1x_2 - y_1y_2] + i[y_1x_2 + x_1y_2].$$

The above formula for multiplication is correct. However, the natural way to understand multiplication in the complex plane is through the use of polar coordinates, discussed in Section 1.7 below.

- **Division** Here, we can use the complex conjugate to replace the complex divisor with a real divisor:

$$\frac{z_1}{z_2} = \frac{1}{z_2} \cdot z_1 = \frac{\overline{z_2}}{|z_2|^2} \cdot z_1 = \frac{z_1 \cdot \overline{z_2}}{|z_2|^2}.$$

1.5 Triangle Inequality

There is no order relationship between complex numbers. However, absolute values allows comparison of complex numbers. The most useful comparison is the "triangle inequality", in the form shown in item (b) of Theorem 1.1. Looking at Figure 1.2, the geometric meaning is clear – the length of any one side of a triangle is less than or equal to the combined lengths of the other two sides.

Theorem 1.1: Triangle Inequality

For $z, w \in \mathbb{C}$, we have:

(a) $|z + w|^2 = |z|^2 + 2Re(z\overline{w}) + |w|^2$;

(b) $|z + w| \leq |z| + |w|$;

(c) $|z - w| \leq |z| + |w|$;

(d) $|z| - |w| \leq |z - w|$, *or equally,* $|z - w| \geq |z| - |w|$, *or equally,* $|w| \geq |z| - |z - w|$;

(e) $||z| - |w|| \leq |z - w|$;

(f) $||z| - |w|| \leq |z + w|$.

Proof (a). By equation (1.3), $\overline{\overline{z}w} = z\overline{w}$. Thus, by equation (1.7), $\overline{z}w + z\overline{w} = 2Re(z\overline{w})$. Therefore

$$|z + w|^2 = (z + w)(\overline{z} + \overline{w}) \qquad \text{(by equation (1.5))}$$
$$= z\overline{z} + z\overline{w} + \overline{z}w + w\overline{w}$$
$$= |z|^2 + 2Re(z\overline{w}) + |w|^2. \qquad \square$$

Proof (b). Using our result from (a), we have

$$|z + w|^2 = |z|^2 + 2Re(z\overline{w}) + |w|^2$$
$$\leq |z|^2 + 2|z\overline{w}| + |w|^2$$
$$= |z|^2 + 2|z||w| + |w|^2$$
$$= (|z| + |w|)^2.$$

Taking the square root of both sides, we have our result. □

Proof (c). Using our result from (b), we have $|z - w| = |z + (-w)| \leq |z| + |-w| = |z| + |w|$. □

Proof (d). Using our result from (b), we have

$$z = (z - w) + w$$
$$|z| = |(z - w) + w| \leq |z - w| + |w|$$
$$|z| - |w| \leq |z - w|.$$
□

Proof (e). Using our result from (d), we have

$$|z| - |w| \leq |z - w| = |w - z|$$
$$|w| - |z| \leq |w - z| = |z - w|.$$

Let $M = |z| - |w|$, so that $|w| - |z| = -M$. We have $M \leq |z - w|$ and $-M \leq |z - w|$. Either $M = 0$ (and we are done), or exactly one of M and $-M$ is positive (so that its value equals its absolute value). It follows immediately that $||z| - |w|| = |M| = |-M| \leq |z - w|$. □

Proof (f). Using our result from (e), we have $||z| - |w|| = ||z| - |(-w)|| \leq |z - (-w)| = |z + w|$. □

> **Remark**
>
> The item (b) classic form of the triangle inequality is seen often in proofs of complex function theory. The item (c) through (f) forms of the triangle inequality, which all follow from (b), can also be very useful.

1.6 The Exponential Function

We assume familiarity with the following Taylor Series expansions of the real-valued exponential, cosine and sine functions, valid (and convergent) for all $x, \theta \in \mathbb{R}$. In the two trigonometric functions, θ represents the angle counterclockwise in radians.

$$e^x = \sum_{n=0}^{\infty} \frac{x^n}{n!} \tag{1.10}$$

$$\cos(\theta) = 1 - \frac{\theta^2}{2!} + \frac{\theta^4}{4!} - + \cdots = \sum_{n=0}^{\infty} \frac{(-1)^n \theta^{2n}}{(2n)!} \tag{1.11}$$

$$\sin(\theta) = \theta - \frac{\theta^3}{3!} + \frac{\theta^5}{5!} - + \cdots = \sum_{n=0}^{\infty} \frac{(-1)^n \theta^{(2n+1)}}{(2n + 1)!} \tag{1.12}$$

Substituting z for x in equation (1.10), we will take

$$e^z = \sum_{n=0}^{\infty} \frac{z^n}{n!}$$

as our formula for the exponential function for all $z \in \mathbb{C}$. Combining the triangle inequality with proof by induction, we have

$$|e^z| \le \sum_{n=0}^{\infty} \frac{|z|^n}{n!} = e^{|z|},$$

so that the power series for e^z is absolutely convergent for all $z \in \mathbb{C}$. That allows term by term differentiation of the power series. We then have $(e^z)' = e^z$:

$$\boxed{(e^z)'} = \frac{d}{dz}(e^z) = \sum_{n=1}^{\infty} \frac{d}{dz}\left(\frac{z^n}{n!}\right) = \sum_{n=1}^{\infty} \frac{nz^{n-1}}{n!} = \sum_{n=1}^{\infty} \frac{z^{n-1}}{(n-1)!} = \sum_{n=0}^{\infty} \frac{z^n}{n!} = \boxed{e^z}.$$

Remark

We will see in Section 10.3.3, that the above extension of the exponential function to the complex plane is *the only possible* complex variable version of the exponential function.

Following are two important proofs regarding the properties of the exponential function in the complex plane. The second proof will be the basis for our study (just ahead) of the polar representation of complex numbers.

Theorem 1.2

For $s, w \in \mathbb{C}$, we have $e^{s+w} = e^s \cdot e^w$.

Proof. Fix $c \in \mathbb{C}$. Define $f(z) = e^z \cdot e^{c-z}$. If the theorem is correct, then $f(z) = f(c)$ and therefore resolves to a constant function. To check that, use the product rule and the chain rule to obtain

$$f'(z) = (e^z)' \cdot e^{c-z} + e^z \cdot (e^{c-z})' = e^z \cdot e^{c-z} - e^z \cdot e^{c-z} = 0.$$

As expected, this shows f is a constant function. Letting $z = 0$, we have $f(0) = e^0 \cdot e^c = e^c$. Thus, $f(z) = e^c$. Now setting $z = s$ and $c = s + w$, we have

$$f(z) = e^z \cdot e^{c-z} = e^s \cdot e^{s+w-s} = \boxed{e^s \cdot e^w = e^{s+w}} = e^c. \qquad \square$$

Remark

Now use $e^0 = 1$ and Theorem 1.2, giving: $1 = e^0 = e^{z-z} = e^z \cdot e^{-z}$. Two results immediately follow: (a) $e^z \ne 0$ for all $z \in \mathbb{C}$, and (b) $e^{-z} = 1/e^z$.

Theorem 1.3

For $\theta \in \mathbb{R}$, $e^{i\theta} = \cos\theta + i\sin\theta$.

Proof. We use that $(-1)^n = (i^2)^n = i^{2n}$ and $i \cdot (-1)^n = i \cdot i^{2n} = i^{(2n+1)}$. Substituting those values into equations (1.11) and (1.12), we have

$$\boxed{\cos\theta + i\sin\theta} = \sum_{n=0}^{\infty} \frac{(-1)^n \theta^{2n}}{(2n)!} + i\sum_{n=0}^{\infty} \frac{(-1)^n \theta^{(2n+1)}}{(2n+1)!} = \sum_{n=0}^{\infty} \frac{(i\theta)^{2n}}{(2n)!} + \sum_{n=0}^{\infty} \frac{(i\theta)^{(2n+1)}}{(2n+1)!} = \boxed{e^{i\theta}}. \qquad \square$$

Remark

Thus, $Re(e^{i\theta}) = \cos\theta$ and $Im(e^{i\theta}) = \sin\theta$, so that $|e^{i\theta}| = \sqrt{\cos^2\theta + \sin^2\theta} = 1$. We see that $e^{i\theta}$ produces points on the unit circle, with θ representing the angle (counterclockwise, in radians) between the positive x axis and the line drawn between 0 and $e^{i\theta}$. Thus, if we allow θ to increase from 0 to 2π, we have exactly scribed the unit circle, counterclockwise, beginning and ending at 1.

Remark

We now make a very important point. The cos and sin functions are 2π periodic. That is, for all $k \in \mathbb{Z}$, we have $\cos\theta = \cos(\theta + 2\pi k)$ and $\sin\theta = \sin(\theta + 2\pi k)$. Thus

$$e^{i\theta} = \cos\theta + i\sin\theta = \cos(\theta + 2\pi k) + i\sin(\theta + 2\pi k) = e^{i(\theta + 2\pi k)}.$$

That means the value of $e^{i\theta}$ is 2π periodic. By way of example, $e^{i0} = e^{i2\pi} = e^{i4\pi} = 1$ and $e^{i\pi} = e^{i3\pi} = -1$.

We can use Theorem 1.3 to obtain useful forms of the trigonometric functions. If we combine $\left[e^{i\theta} = \cos\theta + i\sin\theta\right]$ with $\left[e^{-i\theta} = \cos\theta - i\sin\theta\right]$, and then substitute z for θ, we have expressions valid for all $z \in \mathbb{C}$:

$$\cos z = \frac{e^{iz} + e^{-iz}}{2} \qquad \sin z = \frac{e^{iz} - e^{-iz}}{2i}.$$

With this background, we can now discuss the *polar representation* of any non-zero point in the complex plane.

1.7 Polar Representation

Definition 1.1

*For any non-zero point $z = x + iy$ in the complex plane, we can describe that point in **polar form** (or, equally, using **polar coordinates**). For our given z, let C_R be a circle centered at the origin with radius $R = |z|$ and let L, be a line whose endpoints are the origin and the point z. Then, L has length R and C_R intersects z at the point where L terminates at z. We can therefore write*

$$z = |z|e^{i\theta} = Re^{i\theta},$$

where θ is the angle (with counterclockwise orientation) between the positive x axis and L. The angle θ is important to fully understand, so we include the following figure and definition.

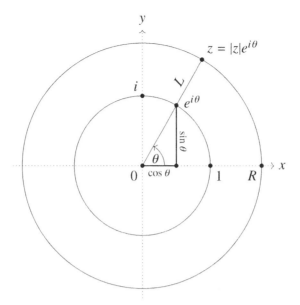

Figure 1.3: Polar Representation

Definition 1.2

*For $z \neq 0$, the **argument** of z, denoted $\arg(z)$, is the angle in radians (with counterclockwise orientation) between the positive x axis and the line that runs between the origin and z. Stated differently, $\arg(z) = \theta$ where θ is the angle such that $z = |z|e^{i\theta}$.*

As shown in Section 1.6, $e^{i\theta}$ is 2π periodic. Thus, for all $k \in \mathbb{Z}$, if $\arg(z) = \theta$ then we also have $\arg(z) = \theta + 2\pi k$. That means $\arg(z)$ is a multi-valued function.

*It will be useful to have a single-valued version of $\arg(z)$. We define the **principal value** of $\arg(z)$, denoted $\mathrm{Arg}(z)$, to be the value of θ in the interval $-\pi < \theta \leq \pi$.*

From the above definition, we see that for all $k \in \mathbb{Z}$ we have

$$z = |z|e^{i \arg(z)} = |z|e^{i \, \mathrm{Arg}(z)} = |z|e^{i[\mathrm{Arg}(z) + 2\pi k]}.$$

Using the *polar form* is helpful in understanding the effect of multiplying two complex numbers $z = |z|e^{i\theta}$ and $w = |w|e^{i\vartheta}$:

$$z \cdot w = |z|e^{i\theta} \cdot |w|e^{i\vartheta} = |z||w| \cdot e^{i(\theta + \vartheta)},$$

so that multiplication results in a rotation (add the two angles) combined with a dilation (multiply the two absolute values).

1.8   The Complex Logarithm

The real variable logarithm is the inverse function to the real variable exponential function. That is, $\log(e^x) = x$ and $e^{\log x} = x$. It is not that simple in the complex plane because the exponential function is 2π periodic.

Before moving to the complex logarithm, we first show how a complex number z can be expressed using polar coordinates and the real logarithm. For any $z \neq 0$, we have $z = |z|e^{i \arg(z)}$. Because $|z|$ is real-valued, we can use the real logarithm and have $|z| = e^{\log|z|}$. Therefore, we can always express z as $z = e^{\log|z|}e^{i\arg(z)} = e^{\log|z|+i\arg(z)}$, where $\arg(z)$ is the multi-valued function in Definition 1.2.

Now to the complex logarithm. The values of $\log(z)$ are *all of* the (infinitely many) complex numbers w such that $e^w = z$. We have seen that if w is a solution to $e^w = z$, then $w + 2\pi i k$ is also a solution, for all $k \in \mathbb{Z}$. Let $\{w_n\}$ be the set of complex numbers solving $e^w = z$ and let $[[\{w_n\}]]$ be a notation that means "pick any one". Then we have

$$e^{[[\{w_n\}]]} = z \quad \text{and} \quad \log(z) = [[\{w_n\}]].$$

The *very important* point is that $\log(z)$ a multi-valued function. For any given $z \neq 0$, $\log(z)$ has infinitely many solutions. Note the difference between a *periodic* function like e^z (at regular intervals of function input, the output repeats the same value) and a *multi-valued* function like $log(z)$ (any single function input can have multiple output values).

Definition 1.3

For $z \neq 0$, we define $\log z$ as

$$\log(z) = \log|z| + i\arg(z)$$
$$= \log|z| + i\operatorname{Arg}(z) + 2\pi i k, \quad k \in \mathbb{Z}$$
$$\operatorname{Log}(z) = \log|z| + i\operatorname{Arg}(z), \quad -\pi < \operatorname{Arg}(z) \leq \pi.$$

*The last above, $\operatorname{Log}(z)$, is the **principal value** of $\log z$ and is a single-valued inverse for $z = e^w$. Each $k \in \mathbb{Z}$, as used above, creates a different **branch** of the logarithm. In the kth branch, we have $\arg(z) \in (2\pi k - \pi, 2\pi k + \pi]$. For $k = 0$, we have $\arg(z) = \operatorname{Arg}(z) \in (-\pi, \pi]$, which we will denote as the **principal branch** of the logarithm.*

If we let $w = \log|z| + i\operatorname{Arg} z$, then

$$e^w = e^{\log|z|+i\operatorname{Arg} z} = e^{\log|z|} \cdot e^{i\operatorname{Arg} z} = |z|e^{i\operatorname{Arg} z} = z.$$

And noting that $e^{2\pi i k} = 1$ for $k \in \mathbb{Z}$, we also have

$$e^w = e^{\log|z|+i\operatorname{Arg} z+2\pi i k} = e^{\log|z|}e^{i\operatorname{Arg} z}e^{2\pi i k} = |z|e^{i\operatorname{Arg} z} \cdot 1 = z.$$

We will have much more to say about the complex logarithm later in this book. You will find that the properties of the complex logarithm play a central role in complex function theory.

1.9 Complex Exponentials

We further demonstrate the properties of the complex logarithm by considering the result of taking a non-zero complex number to a complex power. In real variables, we have $x^a = e^{a\log(x)}$, which suggests the following definition for complex exponents.

Definition 1.4

*For $z, w \in \mathbb{C}$ and $z \neq 0$, we define the multi-valued **power function** to be $z^w = e^{w\log(z)}$. We define the single-valued **principal value** to be $z^w = e^{w\operatorname{Log}(z)}$.*

We therefore have as the values of z^w

$$z^w = e^{w[\log|z|+i\operatorname{Arg}(z)+2\pi ik]} \quad k \in \mathbb{Z}$$
$$= e^{w\operatorname{Log}(z)}e^{w[2\pi ik]}.$$

Note that for $w \in \mathbb{Z}$ we have $e^{w[2\pi ik]} = 1$. Therefore, the power function is single-valued for all integer powers. Also, as you would expect, $z^{-w} = e^{-w\log(z)} = 1/e^{w\log(z)} = 1/z^w$.

An interesting example of a complex power is i^i, giving

$$i^i = e^{i\log(i)} = e^{i\left[\log(1)+i\frac{\pi}{2}+2\pi ik\right]} = e^{-\frac{\pi}{2}[1+4k]}.$$

In the multi-valued result, the value is real for all k. The principal value ($k = 0$) is $e^{-\pi/2}$. For positive k, we have $\lim\limits_{k\to\infty} i^i \to 0$. For negative k, we have $\lim\limits_{k\to-\infty} i^i \to \infty$.

1.10   The Extended Complex Plane

On the real line, there is no difficulty understanding the two points at infinity, $+\infty$ and $-\infty$. Simply traverse the real line in either the positive or negative direction and you are heading towards $\pm\infty$. It is easy to visualize.

In the complex plane, the idea and location of infinity is less clear. You would like to think that any infinite length line in $\mathbb{C}$ is heading towards infinity. But what does that even mean? Is every different line heading towards a different infinity? You have to conclude that $\mathbb{C}$ has no "point at infinity". We remedy that with what Ahlfors [1, 18] says is "an 'ideal' point which we call the *point at infinity*".

> **Definition 1.5**
> *The **extended complex plane**, denoted $\mathbb{C}^*$, is equal to the complex plane plus the **point at infinity**. That is, $\mathbb{C}^* = \mathbb{C} \cup \{\infty\}$.*

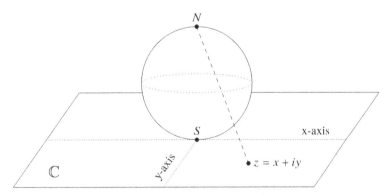

Figure 1.4: The Riemann Sphere

We use the Riemann sphere[1] and stereographic projection to model the extended complex plane. We start with the complex plane on a horizontal surface. On top of that we place a 3-dimensional sphere with coordinates (X, Y, Z) and radius $1/2$. The south pole, $S = (0, 0, 0)$, rests on the origin of the complex plane. The Z coordinate runs perpendicular to the complex plane, increasing from 0 to 1 at the north pole, $N = (0, 0, 1)$. For any fixed $0 < Z < 1$, the X and Y coordinates form a 2-dimensional closed disk parallel to the complex plane, with X and Y equal to their corresponding x and y coordinates in the complex plane (i.e., a line from (X, Y) to (x, y) is perpendicular to the complex plane).

We use stereographic projection to obtain a one-to-one correspondence between points on the surface of the sphere (excluding N) and points in the complex plane. Given any point $z = x + iy$ in the complex plane, draw a line from z to N. That line will intersect exactly one point on the surface of the sphere, and that point on the sphere is unique to z. In the other direction, draw a line from N through any other point P on the surface of the sphere, stopping where you intersect the complex plane. That line will intersect exactly one point on the complex plane, and that point on the plane is unique to P.

The formulae for the one-to-one correspondence between points $P = (X, Y, Z)$ on the sphere and points $z = x + iy$ on the complex plane are as follows:

$$x = \frac{X}{1 - Z} \qquad y = \frac{Y}{1 - Z} \qquad X = \frac{x}{x^2 + y^2 + 1} \qquad Y = \frac{y}{x^2 + y^2 + 1} \qquad Z = \frac{x^2 + y^2}{x^2 + y^2 + 1}.$$

Now consider a circle that is: (1) on the surface of the sphere, and (2) parallel to the complex plane. We will call that circle a "latitude" of the sphere. We necessarily exclude the north and south poles, so any fixed latitude is associated with a fixed $0 < Z < 1$.

For any fixed latitude, we can run lines from N through all points of that latitude, projecting to a circle on the complex plane. A latitude of $Z = 1/2$ projects to the unit circle. The projected circle will be inside the unit disk if $Z < 1/2$ and outside if $Z > 1/2$. With a little geometry, you can calculate the radius of the projected circle as $R = \sqrt{Z/(1 - Z)}$.

As the latitude approaches the north pole, Z approaches 1 and the radius R of the projected circle grows without bound, so that $\lim_{Z \to 1} R \to \infty$. That is, for points z on our projected circle, $\lim_{Z \to 1} |z| \to \infty$.

One final visual. Both $\mathbb{C}$ and the "punctured sphere" $\mathbb{S}^*$ (the sphere minus the north pole) are open sets. We have established a one-to-one correspondence between $\mathbb{C}$ and $\mathbb{S}^*$. Now imagine lifting up the complex plane and laying it on the punctured sphere so that each point on the plane rests on its corresponding point on the sphere. The extended complex plane $\mathbb{C}^*$ is made simply by adding the point at infinity (the north pole). All large z, no matter their orientation in the plane, approach that same point at infinity.

1.11 Supplemental Material

1.11.1 Exercises

Exercises 1.1

(a) *Show that $|z| \leq 1 + |1 - z|$.*

(b) *Show that $|z + w|^2 + |z - w|^2 = 2(|z|^2 + |w|^2)$.*

(c) *For all $n \in \mathbb{N}$, show that $|z_1 + z_2 + \cdots + z_n| \leq \sum_{k=1}^{n} |z_k|$.*

(d) *For $|z| \leq \epsilon < 1$, show that $|e^z - 1| \geq |z|(1 - \epsilon)$.*

> **Remark**

Answers to exercises are in Appendix A.

1.11.2 Cauchy–Schwarz Inequality

> **Theorem 1.4: Cauchy-Schwarz Inequality**
>
> For $z_j, w_j \in \mathbb{C}$
>
> $$\left| \sum_{j=1}^{n} z_j w_j \right|^2 \leq \left(\sum_{j=1}^{n} |z_j|^2 \right) \left(\sum_{j=1}^{n} |w_j|^2 \right).$$

Proof.[2] Let $A = \sum_{j=1}^{n} |z_j|^2$ and $B = \sum_{j=1}^{n} |w_j|^2$ and $T = \sum_{j=1}^{n} z_j w_j$. Then $T \in \mathbb{C}$ and $A, B \in \mathbb{R}$. Note that $A \geq 0$ and $B \geq 0$. If $B = 0$, then all $w_j = 0$ and the proof is complete, so we assume $B > 0$. Next let $S = T/B$ so that $\overline{S} = \overline{T}/B$.

As in Exercise 1.1(b), we use that $0 \leq |z - w|^2 = |z|^2 - 2Re(z\overline{w}) + |w|^2$ and apply that (n times) to the below sum:

$$0 \leq \sum_{j=1}^{n} |z_j - S\overline{w_j}|^2 = \sum_{j=1}^{n} |z_j|^2 + |S|^2 \sum_{j=1}^{n} |w_j|^2 - 2Re\left(\overline{S} \sum_{j=1}^{n} z_j w_j \right)$$

$$= A + |S|^2 B - 2Re\left(\overline{S}T \right)$$

$$= A + \frac{|T^2|}{B} - \frac{2Re\left(\overline{T}T \right)}{B}$$

$$= A + \frac{|T^2|}{B} - 2\frac{|T^2|}{B}$$

$$= A - \frac{|T^2|}{B}.$$

Rearranging and then multiplying both sides by B, we have $|T^2| \leq AB$, as required. $\square$

Chapter 2

Topology of the Complex Plane

The study of complex analysis is, in large part, the study of functions of a complex variable. Often those functions only operate on a limited set of points in the complex plane. The actual makeup of that set of points can significantly impact the operation of the function. Is the set open or closed, bounded, compact? In Section 2.1, just below, we develop the language of sets.

We will often work with sets having a countable number of members. Thus, in Section 2.2, we show certain important properties of countable sets, including a proof that a countable union of countable sets is countable.

In Section 2.3, we focus on a specific sub-group of countable sets - sets (or unions of sets) that contain only rational numbers. For the set of all open disks in $\mathbb{C}$ with rational coordinates and rational radii, we show there exists an open disk small enough to cover any point while remaining in any open disk (no matter how small) centered at that point.

In the next two sections, we use what we have learned above to prove two very important theorems. In Section 2.4, we discuss bounded sets and prove the Bolzano-Weierstrass Theorem (any bounded sequence has a convergent subsequence). We put that theorem to immediate use in Section 2.5, where we turn to compact sets and prove the Heine-Borel Theorem (every open covering of a compact set has a finite subcovering).

2.1   Sets – Basic Definitions and the Language of Sets

Almost all of this section should be familiar to the reader. However, the section is short and worthy of a quick review. At the end of this section, please also note our notations for the open and closed disk and the boundary of a disk. Those notations will be in constant use throughout this book.

2.1.1   Definition of Sets

Definition 2.1
*A **set** is a collection of **elements** of almost any kind. The number of elements may be finite, infinite or even zero (the **empty set**). Also, an element may be included multiple times (even infinite) in the same set. We only care that the elements are selected (and ordered) according to some rule.*

Remark

In this book, we will restrict sets almost exclusively to: (1) *point sets* consisting of real or complex numbers, (2) *sets of sets* consisting of multiple point sets, and (3) *sets of functions* consisting of multiple complex-valued functions.

2.1.2   Functions/Mapping of Sets

Definition 2.2

*Assume that f is a rule that associates element of a set Ω with elements of a set Λ. That is, for every z in Ω, $f(z)$ resolves to some w in Λ. We say that f is a **function** from Ω to Λ, or a **mapping** of Ω into Λ. We will denote this relation by $f : \Omega \mapsto \Lambda$.*

> **Remark**
>
> Unless stated otherwise, any function in this book will be a complex-valued function. Thus, in the mapping $f : \Omega \mapsto \Lambda$, both Ω and Λ will be point sets in the complex plane.

2.1.3   The Cardinality of Sets

Definition 2.3

*Assume a mapping $f : \Omega \mapsto \Lambda$. For $z_1, z_2 \in \Omega$, assume $f(z_1) \neq f(z_2)$ whenever $z_1 \neq z_2$. Assume further that for each $w \in \Lambda$ there exists a $z_n \in \Omega$ with $f(z_n) = w$. In that case, f is said to be a **one-to-one** mapping of Ω into Λ.*

We use the concept of one-to-one mappings to help compare the size of two sets.

Definition 2.4

*If there is a one-to-one mapping of Ω into Λ, then Ω and Λ have the same **cardinal number**, an **equivalence relationship** denoted by $\Lambda \sim \Omega$.*

That equivalence relationship between sets has the following properties:

- *It is **reflexive**: $\Omega \sim \Omega$.*
- *It is **symmetric**: If $\Omega \sim \Lambda$, then $\Lambda \sim \Omega$.*
- *It is **transitive**: If $\Omega_1 \sim \Omega_2$ and $\Omega_2 \sim \Omega_3$, then $\Omega_1 \sim \Omega_3$.*

Definition 2.5

For $n \in \mathbb{N}$, let K_n be the set whose elements are the integers $1, 2, ..., n$ and let K be the set whose elements are all the positive integers. For any set Ω, we say:

- *Ω is **finite** if $\Omega \sim K_n$ for some n, or if Ω is an empty set.*
- *Ω is **infinite** if Ω is not finite.*
- *Ω is **countable** if $\Omega \sim K$.*
- *Ω is **uncountable** if Ω is neither finite nor countable.*

2.1.4   The Union and Intersection of Sets

The *union* of two or more sets is the set of all points which belong to *any* of the included sets. We denote a union of sets by the $\cup$ symbol. Following are examples of the union of a finite, countable or uncountable number of sets, in each case forming a new set K:

$$K = \Omega_1 \cup \Omega_2 \cup \cdots \cup \Omega_n \qquad K = \bigcup_{n=1}^{\infty} S_n \qquad K = \bigcup_{0 \leq w \leq 1} \{z \in \mathbb{C} : |w - z| < 1\}.$$

The *intersection* of two or more sets is the set of all points which belong to *all of* the included sets. We denote an intersection of sets by the ∩ symbol. Following are examples of the intersection of a finite, countable or uncountable number of sets, in each case forming a new set K:

$$K = \Omega_1 \cap \Omega_2 \cap \cdots \cap \Omega_n \qquad K = \bigcap_{n=1}^{\infty} S_n \qquad K = \bigcap_{0 \leq w \leq 1} \{z \in \mathbb{C} : |w - z| < 1\}.$$

Remark

Typically, an intersection of sets will involve a finite number of sets. In the case of the intersection of two sets, $\Omega_1 \cap \Omega_2$, if the intersection is empty then the sets Ω_1 and Ω_2 are said to be *disjoint*.

2.1.5 Classification of Points in a Set

Definition 2.6

*We define a **neighborhood** of w to be the set $\{z \in \mathbb{C} : |z - w| < r\}$ for any (small) $r > 0$.*

Definition 2.7

Given as set Ω, a point w is called:

- *a **limit point** of Ω if an infinite number of points $z \in \Omega$ lie in every neighborhood of w;*
- *an **isolated point** of Ω if $w \in \Omega$ and there exists a neighborhood of w containing no other points of Ω;*
- *an **interior point** of Ω if there exists a neighborhood of w belonging entirely to Ω;*
- *an **exterior point** to Ω if the point w and some neighborhood of w do not belong to Ω;*
- *a **boundary point** of Ω if every neighborhood of w has at least one point which belongs to Ω and at least one point which does not belong to Ω. Note: w itself may or may not belong to Ω.*

There is one type of countable set (the sequence) that is used so often it is separately defined:

Definition 2.8

*A **sequence** is a countable set that is indexed on $n \in \mathbb{N}$. The sequence will often be denoted by $\{z_n\}$, which is understood to mean the countable collection of points $z_1, z_2, z_3, \ldots$. The one-to-one correspondence between the index of $\{z_n\}$ and $\mathbb{N}$ is immediately clear. Often, there will be an associated mapping function f, with $f(n) = z_n$. In fact, rather than a point set, the sequence may be a countable collection of functions, such as $\{f_n\}$.*

2.1.6 Classification of Sets – Open and Closed Sets

Definition 2.9

Given a set Ω,

- *The set consisting of all $\{z \in \mathbb{C} : z \notin \Omega\}$ is the **complement** of Ω, denoted as Ω^c.*
- *A set Ω is **closed** if: (1) it contains all of its limit points[3], or (2) if its complement Ω^c is open.*

- The **closure** of Ω is the union of Ω and its limit points, denoted by $\overline{\Omega}$.
- A set Ω is **open** if, for all $z \in \Omega$, z is an interior point of Ω. Note that a set need not be either open or closed – an example is a set that contains some (but not all) of its limit points.
- The **interior** of Ω consists of all its interior points.
- The **boundary** of Ω is equal to $\overline{\Omega}$ minus the interior of Ω, and is denoted by $\partial\Omega$. Note that points on the boundary of Ω may or may not belong to Ω.

2.1.7 Open and Closed Disks

Definition 2.10

For the radius $r > 0$ and the center point z_0:

*We denote the **open disk** by* $\qquad \mathbf{D}_r(z_0) = \{z \in \mathbb{C} : |z - z_0| < r\}.$

*We denote the **closed disk** by* $\qquad \overline{\mathbf{D}}_r(z_0) = \{z \in \mathbb{C} : |z - z_0| \leq r\}.$

*We denote the **circle** by* $\qquad \mathbf{C}_r(z_0) = \{z \in \mathbb{C} : |z - z_0| = r\}.$

Remark

In the remainder of this book, when we use the above notations for the open disk, closed disk or circle, it is understood that the center and radius are as stated in the notation.

2.2 Countable Sets

In this section, we develop several properties of countable sets. Most importantly, we show that a countable union of countable sets is countable.

2.2.1 Countable Sets - Some Simple Properties

Theorem 2.1

The set $\mathbb{Z}$ of all integers is countable.

Proof. To show that $\mathbb{Z}$ is countable, we must show a one-to-one mapping of $\mathbb{N}$ into $\mathbb{Z}$. Let $f(n) = -(n-1)/2$ for n odd and let $f(n) = n/2$ for n even. Now apply the mapping $f : \mathbb{N} \mapsto \mathbb{Z}$ and we obtain $0, 1, -1, 2, -2, 3, -3, \dots$. It is easily seen that each element of $\mathbb{N}$ is mapped to a unique element of $\mathbb{Z}$ and that all elements of $\mathbb{Z}$ are produced, giving the required one-to-one mapping. $\qquad\square$

Following is a classic proof showing that a countable set is the "smallest" kind of infinite set. Any infinite subset of a countable set must also be countable (and therefore cannot be uncountable).

Theorem 2.2

Every infinite subset of a countable set Ω is countable.

Proof. Suppose $\Lambda \subset \Omega$ and Λ is infinite. Arrange the elements x of Ω in a sequence $\{x_n\}$ of distinct elements. Construct a sequence $\{n_k\}$ as follows:

Let n_1 be the smallest positive integer such that $x_{n_1} \in \Lambda$. Having chosen $n_1, n_2, ..., n_{k-1}$, let n_k be the smallest integer greater than n_{k-1} such that $x_{n_k} \in \Lambda$.

Putting $f(k) = x_{n_k}$ $(k = 1, 2, 3, ...)$, we obtain a one-to-one correspondence between Λ and $\mathbb{N}$. $\qquad\square$

2.2.2 Countable Union of Countable Sets is Countable

Theorem 2.3

For $n \in \mathbb{N}$, let S_n be a countable set with members $\{s(n)_k\}$, enumerated over k. If we define the set S as a countable collection of such countable sets

$$S = \{S_n\} = \bigcup_{n=1}^{\infty} S_n,$$

then the set S is countable.

Proof. We can enumerate the elements of the set S_n by $s(n)_1, s(n)_2, s(n)_3 \ldots$. Using that enumeration, we write the elements of S as follows:

$$
\begin{array}{ccccc}
s(1)_1 & s(2)_1 & s(3)_1 & s(4)_1 & s(5)_1\ldots \\
s(1)_2 & s(2)_2 & s(3)_2 & s(4)_2 & s(5)_2\ldots \\
s(1)_3 & s(2)_3 & s(3)_3 & s(4)_3 & s(5)_3\ldots \\
s(1)_4 & s(2)_4 & s(3)_4 & s(4)_4 & s(5)_4\ldots \\
s(1)_5 & s(2)_5 & s(3)_5 & s(4)_5 & s(5)_5\ldots \\
\vdots & \vdots & \vdots & \vdots & \vdots
\end{array}
$$

The set S_1 is enumerated down the first column, S_2 down the second column, and so on.

For $n, j \in \mathbb{N}$, define an "enumeration helper" function:

$$f(n, j) = \frac{n^2 - n}{2} + j \quad \text{and define a finite set of integers} \quad F_n = \{f(n, 1), f(n, 2), ..., f(n, n)\}.$$

If we order the sets $\{F_1, F_2, ..., F_n\}$, we have an ordered list of integers from 1 to $(n^2 + n)/2$. *It follows that there is a one-to-one correspondence between the elements of the infinite sets $\{F_n\}$ and $\mathbb{N}$.*

Note that the set F_n has n integer elements. Now look back at the array of elements of S shown above. We pair the n integer elements in F_n with the n elements in the diagonal that begins at $s(n)_1$ and ends at $s(1)_n$. By way of example,

- The one element of $F_1 = f(1, 1)$ is paired with $s(1)_1$.
- The two elements of $F_2 = \{f(2, 1), f(2, 2)\}$ are paired with $s(1)_2$ and $s(2)_1$.

- The five elements of $F_5 = \{f(5,1), f(5,2), ..., f(5.5)\}$ are paired with $s(1)_5, s(2)_4, ..., s(5)_1$.

All of the elements of the collection of countable sets $\{S_n\}$ are enumerated by the above technique, with the elements of S arranged in a sequence with a 1-1 correspondence with $\{F_n\}$ and thus $\mathbb{N}$:

$$s(1)_1, \ s(1)_2, \ s(2)_1, \ s(1)_3, \ s(2)_2, \ s(3)_1, \ s(1)_4, \ s(2)_3, \ s(3)_2, \ s(4)_1, ...$$

If any two of the sets S_n have elements in common, these will appear more than once in the above arrangement. We can therefore find a subset $T \subset \mathbb{N}$ such that $S \sim T$. By Theorem 2.2, this shows that S is at most countable. Since $S_1 \subset S$, and S_1 is countable, we see that S is at least countable. We can conclude that S is countable. $\qquad \square$

Corollary 2.1

For $j, k \in \mathbb{N}$, let $\{x_j\}$ and $\{y_k\}$ be two countable sets. Then, the set $\{(x_j, y_k)\}$ constructed by pairing each x_j with each y_k is a countable set.

Proof. For, $j, k \in \mathbb{N}$, let $a(j)_k = (x_j, y_k)$. For j fixed and k ranging over $\mathbb{N}$, we clearly have that $\{a(j)_k\}$ is a countable set. Now define a set K:

$$K = \bigcup_{j=1}^{\infty} \{a(j)_k\}.$$

Thus, K is constructed from a countable union of countable sets, and therefore countable by Theorem 2.3. For all $j, k \in \mathbb{N}$, we have $\{(x_j, y_k)\} \in K$, as required. $\qquad \square$

Corollary 2.2

For $i, j, k \in \mathbb{N}$, let $\{x_j\}$, $\{y_k\}$ and $\{r_i\}$ be three countable sets. Then, the set $\{(x_j, y_k, r_i)\}$ constructed by pairing each x_j with each y_k and then including each such pairing with each r_i is a countable set.

Proof. We use Corollary 2.1 and $K = \{(x_j, y_k)\}$ as defined there, so that K is a countable set. Therefore, for $j, k \in \mathbb{N}$, all possible pairing of $(x_j, y_k) \in K$.

Let $i \in \mathbb{N}$. For i fixed, define $K_i = \{(K, r_i)\}$. We are pairing all $(x_j, y_k) \in K$ with the single ith element of the set $\{r_i\}$. Clearly K_i is a countable set. Now define a set G:

$$G = \bigcup_{i=1}^{\infty} K_i.$$

Thus, G is constructed from a countable union of countable sets, and therefore countable by Theorem 2.3. For all $i, j, k \in \mathbb{N}$, we have $\{(x_j, y_k, r_i)\} \in G$, as required. $\qquad \square$

Remark

In Corollaries 2.1 and 2.2, we have shown we can construct countable sets out of pairs and triples of countable sets. Clearly, we could similarly apply Theorem 2.3 to obtain the same result for any n-tuple of countable sets.

2.3   Sets Using Rational Numbers

In this section, we first show that the set of all rational numbers is countable. Despite "only" being countable, we then prove the rational numbers are dense enough in $\mathbb{R}$ so that there always exists a rational number between any two non-identical real numbers.

Next, using Corollary 2.2, we see that the set of all open disks in $\mathbb{C}$ with rational coordinates and rational radii is a countable set. Finally, for any open disk $\mathbf{D}_\epsilon(w)$ (no matter how small), we prove there exists a rational coordinate/radii disk that can cover w while still remaining inside $\mathbf{D}_\epsilon(w)$. This last proof is a critical component in our later proof of the Heine-Borel Theorem.

Corollary 2.3

$\mathbb{Q}$ *(the set of rational numbers) is countable.*

Proof. For, $n, j \in \mathbb{N}$, let $x(n)_j = j/n$ and $x(-n)_j = j/(-n)$. For n fixed and j ranging over $\mathbb{N}$, we clearly have that both $\{x(n)_j\}$ and $\{x(-n)_j\}$ are countable sets. Now define a set $K \in \mathbb{R}$:

$$K = \left[\bigcup_{n=1}^{\infty} \{x(n)_j\} \right] \cup \left[\bigcup_{n=1}^{\infty} \{x(-n)_j\} \right] \cup \{0\}.$$

As a countable union of countable sets, K is countable by Theorem 2.3. But $\mathbb{Q} \subset K$. Therefore, $\mathbb{Q}$ is a countable set by Theorem 2.2. $\qquad\square$

Theorem 2.4

Let $x, y \in \mathbb{R}$ and $x < y$. Then there exists a rational number $r \in \mathbb{Q}$ with $x < r < y$.

Proof. For our first case, assume $x \geq 0$. We then have $y > 0$ and $y - x > 0$. It follows[4] that there is an $n \in \mathbb{N}$ with $1/n < y - x$ and therefore $1 < ny - nx$ or equally $nx + 1 < ny$. If x is rational, then we have our result using $r = x + 1/n$, because $nr = n(x + 1/n) = nx + 1 < ny$. Thus, we may assume that x is irrational (so that nx is not a whole number). Now, since $nx > 0$ there must be an $A \in \mathbb{N}$ such that $A < nx + 1 < A + 1$. Assembling the above, and setting $r = A/n$ (a rational number), we have

$$nx < A < nx + 1 < ny$$
$$nx < A < ny$$
$$x < A/n < y$$
$$x < r < y,$$

as required.

Now consider the case where $x < 0$. If $y > 0$, we set $r = 0$ and have our result. Finally, if $y < 0$, we set $y' = -x$ and $x' = -y$ and use the first case to find a rational r with $x' < r < y'$. Then $x < -r < y$, as required. $\qquad\square$

> **Corollary 2.4**
>
> *The set of all open disks in $\mathbb{C}$ with rational coordinates and rational radii is countable.*

Proof. The set is represented by all triples of the form $(x_j, y_k, r_i) = \mathbf{D}_{r_i}(x_j + iy_k)$ where x_j, y_k and r_i are rational. The result follows immediately from Corollaries 2.3 and 2.2. □

> **Theorem 2.5**
>
> *Fix $\epsilon > 0$ and fix a point $z = x + iy$, giving the open disk $\mathbf{D}_\epsilon(z)$. Then, for some $z_1 = x_1 + iy_1$ and some $r > 0$, with x_1, y_1 and r rational, we can construct an open disk $\mathbf{D}_r(z_1)$ with (1) $z \in \mathbf{D}_r(z_1)$ and (2) $\mathbf{D}_r(z_1) \subset \mathbf{D}_\epsilon(z)$ and (3) r as small as we like.*

Proof. Fix $n \in \mathbb{N}$, let $\delta > 0$ and fix $\delta < \min(1/n, \epsilon/8)$. We use n to satisfy condition (3) and show that the radius of our disk $\mathbf{D}_r(z_1)$ can be as small as we like.

Using Theorem 2.4, let x_1 be a rational number between x and $x + \delta$, let y_1 be a rational number between y and $y + \delta$, and let r be a rational number between 2δ and 4δ. We construct $\mathbf{D}_r(z_1)$ from those values.

Regarding condition (1) of the lemma, we compute the distance between z and z_1

$$|z - z_1| = \sqrt{(x_1 - x)^2 + (y_1 - y)^2} < \sqrt{\delta^2 + \delta^2} = \sqrt{2 \cdot \delta^2} = \sqrt{2} \cdot \delta < 2\delta.$$

Because the radius of $\mathbf{D}_r(z_1)$ is greater than 2δ and the distance between z and z_1 is less than 2δ, we have $z \in \mathbf{D}_r(z_1)$, satisfying condition (1).

Regarding condition (2), we have $|z - z_1| < 2\delta$ and $r < 4\delta$. For all points in $\mathbf{D}_r(z_1)$, the distance to z is $< 6\delta < 0.75\epsilon$. Therefore, $\mathbf{D}_r(z_1) \subset \mathbf{D}_\epsilon(z)$. □

2.4 Bounded Sets and the Bolzano-Weierstrass Theorem

In this section, we prove the Bolzano-Weierstrass Theorem (every bounded sequence has a convergent subsequence). It is one of the central theorems in both real and complex analysis.

> **Remark**
>
> We assume familiarity with real variable convergent sequences – a sequence of real numbers is convergent if and only if it is a Cauchy sequence. If you need a refresher, you may wish to review Section 6.1, where we extend that convergence test to complex numbers. As a reminder, a sequence $\{z_j\}$ is a *Cauchy sequence* if for every $\epsilon > 0$, there exists and $N \in \mathbb{N}$ such that for all $m, n > N$, we have $|z_m - z_n| < \epsilon$.

> **Definition 2.11**
> *A set Ω is **bounded** if there is a $K > 0$ such that $|z| < K$ for all $z \in \Omega$. If a set is not bounded (i.e., there exists no such K), then the set is **unbounded**. If Ω is bounded, we define its **diameter** by*
>
> $$\text{diam}(\Omega) = \sup_{z, w \in \Omega} |z - w|.$$

An obvious example of an unbounded set is the set of natural numbers $\mathbb{N}$.

Theorem 2.6: Bolzano-Weierstrass Theorem

Let $\{z_n\}$ be a bounded sequence in $\mathbb{C}$ with $|z_n| < M$ for all n. Then $\{z_n\}$ has a convergent subsequence.

Proof. Construct a square $SQ_1 \in \mathbb{C}$ with corners at $(M, iM), (-M, iM), (-M, -iM)$ and $(M, -iM)$, so that the sequence $\{z_n\}$ is wholly contained in SQ_1. (In all that follows, any square SQ_n will include both its boundary and interior).

Step 1. Choose any point z_{j_1} that is a member of $\{z_n\}$ and contained in SQ_1.

Now bisect SQ_1 with a straight horizontal line between the two midpoints on the vertical sides of the square and again bisect the square with a straight vertical line between the two midpoints on the horizontal sides of the square. We now have four equal-sized sub-squares within SQ_1. At least one of those sub-squares contains infinitely many terms of $\{z_n\}$. Call it SQ_2.

Step 2. Choose any point z_{j_2} that is a member of $\{z_n\}$ and contained in SQ_2.

Now bisect SQ_2 with a straight horizontal line between the two midpoints on the vertical sides of the square and again bisect the square with a straight vertical line between the two midpoints on the horizontal sides of the square. We now have four equal-sized sub-squares within SQ_2. At least one of those sub-squares contains infinitely many terms of $\{z_n\}$. Call it SQ_3.

Step n. We continue in similar fashion. By the nth step, we have a subsequence $z_{j_1}, z_{j_2}, \dots z_{j_n}$, with $z_{j_n} \in SQ_n$ and with SQ_n containing infinitely many terms of $\{z_n\}$. All of the remaining terms of our constructed subsequence $\{z_{j_n}\}$ will come from the sub-square SQ_n. The length of any side of sub-square SQ_n is $M/2^{(n-2)}$. We are creating a Cauchy subsequence because for all $m, n > N$ we have $|z_{j_m} - z_{j_n}| < \sqrt{2}M/2^{(N-2)}$. Therefore, $\{z_{j_n}\}$ is a convergence subsequence of $\{z_n\}$. $\qquad \square$

2.5 Compact Sets

We begin this section with the standard definition of a compact set (closed and bounded). Next, we prove that two alternate statements of compactness (convergent subsequence and finite subcover) are equivalent to the standard definition. The latter, known as the Heine-Borel Theorem, appears in many (and sometimes unexpected) places in complex function theory. Finally, we develop a useful lemma regarding nested compact sets.

2.5.1 Closed and Bounded

Definition 2.12
*A set is **compact** if it is closed and bounded.*

A simple consequence of compact sets is the following lemma.

> **Lemma 2.1**
>
> *Let Ω be a compact set, let $\{z_n\}$ be a Cauchy sequence with all $z_n \in \Omega$, and let $\lim\limits_{n\to\infty} z_n = z$. Then, $z \in \Omega$.*

Proof. Let Ω^c be the complement of Ω, so that Ω^c is an open set.

We will assume that $z \notin \Omega$ and obtain a contradiction. If $z \notin \Omega$ then $z \in \Omega^c$. Because Ω^c is open, there is an $\epsilon > 0$ such that, for the open disk $\mathbf{D}_\epsilon(z)$, we have $\mathbf{D}_\epsilon(z) \subset \Omega^c$. But $\{z_n\}$ is a Cauchy sequence. That means there is a $N \in \mathbb{N}$ such that for $n > N$ we have $|z_n - z| < \epsilon$. We have our contradiction because that puts $z_n \in \mathbf{D}_\epsilon(z)$ and therefore $z_n \in \Omega^c$ for an infinity of our z_n. $\qquad\square$

2.5.2 Convergent Subsequence

We can now combine the above lemma with the Bolzano-Weierstrass Theorem to obtain the following theorem regarding compact sets.

> **Theorem 2.7**
>
> *The set Ω is compact if and only if every sequence $\{z_n\}$, with all $z_n \in \Omega$, has a subsequence that converges to a point in Ω.*

Proof. We first assume that Ω is compact. Since Ω is bounded, we apply Theorem 2.6 to see that $\{z_n\}$ has a convergent subsequence. We can then apply Lemma 2.1 to see that the convergent subsequence converges to a point in Ω.

Now assume Ω is not compact, so that Ω is either not closed or not bounded.

Assume Ω is not bounded. Choose some $r_1 > 0$ such that the circle $\mathbf{C}_{r_1}(0)$ intersects Ω. Because Ω is unbounded, r_1 (and all r_n below) must exist. Let z_1 be any point in $\mathbf{C}_{r_1}(0) \cap \Omega$. Next, choose some $r_2 > r_1 + 1$ such that $\mathbf{C}_{r_2}(0)$ intersects Ω and let z_2 be any point in $\mathbf{C}_{r_2}(0) \cap \Omega$. Continuing in this way, we can construct a sequence $\{z_n\}$ with $|z_n|$ monotone increasing and $|z_n - z_{n+1}| \geq 1$. Thus, $\{z_n\}$ has no convergent subsequence.

Finally, assume that Ω is not closed, so that there is some point $z \notin \Omega$ that is on the boundary of Ω. Clearly, for all $\epsilon > 0$ and the disk $\mathbf{D}_\epsilon(z)$ we have $\mathbf{D}_\epsilon(z) \cap \Omega \neq \emptyset$. For all $n \in \mathbb{N}$ let $\epsilon = 1/n$ and choose any $z_n \in \mathbf{D}_{1/n}(z) \cap \Omega$. The sequence $\{z_n\}$ is a Cauchy sequence converging to z, so there can be no convergent subsequences converging to any other point. Thus, no convergent subsequence converges to a point in Ω. $\qquad\square$

2.5.3 Open Covering and the Heine-Borel Theorem

> **Definition 2.13**
>
> *An **open covering** of the set Ω is a family of open sets $\{G_\alpha\}$ (not necessarily countable) such that*
>
> $$\Omega \subset \bigcup_\alpha G_\alpha.$$

Using open coverings, we have the following equivalent formulation of compactness.

Theorem 2.8: Heine-Borel Theorem

The set Ω is compact if and only if every open covering $\{G_\alpha\}$ of Ω has a finite subcovering $\{G_1, G_2, G_3 ..., G_n\}$.

Proof.[5]

Compact $\Rightarrow$ Always Finite Subcover. Assume Ω is compact and $\{G_\alpha\}$ is an open covering.

Let $\mathscr{D}$ be the set of all open disks with rational coordinates and rational radii in $\mathbb{C}$. Then $\mathscr{D}$ is a countable set by Corollary 2.4. Here we will use a subset of $\mathscr{D}$. Let $\{D_j\}$ be the set of all open disks with rational coordinates and rational radii such that any given $D_k \in \{D_j\}$ is wholly in the interior of any one (or more) of the members of $\{G_\alpha\}$. As a subset of $\mathscr{D}$, the set $\{D_j\}$ is countable.

For any given open cover $G_\beta \subset \{G_\alpha\}$, we use Theorem 2.5 to see that every interior point in G_β is covered by some $D_k \in \{D_j\}$. Thus, every point in $\{G_\alpha\}$ is covered by some $D_k \in \{D_j\}$. Therefore $\{G_\alpha\}$ and Ω are both covered by $\{D_j\}$. Note that $\{D_j\} \cap \{G_\alpha\}^c = \emptyset$.

It will be convenient to consider our countable set $\{D_j\}$ in an ordered list $D_1, D_2, ...$. Now build a sequence $\{z_m\}$ of points as follows: let $\{z_1 \in \Omega : z_1 \notin D_1\}$, then $\{z_2 \in \Omega : z_2 \notin D_1 \cup D_2\}$, and so on, with $\{z_n \in \Omega : z_n \notin D_1 \cup D_2 \cup \cdots D_n\}$. We are attempting to build and infinite sequence $\{z_m\}$, which is only possible if no finite subset of $\{D_j\}$ covers Ω.

If we assume our sequence $\{z_m\}$ is infinite, we must have for all m

$$z_m \notin D_1 \cup D_2 \cup D_3 \cup ... \cup D_k, \quad \text{if } m > k. \tag{2.1}$$

By the Bolzano–Weierstrass Theorem, there is a subsequence $\{w_m\}$ of $\{z_m\}$ and a point a such that $\{w_m\} \to a \in \Omega \subset \{D_j\}$. Thus, for some $D_k \in \{D_j\}$, we have $a \in D_k$. Hence, for our Cauchy sequence $\{w_m\}$, there is an N such that for $n > N$, $w_n \in D_k$. This contradicts equation (2.1) because we assumed $z_m \notin D_1 \cup D_2 \cup D_3 \cup ... \cup D_k$ if $m > k$. Therefore, there must be a finite subset of $\{D_j\}$ that covers Ω. Call that finite subset $D_1, D_2, ..., D_n$. Each of those n disks is a subset of some cover in $\{G_\alpha\}$, call those n covers $G_1, G_2, ..., G_n$. We then have $\Omega \subset G_1 \cup G_2 \cup ... \cup G_n$, as required[6].

Not Compact $\Rightarrow$ Not Always Finite Subcover. Now assume Ω is not compact, so that Ω is not closed and/or not bounded. For both cases, we provide an open cover that has no finite subcover. If Ω is not bounded, the open cover $\{D_n\}$ with $D_k = \mathbf{D}_k(0)$ has no finite subcover. If Ω is not closed, we choose a point $a \in \partial\Omega, a \notin \Omega$. The open cover $\{D_n\}$ with $D_k = \{z : |z - a| > 1/k\}$ has no finite subcover. $\square$

2.5.4 Nested Compact Sets

Lemma 2.2

Let $\{\Omega_n\}$ be a collection of non-empty compact sets with $\Omega_{n+1} \subset \Omega_n$ and $\lim\limits_{n\to\infty} \text{diam}(\Omega_n) = 0$. Then there exists a unique point w such that $w \in \bigcap\limits_{n=1}^{\infty} \Omega_n$.

Proof. Form a sequence $\{z_n\}$ by choosing any arbitrary point $z_n \in \Omega_n$. With $\lim\limits_{n\to\infty} \text{diam}(\Omega_n) = 0$, the sequence $\{z_n\}$ must be a Cauchy sequence. Thus, $\lim\limits_{n\to\infty} z_n = w$ for some w. By Theorem 2.7, $w \in \Omega_n$ for all n, proving the existence of w.

To see that w is unique, suppose there exists some other point s that is in all Ω_n. Fix $\epsilon = |w - s|$. Chose N such that for $n > N$ we have $\text{diam}(\Omega_n) < \epsilon/2$. Then for $n > N$ we cannot have both w and s in Ω_n, proving w is unique. $\qquad\square$

2.6 Supplemental Material

We used the Bolzano-Weierstrass Theorem in the proof of the Heine-Borel Theorem. We *did not* use the Heine-Borel Theorem in the proof of the Bolzano-Weierstrass Theorem. (That would have been an invalid use of circular reasoning). However, as an example of using Heine-Borel in a proof, we present another proof of Bolzano-Weierstrass.

Theorem 2.9

Let $\{z_n\}$ be a bounded sequence in $\mathbb{C}$ with $|z_n| < M$ for all n. Then $\{z_n\}$ has a convergent subsequence.

Proof.

Step 1. By assumption, the sequence $\{z_n\} \subset \overline{\mathbf{D}}_M(0)$. Choose any point z_{j_1} that is a member of $\{z_n\}$. Next define

$$A_1 = \bigcup_{w \in \overline{\mathbf{D}}_M(0)} \mathbf{D}_1(w).$$

Then A_1 is an open cover of the compact set $\overline{\mathbf{D}}_M(0)$. By Theorem 2.8, A_1 has a finite subcover. At least one of the disks making up the finite subcover contains infinitely many terms of $\{z_n\}$. Call the disk $\mathscr{D}_1$ and call the subsequence $\{z_n\}_1$.

Step 2. We have $\{z_n\}_1 \subset \overline{\mathscr{D}}_1$. Choose any point z_{j_2} that is a member of $\{z_n\}_1$. Next define

$$A_2 = \bigcup_{w \in \mathscr{D}_1} \mathbf{D}_{1/2}(w).$$

Then A_2 is an open cover of the compact set $\overline{\mathscr{D}}_1$. By Theorem 2.8, A_2 has a finite subcover. At least one of the disks making up the finite subcover contains infinitely many terms of $\{z_n\}_1$. Call the disk $\mathscr{D}_2$ and call the subsequence $\{z_n\}_2$.

Step m. We have $\{z_n\}_{m-1} \subset \overline{\mathscr{D}}_{m-1}$. Choose any point z_{j_m} that is a member of $\{z_n\}_{m-1}$. Define

$$A_m = \bigcup_{w \in \mathscr{D}_{m-1}} \mathbf{D}_{1/m}(w).$$

Then A_m is an open cover of the compact set $\overline{\mathscr{D}}_{m-1}$. By Theorem 2.8, A_m has a finite subcover. At least one of the disks making up the finite subcover contains infinitely many terms of $\{z_n\}_{m-1}$. Call the disk $\mathscr{D}_m$ and call the subsequence $\{z_n\}_m$.

All of the remaining terms of our constructed subsequence $\{z_j\}$ will come from $\mathscr{D}_m$ of radius $1/m$. We are creating a Cauchy subsequence because for all $p, q > N$ we have $|z_{j_p} - z_{j_q}| < 2/N$. Therefore, $\{z_{j_m}\}$ is a convergent subsequence of $\{z_n\}$. $\qquad\square$

Chapter 3

Paths, Connected Sets and Polygons

We continue our survey of the topology of the complex plane. In this chapter, we focus on three particularly important elements: paths, connected sets and polygons. After this chapter, we turn our attention to complex function theory.

3.1 Paths and Contours

There are infinitely many ways to move from point z_0 to point z_1 in the complex plane. And there seem to be as many ways of describing that traversal from z_0 to z_1 as there are authors of textbooks on complex analysis. (To pick a few descriptions: line, arc, curve, trace and path). We use path:

Definition 3.1

*A traversal from z_0 to z_1 in $\mathbb{C}$ is a **path**, and a function that generates a path is a **parameterization** of the path. We say that z_0 and z_1 are **joined** by the path.*

Definition 3.2

***Parameterization** of a path is by a continuous function that maps an interval on the real line to some path in the complex plane. We write the parameterization function as:*

$$\omega(t) = \omega_x(t) + i\omega_y(t), \ a \le t \le b, \ \omega : [a, b] \to \mathbb{C},$$

where $\omega_x(t)$ and $\omega_y(t)$ are continuous (real) functions in the interval $[a, b]$. The interval $[a, b]$ and the resulting path in $\mathbb{C}$ are both assumed to be of finite length. We will often use the symbol γ to reference the path created by a parameterization.

So, for each $a \le t \le b$, $\omega(t)$ is a point on the path in $\mathbb{C}$. We say that the path γ starts at $\omega(a)$ and ends at $\omega(b)$. That is, a path has an orientation: it starts at one end-point and ends at the other. A path whose parameterization traces its points in the opposite direction is a different path.

Definition 3.3

- *A **closed path** is a path that starts and ends at the same point; i.e, $\omega(a) = \omega(b)$.*
- *A **simple path** is a path that does not self-intersect, except possibly at its beginning and ending points (i.e., $\omega(s) \ne \omega(t)$ when $s \ne t$).*
- *A **simple closed path** is a simple path that is also a closed path.*
- *If the **orientation** of a simple closed path is such that the interior lies to the left, it is called **positive** (or **counterclockwise**) orientation; otherwise, **negative** (or **clockwise**) orientation.*
- *A path is **smooth** if $\omega_x'(t)$ and $\omega_y'(t)$ exist and are continuous in the interval $[a, b]$ (only one-sided derivatives needed at the end points).*

> **Remark**
>
> Unless stated otherwise, all paths are assumed to be smooth paths, and all simple closed paths (and contours - see Definition 3.4) are assumed to have positive orientation. The *length* of a path is discussed in Section 5.3.3.

> **Remark**
>
> An important example of a simple closed path is
>
> $$\omega(t) = e^{it} = \cos t + i \sin t, \quad 0 \le t \le 2\pi.$$
>
> This is the unit circle, starting and ending at 1 and traveling in a counterclockwise direction.

3.1.1   Reverse Path

So far, our paths have had an orientation that started at point $\omega(a)$ and ended at point $\omega(b)$. We can create a new path γ^- consisting of the same points in the complex plane but with a reversed orientation so that γ^- starts at point $\omega(b)$ and ends at point $\omega(a)$. As one (of many) parameterizations for γ^-, we define

$$\omega^- : [a, b] \to \mathbb{C} \quad \text{to be the parameterization of } \gamma^- \text{ with } \omega^-(t) = \omega(a + b - t).$$

We call γ^- the **reversed path** of γ.

> **Remark**
>
> Continuing with the example path in the above remark, we reverse the path
>
> $$\omega^-(t) = \omega(0 + 2\pi - t) = \cos(2\pi - t) + i \sin(2\pi - t) = e^{i}(2\pi - t) = e^{-it}, 0 \le t \le 2\pi.$$
>
> This is the unit circle, starting and ending at 1 and traveling in a clockwise direction.

3.1.2   Reparameterization

It is the *image* of a path and its *orientation* that are important. Consider the smooth path γ that is parameterized by

$$\omega : [a, b] \to \mathbb{C}.$$

Let $\phi : [c, d] \to [a, b]$ be an increasing smooth bijection (two-way one-to-one for all members). Then, $\omega \circ \phi : [c, d] \to \mathbb{C}$ parameterizes a path that has the same image and orientation as γ. If ϕ is a decreasing smooth bijection, then the image is the same but the orientation is reversed (i.e., it is a reversed path).

Continuing with the example path $\omega(t) = e^{it}, 0 \leq t \leq 2\pi$, we define

$$\phi(r) = r^2 - 2 \quad \text{so that} \quad \phi : \left[\sqrt{2}, \sqrt{2\pi + 2}\right] \to [0, 2\pi] \quad \text{is an increasing smooth bijection.}$$

Letting $h(r) = \omega(\phi(r)) = \omega \circ \phi : \left[\sqrt{2}, \sqrt{2\pi + 2}\right] \to \mathbb{C}$, we see that $h(r)$ is a reparameterization of $\omega(t)$ that produces the same image (the unit circle) and same orientation in $\mathbb{C}$.

3.1.3 Contour

Often, we want to join several smooth paths together.

Definition 3.4

*A **contour** is a (finite) collection of piecewise smooth paths $\gamma_1, \gamma_2, ... \gamma_n$ where the endpoint of γ_k coincides with the start point of γ_{k+1}.*

We will sometimes denote a contour with a bold path symbol $\boldsymbol{\gamma}$ and sometimes with a $\boldsymbol{\Gamma}$ or $\boldsymbol{C}$. We write

$$\boldsymbol{\gamma} = \gamma_1 + \gamma_2 + ... + \gamma_n.$$

Thus, a contour is a path that is smooth except at finitely many points.

Definition 3.5

- *A **closed contour** is a contour that starts and ends at the same point; i.e, the beginning point of γ_1 is equal to the ending point of γ_n.*
- *A **simple contour** is a contour that does not self-intersect, except possibly at its beginning and ending points.*
- *A **simple closed contour** is a simple contour that is also a closed contour.*
- *The **orientation** (positive of negative) is determined in the same way as a path.*
- *The **length** of a contour is equal to the sum of the lengths of its joined smooth paths.*

3.2 Connected Sets

Definition 3.6

*A set is **disconnected** if it can be partitioned into two nonempty subsets such that each subset has no points in common with the set closure of the other. That is, the set Ω is disconnected if there exists two nonempty subsets X and Y such that $\Omega = X \cup Y$, with $X \cap \overline{Y} = \emptyset$ and $Y \cap \overline{X} = \emptyset$.*

Definition 3.7

*A non-empty set is **connected** if it is not disconnected.*

An example of a set that is disconnected is given by $\Omega = \mathbf{D}_1(0) \cup \mathbf{D}_1(2)$. However, if either of the two open disks includes its closure, such as $\Omega = \overline{\mathbf{D}}_1(0) \cup \mathbf{D}_1(2)$, then Ω is connected.

Definition 3.8

*A set Ω is **path connected** if it is connected and if, for any two points $z_0, z_1 \in \Omega$, there exists a contour γ beginning at z_0 and ending at z_1 with $\gamma \subset \Omega$.*

Definition 3.9

*A set Ω is **simply connected** if it is connected and if, for any simple closed contour $\gamma \subset \Omega$, γ can be contracted to a point while continuously remaining in Ω. (Basically, this means there are no "holes" in Ω).*

Equally, a set Ω in $\mathbb{C}$ is simply connected if and only if it can be constructed by including all of the interior points of some simple closed contour. (The constructed set Ω may include none, some or all of its boundary points).

Every *simply connected* set is *path connected*, and every *path connected* set is *connected*. In the complex plane, sets that are *connected* but not *path connected* are generally quite pathological (pun intended), with names like deleted infinite broom, deleted comb and topologist's sine curve. (In fact, every *open* connected set is path connected). From here forward, we will assume that any connected set is either path connected or simply connected.

Remark

The study of open sets can lead to great complications. As one example, the Jordan Curve Theorem (which we will not prove) makes the intuitively obvious statement that (essentially) a simple closed contour divides the plane into two regions: an interior region and an exterior region, separated by the contour (a "Jordan Curve"). Proof of that simple concept is devilishly difficult and people still argue over the validity of the first proof by Camille Jordan in 1887.

3.3   Regions and Domains

As used in this book, the terms *region* and *domain* are defined below. Often, a complex domain serves as the domain of definition for a complex-valued function.

Definition 3.10

*A **region** in $\mathbb{C}$ is is a subset of $\mathbb{C}$ that is open, non-empty and path connected. A region plus all of its boundary (limit) points is a **closed region**.*

Definition 3.11

*A **domain** in $\mathbb{C}$ is is a subset of $\mathbb{C}$ that is open, non-empty and simply connected. A domain plus all of its boundary (limit) points is a **closed domain**.*

This next theorem is very useful. For any contour inside a region (or domain), it allows us to enclose that contour with a compact set that remains inside the region. We can then apply the properties of compact sets to the points on the contour.

The theorem is also an excellent example of using the Heine-Borel Theorem in a proof.

Theorem 3.1

Let Ω be a region and let $\gamma \subset \Omega$ be a contour. Then there is an $\epsilon > 0$ such that, for every point $z \in \gamma$, the open disk $\mathbf{D}_\epsilon(z) \subset \Omega$.

Proof. [7] For each point $z \in \gamma$, let $[r(z) \cdot 2] > 0$ be small enough so that the open disk $\mathbf{D}_{[r(z)\cdot 2]}(z) \subset \Omega$. Now use only half of that radius, $r(z)$, and define the sets A and A^* as unions of open disks

$$A = \bigcup_{z \in \gamma} \mathbf{D}_{r(z)}(z) \qquad \text{(and as further described below)}: \qquad A^* = \bigcup_{j=1}^{n} \mathbf{D}_{r(z_j)}(z_j). \qquad (3.1)$$

Then $A \subset \Omega$ is an open cover of γ. Because γ is bounded (it is a finite collection of finite length paths) and closed, γ is compact. By Theorem 2.8, the open cover A has a finite subcover A^* consisting of n open disks [see equation (3.1) above]. Let ϵ be the smallest radius of those n open disks.

Fix $w \in \gamma$. Our proof is complete if we can show $\mathbf{D}_\epsilon(w) \subset \Omega$. For at least one of the open disks making up A^*, we must have $w \in \mathbf{D}_{r(z_j)}(z_j)$. We can double the size of that open disk, and still have $\mathbf{D}_{[r(z_j)\cdot 2]}(z_j) \subset \Omega$. With $\epsilon \leq r(z_j)$, that doubling gives $\mathbf{D}_\epsilon(w) \subset \mathbf{D}_{[r(z_j)\cdot 2]}(z_j) \subset \Omega$, as required. $\square$

3.4 Polygons

The simplest possible path, a finite length straight line segment, is the building block for polygons. Polygons can be used to approximate any contour, and play an important role in our proof in Chapter 7 of Cauchy's Integral Theorem. We develop here key properties of polygons.

Definition 3.12

- *A **polygon** consists of a finite number of (finite length) straight line segments (i.e., the simplest possible paths) joined in the usual way to form a contour.*
- *A **closed polygon** and a **simple closed polygon** have the same meaning as any other contour.*
- *A **digon** is a straight line segment (or a part of a straight line segment) that is traversed once in each direction.*

Theorem 3.2

Let Ω be a nonempty open set. Then, Ω is connected if and only if any two points in Ω can be joined by some polygon $P \subset \Omega$.

Proof: (Assume Ω is connected). [8] Fix a point $z_0 \in \Omega$. Let $W \subset \Omega$ be the set of points that can be joined to z_0 by polygons in Ω, and let $S \subset \Omega$ be the set of points that *cannot* be joined.

Now fix any points (we temporarily assume such points exist) $w \in W$ and $s \in S$. Because Ω is open, both points have a neighborhood, say $\mathbf{D}_\epsilon(w)$ and $\mathbf{D}_\delta(s)$, contained in Ω.

Every point in $\mathbf{D}_\epsilon(w)$ can be joined to w by a line segment and therefore to z_0 by a polygon. Thus $\mathbf{D}_\epsilon(w) \subset W$ and W must be open or empty. If any point in $\mathbf{D}_\delta(s)$ can be joined to z_0 by a polygon, then s can also be joined, contrary to assumption; thus, $\mathbf{D}_\delta(s) \subset S$ and S must be open or empty.

Note that the open set W must be non-empty because, at a minimum, it contains a neighborhood of z_0. Reviewing, we have Ω and W open and non-empty with $\Omega = W \cup S$ and $W \cap S = \emptyset$. That means S is the complement of W in Ω and therefore not open. Having previously shown that S is open or empty, we conclude S is empty. Thus, $W = \Omega$, as required. $\qquad\square$

Proof: (Assume Ω is not connected). Because Ω is not connected, there exists two nonempty subsets W and S such that $\Omega = W \cup S$, with $W \cap \overline{S} = \emptyset$ and $S \cap \overline{W} = \emptyset$.

Now fix any points $w \in W$ and $s \in S$ and assume they can be joined by a polygon in Ω. At least one segment of the polygon must connect a point in W to a point in S. Without loss of generality, we may assume that w and s are joined by a line segment. Parameterize that line segment by

$$\omega(t) = w + t(s - w), \ 0 \le t \le 1.$$

Because W is open, there is some t_w such that $\omega(t) \in W$ for $0 \le t < t_w < 1$. Similarly, there is some t_s such that $\omega(t) \in S$ for $0 < t_s < t \le 1$. We must have $t_w < t_s$, otherwise there would be a point $\omega(t)$ in both W and S. But that makes the line segment disconnected, showing that no polygon can connect points w and s. $\qquad\square$

> **Remark**
>
> The importance of the next two theorems will not be seen until later in this book. The underlying idea is that certain integrals over digons, triangles and rectangles evaluate to zero. If we can decompose a closed polygon into smaller parts that consist only of digons, triangles and rectangles, then (under certain circumstances) an integral over that closed polygon will evaluate to zero.
>
> Using the idea that digons "self-erase", we explain what we mean by decompose. When we decompose a given closed polygon into component parts, we mean that if we remove any digons created by the decomposition (or add back any digon removed by the decomposition) what remains is the original polygon.
>
> Thus, when the integral over digons evaluates to zero, the integral over the original polygon will be equal to the integral over the component parts of the decomposed polygon.

> **Remark**
>
> The *results* of the next two theorems are important, but the proofs can be skipped without harm to the reader's understanding of complex analysis.

Theorem 3.3

Every oriented closed polygon P can be decomposed into a finite number of digons and a finite number of oriented simple closed polygons.

Proof.[9]

The Setup. Assume that P is composed of n straight line segments. Stating at the beginning point (and following the oriented traversal) of P, we will denote the n straight line segments of P as $A_1A_2, A_2A_3 \cdots A_nA_{n+1}$, where A_kA_{k+1} is a straight line segment beginning at point A_k and ending at point A_{k+1}. In the same order, we will refer to those line segments as the sides of P, denoted by $s_1, s_2, ..., s_n$. Because P is a closed polygon, we must have $A_1 = A_{n+1}$.

We assume, without loss of generality, that no sides s_k and s_{k+1} have only one point in common and are on the same straight line. That is, s_{k+1} is not just an *extension* of s_k further along the same straight line.

Let k be the current side number, beginning with $k = 2$. We process side s_k of P by applying *Rule (a)* through *Rule (d)*, below.

Rule (a). We apply this rule if s_k has more than one point in common with s_{k-1}. This is only possible if s_k does a partial or full retrace back onto s_{k-1} (creating a digon). In the partial retrace case, there is a point B_{k-1} of s_{k-1} such that $B_{k-1} = A_{k+1}$. In other words, there is a point in s_{k-1} that is the endpoint of s_k. We can therefore modify our polygon P by eliminating the digon $B_{k-1} \rightarrow A_k \rightarrow A_{k+1}$. This eliminates side s_k of the polygon and modifies side s_{k-1} so the line segments are now $A_1A_2, A_2A_3 \cdots A_{k-1}B_{k-1}, A_{k+1}A_{k+2} \cdots A_nA_{n+1}$, making a closed polygon P'.

In the full retrace case, there is a point B_k of s_k such that $B_k = A_{k-1}$. In other words, there is a point in s_k that is the beginning point of s_{k-1}. We therefore modify our polygon P by eliminating the digon $A_{k-1} \rightarrow A_k \rightarrow B_k = A_{k-1}$. That is, we eliminate s_{k-1} and use only the "tail end" (if any) of s_k. The line segments are now $A_1A_2, A_2A_3 \cdots A_{k-2}A_{k-1}, B_kA_{k+1} \cdots A_nA_{n+1}$, making a closed polygon P'.

In either the partial or full retrace case, we have decomposed P into a digon and a closed polygon P'. If *Rule (a)* has been applied, proceed to *Rule (c)*. Otherwise, proceed to *Rule (b)*.

Rule (b). If $k \geq 3$, let $1 \leq u \leq (k-2)$. We only apply this rule if $k \geq 3$ *and* s_k has at least one point in common with one or more of the s_u.

Recall that side s_k is the line segment A_kA_{k+1}. Choose the point in common that is nearest to A_k and call that point B_k. That same B_k is also a point on one of the sides s_u. Call that side s_r and let $B_r = B_k$. Note that no other of the sides s_u can pass through the point B_k. Otherwise, two of the s_u would have B_k as a point in common – something that would have been eliminated in a previous pass through this *Rule (b)*. Now consider the closed polygon

$$Q' = B_rA_{r+1}, A_{r+1}A_{r+2} \cdots A_kB_k.$$

Accounting for the previous passes through this *Rule (b)* and noting how B_k was selected (the point in common nearest to A_K), Q' must be a simple closed polygon. Clearly, Q' has the same orientation as P. Because Q' is a simple closed polygon, the remainder

$$A_1A_2, A_2A_3 \cdots A_rB_r, B_kA_{k+1} \cdots A_nA_{n+1}$$

is a closed polygon P'. We have decomposed P into a simple closed polygon and a closed polygon P'.

Rule (c). If either *Rule (a)* or *Rule (b)* has been applied during this pass through the rules, begin all over again at *The Setup*, with $P = P'$. Without loss of generality, continue to assume that P has n sides. If neither *Rule (a)* nor *Rule (b)* has been applied, proceed to *Rule (d)*.

Rule (d). If $k < n$, increase k by 1 and begin again at *Rule (a)*. If $k = n$, we have made a pass though *Rule (a)* and *Rule (b)* without applying either. Therefore, every s_k ($k > 1$) has only one point in common with s_{k-1} and no points in common with s_u ($1 \le u \le k - 2$). Therefore, the P remaining after this pass through the rules is a simple closed polygon. We have therefore (after a finite number of steps) decomposed the original P into a finite number of digons and a finite number of simple closed polygons, completing the proof. □

Theorem 3.4

Let P be a simple closed polygon with 4 or more sides. Then

    (a) P can be decomposed into triangles by means of digons in the interior of P.

    (b) All such triangles in (a) have the same orientation as P.

Proof (a) - Triangles. [10] Let n equal the number of sides of P. If $n = 4$, the result is immediate, so assume $n > 4$. We prove the result by induction. We assume the result is true for polygons having less than n sides and prove the result for polygons having n sides.

Our strategy is to show that we can insert a digon in the interior of P which decomposes P into two polygons P_1 and P_2. Note that both P_1 and P_2 have less than n sides. (The interior digon adds one side to each sub-polygon, but each sub-polygon loses at least two sides to the other sub-polygon). With less than n sides, P_1 and P_2 satisfy assertion (a) and our proof by induction is complete.

Choose a Convex Vertex. Let L be a straight line in the plane of infinite length that does not intersect P. Remaining parallel to its original position, move L towards P until L and P intersect. At such intersection, one (or more) vertices and (possibly) one or more line segments of P intersect L. Chose one such vertex and call it A. The point A must be a convex vertex of P (the angle interior to P is less that π).

Construct a Triangle. Let B and C denote the two vertices adjacent to A and construct from those three points a "guiding triangle" ABC. Also, let (B, C) be the open line segment between points B and C. Note that the polygon P cannot completely cover (B, C) because that would make triangle ABC a closed polygon and we have assumed $n > 4$.

Consider Three Cases. With our construction, we have obtained one of three cases.

Case 1. No point on P intersects either the interior of triangle ABC or the open line segment (B, C). Thus, we can use BC as our digon in the interior of P, so our inductive proof is complete.

Case 2. No point on P intersects the interior of triangle ABC. However, one (or more) vertices and (possibly) one or more line segments of P intersect (B, C). Choose one such vertex and call it V. Then, we can use AV as our digon in the interior of P, so our inductive proof is complete.

Case 3. Some part of the polygon P intersects the interior of triangle ABC. Let L be a straight line in the plane of infinite length that includes A and is parallel to BC. Remaining parallel to BC, move L towards BC until L first intersects P in the interior of triangle ABC. At that intersection, let L' be the intersection of L and the interior of triangle ABC. As in case 2, the intersection of L' and P includes one (or more) vertices and (possibly) one or more line segments of P. Choose one such vertex and call it V. Then, we can use AV as our digon in the interior of P, so our inductive proof is complete. □

Proof (b) - Orientation. We assume without loss of generality that P is oriented in the positive direction. The first step in the decomposition creates two sub-polygons from P by use of exactly one digon in the interior of P.

We see from (a) that the digon has as its endpoints two of the vertices of P. Call those endpoints B and C. One sub-polygon is traced by beginning at B, continuing in the positive direction along P until C, then turning "left" and continuing from C to B. The other sub-polygon is traced in the same way, except it begins at C. Both sub-polygons are oriented in the positive direction. The digon has been used in one direction by one sub-polygon and in the other direction by the other sub-polygon.

In the same way, and with the same results, further decompositions of sub-polygons always result in positive orientations for the next generation of sub-polygons. Eventually, we end up with sub-polygons of 4 sides. Using the same reasoning, the final decomposition of that 4-sided polygon results in two triangles oriented in the positive direction. $\qquad\square$

3.5   Supplemental Material

The following theorem demonstrates ideas from our discussion of sets, contours and polygons. This theorem will be used in the proof of Theorem 7.7. We begin with a definition that will be used only for the below theorem.

Definition 3.13

For $w \neq 0 \in \mathbb{C}$, define $\mathcal{P}(w)$ to be a polygon traversing from 0 to w as follows:

- *First, a horizontal line (if needed) from 0 to $Re(w)$.*

- *Then, a vertical line (if needed) from $Re(w)$ to w.*

Define $-\mathcal{P}(w)$ to be the same polygon oriented in the opposite direction (traversing from w to 0).

Theorem 3.5

Fix $z \neq 0$ and let $\mathbf{D}_\delta(z)$ be a neighborhood of z small enough such that: (1) if z is not on the real or imaginary axis, $\mathbf{D}_\delta(z)$ remains in the same quadrant as z, and (2) if z is on the real or imaginary axis, $\mathbf{D}_\delta(z)$ remains in the same half-plane as z.

For $z_0 \neq z$, fix $z_0 \in \mathbf{D}_\delta(z)$ and let $\Delta z = z_0 - z$ so that $z_0 = z + \Delta z$.

Let $\mathbf{P}$ be a set, initially containing $\{\mathcal{P}(z + \Delta z), -\mathcal{P}(z)\}$. Then, by including in $\mathbf{P}$ (if necessary) a particular digon or oriented triangle, $\mathbf{P}$ can be decomposed into (1) a line segment traversing from z to $(z + \Delta z)$, plus (2) zero or more digons, oriented triangles and oriented rectangles.

Proof. [11]   To prove the theorem, we consider several cases.

Case 1. $Im(z) = Im(z + \Delta z) = 0$ or $Re(z) = Re(z + \Delta z) = 0$. Both $\mathcal{P}(z + \Delta z)$ and $-\mathcal{P}(z)$ are single-leg polygons on either the real or imaginary axis. The reverse traversal of $-\mathcal{P}(z)$ leaves only a digon plus the line segment from z to $(z + \Delta z)$, as required.

Case 2. $Re(z) = Re(z + \Delta z) \neq 0$. This is another simple case. Both polygons trace the same path, with one stopping short of the other. Again, the reverse traversal of $-\mathcal{P}(z)$ leaves only a digon plus the line segment from z to $(z + \Delta z)$, as required.

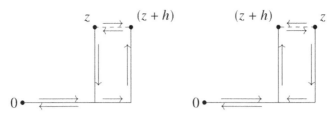

Figure 3.1: Case 4a (Examples)

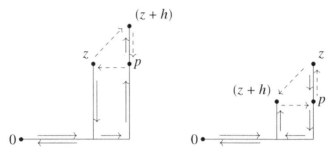

Figure 3.2: Case 4b (Examples)

Case 3. $Im(z) = 0$ but $Im(z + \Delta z) \neq 0$. Here, $-\mathscr{P}(z)$ is a single-leg polygon on the real axis, but $\mathscr{P}(z + \Delta z)$ departs the real axis. First note the two paths create a digon that cancels between 0 and $\min(Re(z), Re(z + \Delta z))$. Now insert a digon between z and $(z + \Delta z)$. One direction of the digon completes an oriented traversal of a triangle from z to $Re(z + \Delta z)$ to $(z + \Delta z)$ back to z. The other direction of the digon is the line segment from z to $(z + \Delta z)$, as required.

Case 4. In the remaining cases, z is not on the real axis, but may be on the imaginary axis. We also have that $Re(z) \neq Re(z + \Delta z)$. We consider cases 4a and 4b.

Case 4a. $Im(z) = Im(z + \Delta z)$. We insert a digon between z and $(z + \Delta z)$. One direction of the digon completes an oriented traversal of a rectangle with points $Re(z), Re(z + \Delta z), (z + \Delta z), z$. The path on the real axis between 0 and the rectangle is a digon due to the reverse transversal of $-\mathscr{P}(z)$. All that remains is the other direction of the inserted digon: the line segment from z to $(z + h)$, as required.

Case 4b. In this final case, $Re(z) \neq Re(z + \Delta z)$ and $Im(z) \neq Im(z + \Delta z)$. We first define a point p as follows. If $Im(z) < Im(z + \Delta z)$, let $Re(p) = Re(z + \Delta z)$ and $Im(p) = Im(z)$. If $Im(z) > Im(z + \Delta z)$, let $Re(p) = Re(z)$ and $Im(p) = Im(z + \Delta z)$. Now insert an oriented triangle as follows: begin at z, move to $(z + \Delta z)$, move to p and then return to z. One leg of the triangle completes an oriented rectangle and one leg creates a digon. The path on the real axis between 0 and the rectangle is a digon due to the reverse transversal of $-\mathscr{P}(z)$. All that remains (the unused segment of the triangle) is the line segment from z to $(z + \Delta z)$, as required. $\square$

Chapter 4

Derivatives and the Cauchy-Riemann Equations

In this chapter we study functions of a complex variable that are complex differentiable. We begin by defining when complex functions are continuous or complex differentiable – definitions which should be familiar from real variable calculus. After developing some basic properties of complex derivatives, we get to the heart of the chapter. We show that functions are complex differentiable (i.e., holomorphic) if and only if they satisfy the Cauchy-Riemann equations. We then show that holomorphic functions are harmonic (think very well behaved). Finally, we continue our study of the complex logarithm by proving that any fixed branch of $\log(z)$ is holomorphic in the slit plane $\mathbb{C}\backslash(-\infty, 0]$.

4.1 Some Preliminary Definitions

4.1.1 Continuity

Definition 4.1

*For the domain Ω, the function $f(z) : \Omega \mapsto \mathbb{C}$ is **continuous** at the point $z_0 \in \Omega$ if for every $\epsilon > 0$ there exists a $\delta > 0$ such that whenever $z \in \mathbf{D}_\delta(z_0) \subset \Omega$ then $f(z) \in \mathbf{D}_\epsilon(f(z_0))$.*

Note that our domain Ω is, by definition, open. Thus, we can always choose a δ small enough so that $\mathbf{D}_\delta(z_0) \subset \Omega$.

The function $f(z)$ is continuous in Ω if it is continuous at all $z \in \Omega$.

> **Remark**
>
> As shorthand, we might say that $f(z)$ is continuous at z_0 if $f(z) \to f(z_0)$ as $z \to z_0$.
>
> A fully equivalent definition is that for every sequence $\{z_n\} \subset \Omega$ such that $\lim_{n\to\infty} z_n = z_0$, then $\lim_{n\to\infty} f(z_n) = f(z_0)$.

It is easily shown that sums and products of continuous functions are continuous, and so are quotients, provided that the denominator is not zero. Further, the composition of continuous functions is continuous.

4.1.2 Continuity on a Boundary

Continuity is usually defined with respect to points in an open set. However, we must sometimes consider continuity with respect to the boundary points of a closed set. We consider next two types of closed sets: closed domains and contours.

Definition 4.2

*For the closed domain $\overline{\Omega}$, we say $f(z) : \overline{\Omega} \mapsto \mathbb{C}$ is continuous on $\overline{\Omega}$ if: (1) the usual conditions of continuity apply for $z \in \Omega$, and (2) for all $w \in \partial\Omega$, the usual conditions of continuity apply for some **partial neighborhood** $z \in \mathbf{D}_\delta(w) \cap \overline{\Omega}$. The latter condition is sometimes called **continuity from the interior**.*

*For the contour $\mathbf{C}$, we first consider continuity with respect its component smooth paths. For the smooth path γ, we say $f(z) : \gamma \mapsto \mathbb{C}$ is continuous on γ if for all $w \in \gamma$, the usual conditions of continuity apply for some **path neighborhood** $z \in \mathbf{D}_\delta(w) \cap \gamma$. The latter condition is sometimes called **continuity along a path**. If all component smooth paths of $\mathbf{C}$ meet the requirements for continuity along a path, we say that $f(z)$ is **piecewise continuous** along $\mathbf{C}$.*

4.1.3 Uniform Continuity

A much stronger type of continuity is uniform continuity. In regular continuity, the epsilon-delta test is applied *locally* to a point and its neighborhood. In uniform continuity, the same epsilon-delta values apply *uniformly* throughout the domain. Think of continuity as being defined at a point, while uniform continuity is defined on a set.

Definition 4.3

*For the domain Ω, the function $f(z) : \Omega \mapsto \mathbb{C}$ is **uniformly continuous** in Ω if for every $\epsilon > 0$ there exists a $\delta > 0$ such that whenever $z_1, z_2 \in \Omega$ and $|z_1 - z_2| < \delta$ then $|f(z_1) - f(z_2)| < \epsilon$.*

4.1.4 Differentiable / Derivative

Definition 4.4

*For the domain Ω, the function $f(z) : \Omega \mapsto \mathbb{C}$ is **complex differentiable** at the point $z_0 \in \Omega$ if the quotient*

$$\frac{f(z) - f(z_0)}{z - z_0} \qquad \text{for } z \in \Omega \text{ and } (z - z_0) \neq 0,$$

*has a limit as $z \to z_0$. We refer to that limit as the **complex derivative** of f at z_0 and write*

$$f'(z_0) = \frac{df}{dz}(z_0) = \lim_{z \to z_0} \frac{f(z) - f(z_0)}{z - z_0}.$$

The function $f(z)$ is complex differentiable on Ω if it is complex differentiable at all $z \in \Omega$.

> **Remark**
>
> We often rewrite the above definition by using $\Delta z = z - z_0$, so that (if a limit exists)
>
> $$f'(z_0) = \lim_{\Delta z \to 0} \frac{f(z_0 + \Delta z) - f(z_0)}{\Delta z}.$$
>
> The ability of Δz to approach 0 from any direction is key to the study of complex derivatives.

4.1.5 Holomorphic Functions

> **Definition 4.5**
> *For the domain Ω, the function $f(z) : \Omega \mapsto \mathbb{C}$ is **holomorphic** at the point $z_0 \in \Omega$ if it is complex differentiable at z_0. The function $f(z)$ is holomorphic in Ω if $f(z)$ is holomorphic at all $z \in \Omega$.*
> *If the function $f(z)$ is holomorphic in all of $\mathbb{C}$ we say that $f(z)$ is **entire**.*

Remark

Like continuity, the complex derivative is defined with respect to an open set. That ensures each complex differentiable point in the set has an open neighborhood also in the set. Complex differentiability on the boundary of a set is a complicated and advanced topic. Unless specifically stated otherwise, we assume that our complex differentiable points are members of an open set.

With respect to a closed set G, if we say that $f(z)$ is holomorphic on G it is implied that $f(z)$ is holomorphic in some open set containing G.

4.2 Component Parts of Complex Functions

Let Ω and Λ be sets in $\mathbb{C}$. Here we consider a complex function $f : \Omega \mapsto \Lambda$. For $z = x + iy \in \Omega$ and $w = s + it \in \Lambda$, we will assume $f(z) = w$.

We could equally think of Ω and Λ as sets in $\mathbb{R}^2$ and a mapping $F : \Omega \subset \mathbb{R}^2 \mapsto \Lambda \subset \mathbb{R}^2$. Using the real parts of z and w, and our equivalent function F, then $f(z) = w$ maps to $F(x, y) = (s, t)$. In $\mathbb{R}^2$, there also exist functions $s = U(x, y)$ and $t = V(x, y)$ with $F(x, y) = (U(x, y), V(x, y))$.

That brings us back to $f(z)$ where, likewise, there are real-valued functions of two real variables $u(x, y)$ and $v(x, y)$ with $f(z) = u(x, y) + iv(x, y)$. That is, $u(x, y) = Re(f(z))$ and $v(x, y) = Im(f(z))$. The last is sometimes written in shorthand as $f(z) = u + iv$.

Remark

The $f(z) = u(x, y) + iv(x, y)$ form will be useful when we consider partial derivatives of $f(z)$. That is, $dz = dx + idy$.

Remark

Assume that $f(z) = u(x, y) + iv(x, y)$ is continuous at a point. Then, both $u(x, y)$ and $v(x, y)$ must be continuous at that point. (Any jump discontinuity at either the x- or y-coordinate will cause a jump discontinuity at $f(z)$).

Remark

The easiest way to visualize the plotting of the values of $f(z) = w$ from Ω to Λ is to think of a mapping $\mathbb{C} \mapsto \mathbb{C}$ from one complex "z-plane" to another complex "w-plane".

4.3 Basics of Complex Derivatives

Theorem 4.1

If $f(z)$ is differentiable at z_0, then $f(z)$ is continuous at z_0.

Proof. We begin with the following expression for $f(z)$, and evaluate it as $z \to z_0$:

$$f(z) = f(z_0) + \left(\frac{f(z) - f(z_0)}{z - z_0} \right)(z - z_0)$$

$$\lim_{z \to z_0} f(z) = \lim_{z \to z_0} \left[f(z_0) + \left(\frac{f(z) - f(z_0)}{z - z_0} \right)(z - z_0) \right]$$

$$= f(z_0) + \lim_{z \to z_0} \left[(f'(z_0))(z - z_0) \right]$$

$$= f(z_0) + f'(z_0) \left[\lim_{z \to z_0} (z - z_0) \right]$$

$$= f(z_0) + f'(z_0)[0]$$

$$= f(z_0).$$

We see that $f(z) \to f(z_0)$ as $z \to z_0$, as required. $\qquad\square$

Theorem 4.2

Assume $f(z)$ and $g(z)$ are differentiable at z, and that c is any complex constant. Then, the complex derivative satisfies the following rules for differentiating sums, products, and quotients. In all such cases, the resulting formula is also differentiable at z.

$$(cf)'(z) = cf'(z) \tag{4.1}$$

$$(f + g)'(z) = f'(z) + g'(z) \tag{4.2}$$

$$(f(z) \cdot g(z))' = (fg)'(z) = f(z)g'(z) + f'(z)g(z) \tag{4.3}$$

$$(f(z)/g(z))' = (f/g)'(z) = \frac{g(z)f'(z) - f(z)g'(z)}{g(z)^2}, \quad g(z) \neq 0. \tag{4.4}$$

Proof. Equations (4.1) and (4.2) are easily shown. For equation (4.3) we have

$$(fg)'(z) = \lim_{\Delta z \to 0} \frac{(fg)(z + \Delta z) - (fg)(z)}{\Delta z},$$

$$= \lim_{\Delta z \to 0} \frac{[f(z + \Delta z) \cdot g(z + \Delta z)] - [f(z) \cdot g(z)]}{\Delta z},$$

$$= \lim_{\Delta z \to 0} \left(f(z + \Delta z)\frac{g(z + \Delta z) - g(z)}{\Delta z} + \frac{f(z + \Delta z) - f(z)}{\Delta z}g(z) \right)$$

$$= \lim_{\Delta z \to 0} \left[f(z + \Delta z)g'(z) + f'(z)g(z) \right]$$

$$= f(z)g'(z) + f'(z)g(z).$$

Finally, for equation (4.4), we have

$$
\begin{aligned}
(f/g)'(z) &= \lim_{\Delta z \to 0} \frac{(f/g)(z + \Delta z) - (f/g)(z)}{\Delta z} \\
&= \lim_{\Delta z \to 0} \left[\frac{(f/g)(z + \Delta z) - (f/g)(z)}{\Delta z} \right] \cdot \left[\frac{g(z + \Delta z)g(z)}{g(z + \Delta z)g(z)} \right] \\
&= \lim_{\Delta z \to 0} \frac{f(z + \Delta z)g(z) - f(z)(g)(z + \Delta z)}{\Delta z \cdot g(z + \Delta z) \cdot g(z)} \\
&= \lim_{\Delta z \to 0} \frac{f(z + \Delta z)g(z) - f(z)g(z) + f(z)g(z) - f(z)(g)(z + \Delta z)}{\Delta z \cdot g(z + \Delta z) \cdot g(z)} \\
&= \lim_{\Delta z \to 0} \frac{1}{g(z + \Delta z) \cdot g(z)} \left(\frac{f(z + \Delta z)g(z) - f(z)g(z) + f(z)g(z) - f(z)(g)(z + \Delta z)}{\Delta z} \right) \\
&= \lim_{\Delta z \to 0} \frac{1}{g(z + \Delta z) \cdot g(z)} \left(\frac{g(z)\left[f(z + \Delta z) - f(z) \right]}{\Delta z} + \frac{f(z)\left[g(z) - g(z + \Delta z) \right]}{\Delta z} \right) \\
&= \lim_{\Delta z \to 0} \frac{1}{g(z + \Delta z) \cdot g(z)} \left(g(z)\left[\frac{f(z + \Delta z) - f(z)}{\Delta z} \right] - f(z)\left[\frac{g(z + \Delta z) - g(z)}{\Delta z} \right] \right) \\
&= \lim_{\Delta z \to 0} \frac{g(z)f'(z) - f(z)g'(z)}{g(z + \Delta z) \cdot g(z)} \\
&= \frac{g(z)f'(z) - f(z)g'(z)}{g(z)^2}. \qquad \square
\end{aligned}
$$

Theorem 4.3

Suppose that $g(z)$ is differentiable at z_0, and suppose that $f(w)$ is differentiable at $w_0 = g(z_0)$. Then the composition $(f \circ g)(z) = f(g(z))$ is differentiable at z_0 and

$$
(f \circ g)(z) = f'(g(z_0))g'(z_0).
$$

Proof.

Case 1. First assume $g'(z_0) \neq 0$, so that for ϵ small enough, $g(z) \neq g(z_0)$ for $0 < |z - z_0| < \epsilon$. This allows:

$$
\frac{f(g(z)) - f(g(z_0))}{z - z_0} = \left[\frac{f(g(z)) - f(g(z_0))}{g(z) - g(z_0)} \right] \cdot \frac{g(z) - g(z_0)}{z - z_0}.
$$

Since $g(z)$ is differentiable at z_0, it is continuous at z_0; that is, $g(z) \to g(z_0)$ as $z \to z_0$. Consequently, for the fraction in brackets we have [fraction] $\to f'(g(z_0))$ as $z \to z_0$. Therefore, passing the full right-hand side to the limit, we obtain $f'(g(z_0))g'(z_0)$, as required.

Case 2. Assume $g'(z_0) = 0$. Since $f(w)$ is differentiable at w_0, the following difference quotient is bounded near w_0. That is, for $0 < |w - w_0| < \epsilon$ and some constant C, we have

$$
\left| \frac{f(w) - f(w_0)}{w - w_0} \right| \leq C.
$$

For z near enough to z_0, that mean $|f(g(z)) - f(g(z_0))| \leq C|g(z) - g(z_0)|$. Thus,

$$
\left| \frac{f(g(z)) - f(g(z_0))}{z - z_0} \right| \leq C \left| \frac{g(z) - g(z_0)}{z - z_0} \right|.
$$

Since the right-hand side tends to 0 as $z \to z_0$, we obtain $(f \circ g)(z_0) = 0$, as required. $\qquad \square$

4.4 The Cauchy-Riemann Equations

In the Cauchy–Riemann equations below, we will see that a holomorphic function is very constrained by the rigid relationship between that function's complex derivative, its real and imaginary parts, and its partial derivatives. In fact, using the Cauchy–Riemann equations, we will show that all holomorphic functions are *harmonic functions*, a special class of functions that is very well behaved.

Theorem 4.4: Cauchy-Riemann Equations (part 1)

For $z = x + iy$, let $f(z) = u(x, y) + iv(x, y)$ be defined in the domain Ω and holomorphic at the point $z \in \Omega$. Then

$$f'(z) = \frac{\partial u}{\partial x}(x, y) + i\frac{\partial v}{\partial x}(x, y) = \frac{\partial v}{\partial y}(x, y) - i\frac{\partial u}{\partial y}(x, y),$$

and therefore

$$\frac{\partial u}{\partial x}(x, y) = \frac{\partial v}{\partial y}(x, y) \quad and \quad \frac{\partial u}{\partial y}(x, y) = -\frac{\partial v}{\partial x}(x, y). \tag{4.5}$$

Proof. [12] We are given that $f(z)$ is complex differentiable at our fixed z. Thus, in our difference quotient for the derivative, we can have $\Delta z = \Delta x + i\Delta y \to 0$ from any direction. In particular, we can hold Δy constant and approach zero along the x-axis or hold Δx constant and approach zero along the y-axis. Therefore, all three of the following difference quotients must obtain the same value

$$f'(z) = \lim_{\Delta z \to 0} \frac{f(z + \Delta z) - f(z)}{\Delta z} = \lim_{\Delta x \to 0} \frac{f(z + \Delta x) - f(z)}{\Delta x} = \lim_{\Delta y \to 0} \frac{f(z + i\Delta y) - f(z)}{i\Delta y}.$$

First assume $\Delta y = 0$ so that $\Delta z = \Delta x$.

$$\lim_{\Delta x \to 0} \frac{f(z + \Delta x) - f(z)}{\Delta x} = \lim_{\Delta x \to 0} \left[\frac{u(x + \Delta x, y) + iv(x + \Delta x, y) - (u(x, y) - iv(x, y))}{\Delta x} \right]$$
$$= \lim_{\Delta x \to 0} \left[\frac{u(x + \Delta x, y) - u(x, y)}{\Delta x} + i\frac{v(x + \Delta x, y) - v(x, y)}{\Delta x} \right].$$

We have obtained the partial derivatives $\partial u/\partial x$ and $\partial v/\partial x$

$$f'(z) = \frac{\partial u}{\partial x}(x, y) + i\frac{\partial v}{\partial x}(x, y). \tag{4.6}$$

Now assume $\Delta x = 0$ so that $\Delta z = i\Delta y$.

$$\lim_{\Delta y \to 0} \frac{f(z + i\Delta y) - f(z)}{i\Delta y} = \lim_{\Delta y \to 0} \left[\frac{u(x, y + \Delta y) + iv(x, y + \Delta y) - (u(x, y) - iv(x, y))}{i\Delta y} \right]$$
$$= \lim_{\Delta y \to 0} \left[\frac{v(x, y + \Delta y) - v(x, y)}{\Delta y} - i\frac{u(x, y + \Delta y) - u(x, y)}{\Delta y} \right].$$

We have obtained the partial derivatives $\partial v/\partial y$ and $\partial u/\partial y$

$$f'(z) = \frac{\partial v}{\partial y}(x, y) - i\frac{\partial u}{\partial y}(x, y). \tag{4.7}$$

Now using our two expressions for $f'(z)$ in equations (4.6) and (4.7), we equate their real and imaginary parts, and obtain equations (4.5), as required. $\square$

Definition 4.6

*Equations (4.5) are called the **Cauchy-Riemann equations**.*

Remark

As we get deeper into complex function theory, we will show that all holomorphic functions have complex derivatives of all orders and therefore continuous partial derivatives of all orders. Anticipating that result, we will assume below that all holomorphic functions have continuous partial derivatives of both the first and second order.

We have shown that all holomorphic functions satisfy the Cauchy-Riemann equations. We now show that all functions that satisfy the Cauchy-Riemann equations are holomorphic.

Theorem 4.5: Cauchy-Riemann Equations (part 2)

For $z = x + iy$, let $f(z) = u(x, y) + iv(x, y)$ be defined in the domain Ω. Assume that $u(x, y)$ and $v(x, y)$ have continuous first order partial derivatives that satisfy the Cauchy-Riemann equations in Ω, Then, $f(z)$ is holomorphic in Ω.

Proof. [13] Fix $z = x + iy \in \Omega$. Using Taylor's Remainder Theorem, we have

$$u(x + \Delta x, y + \Delta y) = u(x, y) + \frac{\partial u}{\partial x}(x, y)\Delta x + \frac{\partial u}{\partial y}(x, y)\Delta y + R_u(\Delta x, \Delta y)$$

$$v(x + \Delta x, y + \Delta y) = v(x, y) + \frac{\partial v}{\partial x}(x, y)\Delta x + \frac{\partial v}{\partial y}(x, y)\Delta y + R_v(\Delta x, \Delta y),$$

where $R_u(\Delta x, \Delta y)$ and $R_v(\Delta x, \Delta y)$ are the remainder/error terms in the linear approximation given by Taylor's theorem. By way of example, we consider the error term $R_u(\Delta x)$ for $\partial u / \partial x$:

$$|R_u(\Delta x)| \leq \max_{x-|\Delta x| \leq x_0 \leq x+|\Delta x|} |u(x_0, y) - u(x, y)| |\Delta x|.$$

The continuity of the partial derivatives means we can choose a $\delta(n)$ such that if $|\Delta x| < \delta(n)$ then we have $|u(x_0, y) - u(x, y)| < 1/4n$. Thus, $|R_u(\Delta x)| \leq |\Delta x|/4n$. Applying the same reasoning to all four partial error terms, there is a $\delta(n)$ such that

$$R_u(\Delta x, \Delta y) + R_v(\Delta x, \Delta y) = R_u(\Delta z) + R_v(\Delta z) \leq \frac{|\Delta z|}{n}, \tag{4.8}$$

where n can be as large as we like by choosing the appropriate $\delta(n)$.

We then have

$$f(z + \Delta z) = u(x + \Delta x, y + \Delta y) + iv(x + \Delta x, y + \Delta y)$$

$$= u(x, y) + \frac{\partial u}{\partial x}(x, y)\Delta x + \frac{\partial u}{\partial y}(x, y)\Delta y + R_u(\Delta z)$$

$$+ iv(x, y) + i\frac{\partial v}{\partial x}(x, y)\Delta x + i\frac{\partial v}{\partial y}(x, y)\Delta y + iR_v(\Delta z)$$

$$= f(z) + \frac{\partial u}{\partial x}(x, y)\Delta x + \frac{\partial u}{\partial y}(x, y)\Delta y + i\frac{\partial v}{\partial x}(x, y)\Delta x + i\frac{\partial v}{\partial y}(x, y)\Delta y + R_u(\Delta z) + iR_v(\Delta z).$$

By assumption, $u(x, y)$ and $v(x, y)$ satisfy the Cauchy-Riemann equations. Thus, we can use equation (4.5) and substitute the ∂x formulae for the ∂y formulae, giving

$$f(z + \Delta z) = f(z) + \frac{\partial u}{\partial x}(x, y) \Delta x - \frac{\partial v}{\partial x}(x, y) \Delta y + i\frac{\partial v}{\partial x}(x, y) \Delta x + i\frac{\partial u}{\partial x}(x, y) \Delta y + R_u(\Delta z) + iR_v(\Delta z)$$

$$= f(z) + \frac{\partial u}{\partial x}(x, y)(\Delta x + i\Delta y) + i\frac{\partial v}{\partial x}(x, y)(\Delta x + i\Delta y) + R_u(\Delta z) + iR_v(\Delta z)$$

and now using that $\Delta z = \Delta x + i\Delta y$

$$= f(z) + \left[\frac{\partial u}{\partial x}(x, y) + i\frac{\partial v}{\partial x}(x, y) \right] \Delta z + R_u(\Delta z) + iR_v(\Delta z).$$

Rearranging and dividing both sides by Δz

$$\frac{f(z + \Delta z) - f(z)}{\Delta z} = \left[\frac{\partial u}{\partial x}(x, y) + i\frac{\partial v}{\partial x}(x, y) \right] + \frac{R_u(\Delta z) + iR_v(\Delta z)}{\Delta z}$$

$$f'(z) = \lim_{\Delta z \to 0} \frac{f(z + \Delta z) - f(z)}{\Delta z} = \left[\frac{\partial u}{\partial x}(x, y) + i\frac{\partial v}{\partial x}(x, y) \right] + \lim_{\Delta z \to 0} \frac{R_u(\Delta z) + iR_v(\Delta z)}{\Delta z}.$$

We have shown in equation (4.8) that the right-most term above goes to zero. Thus, $f'(z)$ is equal to the continuous partial derivatives of equation (4.6), and is therefore holomorphic in Ω. $\qquad\square$

Theorem 4.6

For $z = x + iy$, let $f(z) = u(x, y) + iv(x, y)$ be holomorphic in the domain Ω. For $z \in \Omega$, if either $Re(f(z))$ or $Im(f(z))$ is constant, then $f(z)$ is constant.

Proof. Assume first that $Re(f(z))$ is constant, so that

$$\frac{\partial u}{\partial x}(x, y) = \frac{\partial u}{\partial y}(x, y) = 0.$$

By the Cauchy-Riemann equations

$$\frac{\partial v}{\partial x}(x, y) = -\frac{\partial u}{\partial y}(x, y) = 0.$$

Thus, by Theorem 4.4

$$f'(z) = \frac{\partial u}{\partial x} + i\frac{\partial v}{\partial x} = 0 + 0 = 0.$$

The proof where $Im(f(z))$ is constant proceeds in similar fashion. $\qquad\square$

Remark

This theorem shows that a non-constant holomorphic function cannot have only real or only imaginary values.

4.5 Harmonic Functions

> **Definition 4.7**
>
> *For the real space $\mathbb{R}^n$, with elements $(x_1, x_2, \cdots, x_n)$, let U be an open subset of $\mathbb{R}^n$. Suppose the function $f : U \mapsto \mathbb{R}$ has continuous partial derivatives of the first and second order and satisfies **Laplace's equation**:*
>
> $$\frac{\partial^2 f}{\partial x_1^2} + \frac{\partial^2 f}{\partial x_2^2} + \cdots \frac{\partial^2 f}{\partial x_n^2} = 0.$$
>
> *Then, f is a **harmonic function**.*

Harmonic function of two real variables are among the most well-behaved functions in $\mathbb{R}^2$. A discussion of all of their important properties is beyond the scope of this book. We briefly note here that a harmonic function on a set Ω has the following properties on Ω: (1) it is analytic (it can be locally expressed as a power series), (2) it is infinitely differentiable and (3) partial derivatives of all orders are harmonic.

We now show that the real and imaginary parts of a holomorphic function are harmonic.

Theorem 4.7

Let $f(z) = u(x, y) + iv(x, y)$ be holomorphic in the domain Ω. Assume that $f(z)$ has continuous partial derivatives of the first and second order. Then, $u(x, y)$ and $v(x, y)$ are harmonic for $z = x + iy \in \Omega$.

Proof. We recall the Cauchy-Riemann equations:

$$\frac{\partial u}{\partial x} = \frac{\partial v}{\partial y} \quad \text{and} \quad \frac{\partial u}{\partial y} = -\frac{\partial v}{\partial x}.$$

Using those equations, we have

$$\boxed{\frac{\partial^2 u}{\partial x^2}} = \frac{\partial}{\partial x}\frac{\partial u}{\partial x} = \frac{\partial}{\partial x}\frac{\partial v}{\partial y} = \frac{\partial}{\partial y}\frac{\partial v}{\partial x} = -\frac{\partial}{\partial y}\frac{\partial u}{\partial y} = \boxed{-\frac{\partial^2 u}{\partial y^2}}$$

$$\boxed{\frac{\partial^2 v}{\partial y^2}} = \frac{\partial}{\partial y}\frac{\partial v}{\partial y} = \frac{\partial}{\partial y}\frac{\partial u}{\partial x} = \frac{\partial}{\partial x}\frac{\partial u}{\partial y} = -\frac{\partial}{\partial x}\frac{\partial v}{\partial x} = \boxed{-\frac{\partial^2 v}{\partial x^2}}.$$

From the boxed equations, it follows immediately that

$$\frac{\partial^2 u}{\partial x^2} + \frac{\partial^2 u}{\partial y^2} = 0 \quad \text{and} \quad \frac{\partial^2 v}{\partial x^2} + \frac{\partial^2 v}{\partial y^2} = 0. \qquad \square$$

> **Definition 4.8**
>
> *We have shown that the real and imaginary parts of holomorphic functions are harmonic. For our holomorphic function $f = u + iv$, the harmonic function v is called the **harmonic conjugate** of u.*

Theorem 4.8

Let $f_1 = u_1 + iv_1$ and $f_2 = u_1 + iv_2$ be holomorphic in the domain Ω, so that u_1, v_1 and v_2 are harmonic functions and both v_1 and v_2 are harmonic conjugates of u_1. Then, v_1 and v_2 differ by a constant.

Proof. Because f_1 and f_2 are both holomorphic, then $g = (f_1 - f_2) = i(v_1 - v_2)$ is a purely imaginary holomorphic function on Ω. Because $Re(g)$ is constant, by Theorem 4.6, that means g is constant. Therefore $(v_1 - v_2)$ is constant. $\qquad\square$

4.6 Holomorphy of the Complex Logarithm

We continue to add color to the very important complex logarithm. Our next theorem demonstrates a critical property: every branch of the complex logarithm is only holomorphic in the slit plane.

Theorem 4.9

For any fixed $k \in \mathbb{Z}$, let $\log(z) = \log|z| + i\operatorname{Arg}(z) + 2\pi ik$ be a branch of the complex logarithm. Then, $\log(z)$ is holomorphic in the slit plane $\mathbb{C}\backslash(-\infty, 0]$.

Proof. We first demonstrate that $\operatorname{Arg} z$ (and therefore $\operatorname{Log}(z)$) is discontinuous at each point on the negative real axis. Let $z = x_0 + iy$ for some fixed $x_0 < 0$. For $y > 0$, $\lim\limits_{y \to 0} \operatorname{Arg}(z) = \pi$. On the other hand, for $y < 0$, $\lim\limits_{y \to 0} \operatorname{Arg}(z) = -\pi$, a clear discontinuity. A function cannot be holomorphic at a point of discontinuity. Thus, combined with $\log(z)$ being undefined for $z = 0$, we must be restricted to the slit plane.

For our fixed branch of the logarithm, we have $\log(z) = \log|z| + i\operatorname{Arg}(z) + 2\pi ik$. In any derivative of $\log(z)$, the $2\pi ik$ constant term will vanish, so it suffices to prove the assertion for $\log(z) = \log|z| + i\operatorname{Arg}(z) = \operatorname{Log}(z)$, the principal branch of the logarithm and the principal value for $\log(z)$.

Our proof is therefore complete if we can show that $\operatorname{Log}(z)$ satisfied the Cauchy-Riemann equations on the slit plane. Using that $\operatorname{Arg}(z) = \operatorname{atan2}(y, x)$ for $z = x + iy$, we have

$$\operatorname{Log}(z) = u(x, y) + iv(x, y) \quad \text{where} \quad u(x, y) = \log\left(\sqrt{x^2 + y^2}\right) \quad \text{and} \quad v(x, y) = \operatorname{atan2}(y, x).$$

Applying the chain rule, it is easily seen that

$$\frac{\partial u}{\partial x}(x, y) = \frac{\partial u}{\partial x}\log\left(\sqrt{x^2 + y^2}\right) = \frac{\partial u}{\partial x}\left[\frac{1}{2}\log\left(x^2 + y^2\right)\right] = \frac{1}{2} \cdot \frac{1}{x^2 + y^2} \cdot 2x = \frac{x}{x^2 + y^2}$$

$$\frac{\partial u}{\partial y}(x, y) = \frac{\partial u}{\partial y}\log\left(\sqrt{x^2 + y^2}\right) = \frac{y}{x^2 + y^2}.$$

Reading off the known partial derivatives of $\operatorname{atan2}(y, x)$, we have

$$\frac{\partial v}{\partial x}(x, y) = \frac{\partial}{\partial x}\operatorname{atan2}(y, x) = \frac{-y}{x^2 + y^2} \quad \text{and} \quad \frac{\partial v}{\partial y}(x, y) = \frac{\partial}{\partial y}\operatorname{atan2}(y, x) = \frac{x}{x^2 + y^2}.$$

We therefore have

$$\frac{\partial u}{\partial x}(x, y) = \frac{\partial v}{\partial y}(x, y) \quad \text{and} \quad \frac{\partial u}{\partial y}(x, y) = -\frac{\partial v}{\partial x}(x, y),$$

showing the Cauchy-Riemann equations are satisfied, as required. □

Theorem 4.10

For any fixed $k \in \mathbb{Z}$, let $\log(z) = \log|z| + i\operatorname{Arg}(z) + 2\pi ik$ be a branch of the complex logarithm. Then, on the slit plane $\mathbb{C}\backslash(-\infty, 0]$, we have

$$\frac{d}{dz}\log(z) = \frac{1}{z}.$$

Proof #1. Let $z = x + iy$. Applying Theorem 4.4 and Theorem 4.9, we have

$$\frac{d}{dz}\log(z) = \frac{\partial u}{\partial x} + i\frac{\partial v}{\partial x} = \frac{x}{x^2 + y^2} + i\left(\frac{-y}{x^2 + y^2}\right) = \frac{x - iy}{x^2 + y^2} = \frac{(x - iy)}{(x - iy)(x + iy)} = \frac{1}{z}. \qquad \square$$

Proof #2. For our fixed branch of the logarithm, $\log(z)$ is single-valued. We start with the identity $e^{\log(z)} = z$ and take the derivative of both sides (using the chain rule)

$$1 = \frac{d}{dz}z = \frac{d}{dz}e^{\log(z)} = e^{\log(z)}\frac{d}{dz}\log(z)$$

$$= z\frac{d}{dz}\log(z) \qquad \text{(substituting } z \text{ for } e^{\log(z)})$$

$$\frac{1}{z} = \frac{d}{dz}\log(z). \qquad \square$$

4.7 Supplemental Material

4.7.1 Exercises

Exercises 4.1

(a) *Below, we use compactness and the Bolzano-Weierstrass Theorem to prove Theorem 4.11. Instead, prove the theorem by use of compactness and the Heine-Borel Theorem.*

(b) *Show that the function $f(z) = \bar{z}$ is not differentiable at any point.*

(c) *Let $f(z) = z^n$ for $n \in \mathbb{Z}$. Show that $f(z)$ is holomorphic in $\mathbb{C}$ for $n \geq 1$ and holomorphic in $\mathbb{C}\backslash\{0\}$ for $n \leq 0$ with (in both cases) $f'(z) = nz^{n-1}$.*

(d) *Let $f(z)$ be holomorphic and non-zero in the domain Ω. Show that $g(z) = 1/f(z)$ is also holomorphic in Ω.*

Remark

Answers to exercises are in Appendix A.

4.7.2 Continuous on Compact Set

> **Theorem 4.11**
>
> *Let $f(z)$ be continuous on the compact set G. Then f is uniformly continuous on G.*

Proof. We assume that f is not uniformly continuous on the compact set G and look for a contradiction.

Because f is not uniformly continuous, there must be some $\epsilon > 0$ for which there is no uniform δ. Fix that ϵ and let $n \in \mathbb{N}$. By assumption, there can be no n such that $1/n$ can be our uniform δ. Therefore, for each n, there exist points $z_n, w_n \in G$ such that

$$|z_n - w_n| < 1/n \qquad \text{and} \qquad |f(z_n) - f)w_n)| \geq \epsilon.$$

As we step through each n, we are building two sequences $\{z_n\}$ and $\{w_n\}$. Using the compactness of G and Theorem 2.6, the sequence $\{z_n\}$ has a convergent subsequence that converges to some point $p \in G$. Discarding any index n that is not in that convergent subsequence, we form two new sequences $\{z_n^*\}$ and $\{w_n^*\}$ that consist only of the index n's that were in the above convergent subsequence.

The sequence $\{z_n^*\}$ converges to p and $|z_n - w_n| < 1/n$ for each n. Therefore, $\{w_n^*\}$ also converges to p. This gives

$$\lim_{n \to \infty} z_n^* = \lim_{n \to \infty} w_n^* = p \qquad \text{(and by continuity of } f\text{)} \qquad \lim_{n \to \infty} f(z_n^*) = \lim_{n \to \infty} f(w_n^*) = f(p).$$

For some N, we must therefore have $|f(z_n^*) - f(w_n^*)| < \epsilon$ for $n > N$, contrary to assumption, completing our proof by contradiction. $\qquad\qquad\square$

> **Remark**
>
> Note that, in the case of a point on the boundary of our compact set G, the theorem only assumes *continuity from the interior* as described in Section 4.1.2.
>
> Of course, if $f(z)$ is continuous in some open set that contains G, then normal continuity in a neighborhood can be assumed.

Complex Integration

5.1 Introduction

We start with a brief reminder of the Riemann integral of a real-valued function.

Let f be a real-valued function defined on the interval $[a, b]$. We partition $[a, b]$ into n subintervals:

$$a = x_0 < x_1 < x_2 < ... < x_n = b.$$

To keep it simple we will assume that all the subintervals are of equal (non-zero) length $(b-a)/n$.

Now let $t_1, t_2, , , , t_n$ be a sequence of n numbers with $t_k \in [x_{k-1}, x_k]$. The *Riemann sum* with respect the function f, the interval $[a, b]$ and the above partition is:

$$S_n = \sum_{k=1}^{n} f(t_k) \cdot (x_k - x_{k-1}).$$

For each interval, we obtain an "interval value" by multiplying the length of the interval by our estimate of the value of f in the interval. Then, S_n sums all of those interval values. The *Riemann integral* is the limit of the Riemann sums as the partition gets finer (i.e., n gets larger):

$$\lim_{n \to \infty} S_n = \int_a^b f(x) \, dx.$$

If the limit exists, the function is said to be *Riemann-integrable*.

It is easy to visualize this in the two-dimensional (x, y) plane, where the x-axis consists of the points in the $[a, b]$ interval, and the y-axis consists of $y = f(x)$. In the complex plane, things get more complicated. Consider, for example, the real integral

$$\int_a^b f(x) \, dx,$$

which we would simply describe as "the integral of f from a to b". Now consider the complex integral

$$\int_{z_0}^{z_1} f(z) \, dz.$$

We want to start at z_0, move through the complex plane to z_1, integrating f as we go. But in the complex plane there are infinitely many ways to move from z_0 to z_1. We will use the language of *paths* and *contours*, defined in Section 3.1, to describe the transversal from z_0 to z_1.

In this chapter, we use a complex-valued Riemann sum approach to describe integration along a path or contour. We will call these integrals *contour integrals* (they are sometimes referred to as *line integrals* or *path integrals* in the literature).

5.2 The Contour Integral

5.2.1 The Complex-Valued Riemann Sum

In our initial discussion of the complex-valued Riemann sum, we assume that

- $f(z)$ is continuous (except possibly at finitely many points) on the domain Ω,
- $\gamma \subset \Omega$ is a smooth path of finite length parameterized by $\omega : [a, b] \to \mathbb{C}$, and
- we are integrating $f(z)$ over our smooth path γ, beginning at $\omega(a)$ and ending at $\omega(b)$.

The integral

$$\int_\gamma f(z)\, dz$$

is approximated by the complex-valued Riemann sum as follows. We subdivide the interval $[a, b]$ into n equal-width subintervals $a = x_0 < x_1 < x_2 < \ldots < x_n = b$, so that $\omega(x_0), \omega(x_1) \cdots \omega(x_n)$ are $n + 1$ oriented points along the path γ. Connecting those points by straight line segments creates an n-sided polygon. As n increases, the polygon becomes a closer and closer fit to the smooth path γ.

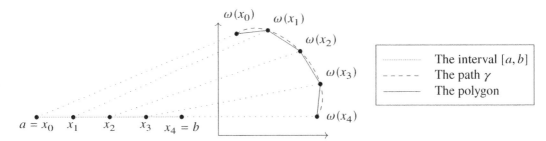

Figure 5.1: Estimation by Polygon

We then evaluate

$$S_n = \sum_{k=1}^{n} f(\omega(x_k)) \cdot \left[\omega(x_k) - \omega(x_{k-1}) \right],$$

where the sum is over the n polygon sides. For polygon side k, we compute a value by multiplying the following two numbers:

(a) **Function Value.** We use $f(\omega(x_k))$ as an estimate of the value of f on polygon side k, and

(b) **Side Value.** We use $\left[\omega(x_k) - \omega(x_{k-1}) \right]$ to compute the length and slope of polygon side k. Let the point p be the result of that subtraction. In polar coordinates, $p = Re^{i\theta}$, where R is the length of the polygon side and θ is $\operatorname{Arg} p$ (the slope of the polygon side).

This should become clearer after Theorem 5.1, just below, on the parameterization function ω.

5.2.2 The Parameterization Function

We assume here that ω generates a *smooth path*. As described in Section 3.1, we then have

$$\omega(t) = \omega_x(t) + i\omega_y(t),\ a \le t \le b,\ \omega : [a, b] \to \mathbb{C},$$

where $\omega_x(t)$ and $\omega_y(t)$ are continuous (real) functions in the interval $[a,b]$ and $\omega'_x(t)$ and $\omega'_y(t)$ exist and are continuous in the interval $[a,b]$ (only one-sided derivatives needed at the end points).

Theorem 5.1

Let $\gamma \in \mathbb{C}$ be a smooth path parameterized by $\omega : [a,b] \to \mathbb{C}$. Then, for $a \leq t_1 < t_2 \leq b$

$$\omega(t_2) - \omega(t_1) = \int_{t_1}^{t_2} \omega'(t)\, dt.$$

Proof. We have

$$\int_{t_1}^{t_2} \omega'(t)\, dt = \int_{t_1}^{t_2} \left(\omega'_x(t) + i\omega'_y(t) \right) dt = \int_{t_1}^{t_2} \omega'_x(t)\, dt + i \int_{t_1}^{t_2} \omega'_y(t)\, dt.$$

The integral has been reduced to two purely real-valued integrals, giving

$$= \left[\omega_x(t_2) - \omega_x(t_1) \right] + i \left[\omega_y(t_2) - \omega_y(t_1) \right] = \left[\omega_x(t_2) + i\omega_y(t_2) \right] - \left[\omega_x(t_1) + i\omega_y(t_1) \right]$$

$$= \omega(t_2) - \omega(t_1). \qquad \square$$

5.2.3 The Contour Integral - Final Form

Returning to the Riemann sum, we can use Theorem 5.1 to obtain

$$S_n = \sum_{k=1}^{n} f(\omega(x_k)) \cdot \left[\omega(x_k) - \omega(x_{k-1}) \right] = \sum_{k=1}^{n} \left[f(\omega(x_k)) \cdot \left(\int_{x_{k-1}}^{x_k} \omega'(t)\, dt \right) \right]$$

$$= \sum_{k=1}^{n} \int_{x_{k-1}}^{x_k} f(\omega(x_k))\, \omega'(t)\, dt.$$

The Riemann integral is then the limit of this Riemann sum as the lengths of the subintervals approach zero:

$$\int_{\gamma} f(z)\, dz = \lim_{n \to \infty} \sum_{k=1}^{n} \int_{x_{k-1}}^{x_k} f(\omega(x_k))\, \omega'(t)\, dt = \int_{a}^{b} f(\omega(t))\, \omega'(t)\, dt. \qquad (5.1)$$

This is our definition of the complex contour integral of $f(z)$ integrating over the smooth path γ.

5.2.4 Parts of the Contour Integral

We can write $\omega(t) = \omega_x(t) + i\omega_y(t)$ where $\omega_x(t)$ and $\omega_y(t)$ are real-valued. Similarly, we can write $f(z) = f(x + iy) = u(x,y) + iv(x,y)$, where $u(x,y)$ and $v(x,y)$ are real-valued functions of two real variables. This allows

$$f(\omega(t)) = u(\omega_x(t), \omega_y(t)) + iv(\omega_x(t), \omega_y(t)).$$

Thus, the right-hand side of equation (5.1) can be written as:

$$\int_{a}^{b} f(\omega(t))\, \omega'(t)\, dt = \int_{a}^{b} \left[u(\omega_x(t), \omega_y(t)) + iv(\omega_x(t), \omega_y(t)) \right] \cdot \left[\omega'_x(t) + i\omega'_y(t) \right] dt$$

$$= \int_{a}^{b} \left[u(\omega_x(t), \omega_y(t)) \right] \omega'_x(t) - \left[v(\omega_x(t), \omega_y(t)) \right] \omega'_y(t)\, dt$$

$$+ i \int_{a}^{b} \left[u(\omega_x(t), \omega_y(t)) \right] \omega'_y(t) + \left[v(\omega_x(t), \omega_y(t)) \right] \omega'_x(t)\, dt. \qquad (5.2)$$

As shorthand, we can say:

$$\int f(z)\,dz = \int (u + iv)(dx + idy) = \int (udx - vdy) + i \int (vdx + udy).$$

We have reduced our contour integral to integrals of real-valued functions. This allows us to use much of the theory of real-valued integrals in evaluating the complex contour integral.

5.3 Properties of the Contour Integral

5.3.1 The Basic Rules

For our statement of basic rules, we assume the following:

- f and g are continuous complex functions on the open set Ω.

- α and β are constant values (real or complex).

- γ is a smooth path of finite length parameterized by $\omega : [a, b] \rightarrow \Omega$, with γ^- as its reversed path. On the real non-zero length interval $[a, b]$, there exists an m with $a < m < b$.

- $\gamma_1, \gamma_2, ... \gamma_n$ are smooth paths of finite length parameterized by $\omega_i : [a_i, b_i] \rightarrow \Omega$, where the endpoint of γ_r coincides with the start point of γ_{r+1}.

- C is a contour consisting of $C = \gamma_1 + \gamma_2 + ... + \gamma_n$.

Theorem 5.2

Using the assumptions stated immediately above, we have

(a) $\int_\gamma [\alpha f(z) + \beta g(z)]\,dz = \alpha \int_\gamma f(z)\,dz + \beta \int_\gamma g(z)\,dz$

(b) $\int_C f(z)\,dz = \sum_{k=1}^n \int_{\gamma_k} f(z)\,dz$

(c) $\int_{\gamma^-} f(z)\,dz = - \int_\gamma f(z)\,dz$

(d) $\int_\gamma f(z)\,dz = \int_a^b f(\omega(t))\omega'(t)\,dt = \int_a^m f(\omega(t))\omega'(t)\,dt + \int_m^b f(\omega(t))\omega'(t)\,dt$

Proof. Each of (a) through (d) can be shown by making the appropriate substitutions in equation (5.2) and then applying the standard rules of real variable integrals. □

Remark

It is tempting to think $Re\left(\int_\gamma f(z)\,dz\right) = \int_\gamma Re(f(z))\,dz$ and $Im\left(\int_\gamma f(z)\,dz\right) = \int_\gamma Im(f(z))\,dz$. To see this is not true, we give a counter-example. Let $f(z) = 1$ and $\gamma = [0, i]$. Then we have $Re\left(\int_\gamma f(z)\,dz\right) = Re\left(\int_\gamma dz\right) = Re(i) = 0$ and $\int_\gamma Re(f(z))\,dz = \int_\gamma dz = i$.

> **Remark**

In light of Theorem 5.2(b), an integral over the contour **C** can be treated as an integral over a single smooth path because the "corners" of **C** (at the junctions of the finite number of smooth paths) have measure zero. This is also shown in the first proof found in Theorem 5.4.

Similarly, it is sufficient that $f(z)$ is piecewise continuous, with a finite number of discontinuities of measure zero. In that case, the integral of $f(z)$ over any γ_k can be summed over the continuous pieces of $f(z)$.

5.3.2 Change of Parameterization

> **Theorem 5.3**
>
> Let γ be a smooth path parameterized by $\omega(t)$, $a \leq t \leq b$, $: [a,b] \to \mathbb{C}$, and let the function $\phi(r)$, $c \leq r \leq d$, $: [c,d] \to [a,b]$ be an increasing smooth bijection. Now let λ be a smooth path parameterized by $\omega(\phi(r))$, $c \leq r \leq d$, $: [c,d] \to \mathbb{C}$. Then
>
> $$\int_\gamma f(z)\, dz = \int_\lambda f(z)\, dz.$$

Proof. As discussed in Section 3.1.2, the path γ has the same image and oreientation as λ.

By the chain rule, $[\omega(\phi(r))]' = \omega'(\phi(r))\phi'(r)$. With $t = \phi(r)$, we have $dt = \phi'(r)\, dr$. Putting that together, we have

$$
\begin{aligned}
\int_\lambda f(z)\, dx &= \int_c^d f(\omega(\phi(r)))[\omega(\phi(r))]'\, dr \\
&= \int_c^d f(\omega(\phi(r)))[\omega'(\phi(r))]\phi'(r)\, dr \\
&= \int_a^b f(\omega(t))\omega'(t)\, dt \quad \text{(after letting } t = \phi(r)\text{)} \\
&= \int_\gamma f(z)\, dz.
\end{aligned}
$$

$\square$

5.3.3 Length of the Path

Let γ be a smooth path parameterized by $\omega : [a,b] \to \mathbb{C}$. We denote the length of γ by $L(\gamma)$. We can approximate $L(\gamma)$ using a Riemann sum approach.

For the partition $a = t_0 < t_1 < t_2 < ... < t_n = b$, we build a polygonal path consisting of n sides of the form $[\omega(t_{i-1}), \omega(t_i)]$. As n increases, the length of our polygon better approximates (but never exceeds) $L(\gamma)$. As explained in Section 5.2.1, let $p = \omega(t_i) - \omega(t_{i-1}) = Re^{i\theta}$. Then, $|Re^{i\theta}| = R = |\omega(t_i) - \omega(t_{i-1})|$, is equal to the length of the polygon side.

To compute the length of the path, apply Theorem 5.1 to obtain

$$L(\gamma) = \lim_{n\to\infty} \sum_{i=1}^n |\omega(t_i) - \omega(t_{i-1})| = \int_a^b |\omega'(t)|\, dt.$$

This motivates the following definition:

Definition 5.1

*The **length** of the smooth path γ is equal to the following (real) integral:*

$$L(\gamma) = \int_a^b |\omega'(t)|\, dt = \int_a^b \sqrt{\omega'_x(t)^2 + \omega'_y(t)^2}\, dt.$$

We use the above to compute the length of a circle centered at complex point c, with radius r. Parameterize the circle with $\omega(t) = c + re^{it}$, $0 \le t \le 2\pi$. Now since $|\omega'(t)| = |re^{it}| = r$ we have:

$$\int_0^{2\pi} |\omega'(t)|\, dt = \int_0^{2\pi} r\, dt = r \int_0^{2\pi} dt = 2\pi r \quad \text{or, equally...}$$

$$\int_0^{2\pi} \sqrt{r^2 \sin(t)^2 + r^2 \cos(t)^2}\, dt = \int_0^{2\pi} r\sqrt{1}\, dt = 2\pi r.$$

5.3.4   The Inequality and Estimation Lemmas

The next lemma could be proved by applying the triangle inequality to S_n (the nth Riemann sum), and then applying induction to show it holds at the limit. To demonstrate an interesting technique, we provide a different proof.

Lemma 5.1: The Inequality Lemma

Let $g : [a, b] \to \mathbb{C}$ be continuous functions. Then:

$$\left| \int_a^b g(t)\, dt \right| \le \int_a^b |g(t)|\, dt.$$

Proof. There is nothing to prove if the LHS integral is zero, so we assume otherwise. Choose $R > 0$ and $0 \le \theta \le 2\pi$ such that

$$\int_a^b g(t)\, dt = Re^{i\theta}.$$

We have

$$\left| \int_a^b g(t)\, dt \right| = R = \int_a^b e^{-i\theta} g(t)\, dt = \int_a^b \left[Re(e^{-i\theta} g(t)) + i\, Im(e^{-i\theta} g(t)) \right] dt$$

$$= \int_a^b Re\left(e^{-i\theta} g(t) \right) dt + i \int_a^b Im\left(e^{-i\theta} g(t) \right) dt$$

But R is real, so our integral reduces to

$$= \int_a^b Re\left(e^{-i\theta} g(t) \right) dt$$

$$\le \int_a^b \left| Re\left(e^{-i\theta} g(t) \right) \right| dt$$

$$\le \int_a^b \left| e^{-i\theta} g(t) \right| dt \qquad \text{(because } |Re(z)| \le |z|)$$

$$= \int_a^b \left| e^{-i\theta} \right| |g(t)|\, dt$$

$$= \int_a^b |g(t)|\, dt. \qquad \qquad \square$$

CHAPTER 5. COMPLEX INTEGRATION

> **Lemma 5.2: The Estimation Lemma (The "ML Inequality")**
>
> *Let f be continuous in the domain Ω and let $\gamma \subset \Omega$ be a smooth path. Suppose that $|f(z)| \leq M$ for all $z \in \gamma$. Then:*
> $$\left| \int_\gamma f(z)\, dz \right| \leq M \cdot L(\gamma).$$

Proof. By Lemma 5.1 we have:

$$\left| \int_\gamma f(z)\, dz \right| = \left| \int_a^b f(\omega(t))\omega'(t)\, dz \right| \leq \int_a^b |f(\omega(t))||\omega'(t)|\, dz \leq M \int_a^b |\omega'(t)|\, dz = M \cdot L(\gamma). \qquad \square$$

Remark

The Estimation Lemma appears constantly in complex analysis. We will follow many others and refer to the lemma as the *ML inequality*.

5.4 Fundamental Theorem of Calculus for Contour Integrals

It is quite useful that the real variable concept of Riemann sums applies in the complex plane (at least for *Riemann integrable* complex-valued functions). It allows us to compute the integral of $f(z)$ over a path in the complex plane beginning at z_0 and ending at z_1. The remaining problem is that there are infinitely many ways a path can traverse from z_0 to z_1. Does the value of the integral depend upon the exact course the path takes?

To answer that question, we turn to another concept well-known in real variable analysis: The Fundamental Theorem of Calculus. On the interval $[a, b]$, suppose F is continuous, f is continuous almost everywhere and $F'(x) = f(z)$. Then

$$\int_a^b f(x)\, dx = F(b) - F(a).$$

Is there a class of complex-valued functions where the integral over a path can be similarly reduced to evaluating the endpoints of the path? In this section, we describe the *conditions* needed before you can apply the Fundamental Theorem of Calculus to complex contour integrals. In Chapter 7, we prove Cauchy's Integral Theorem, which shows the *circumstances* where those conditions are obtained.

Definition 5.2
*A **primitive** for f on the region $\mathcal{R}$ is a function F that is holomorphic in $\mathcal{R}$ and such that: $F'(z) = f(z)$ for all $z \in \mathcal{R}$.*

Remark

The terms "primitive" and "antiderivative" are interchangeable, with the term primitive more common in Europe and antiderivative more common in the United States. In this book, we have elected to use the term primitive.

Theorem 5.4: Fundamental Theorem of Calculus

Let $f(z)$ be continuous in the region $\mathcal{R}$. For any $z_0, z_1 \in \mathcal{R}$, let $\boldsymbol{C} \subset \mathcal{R}$ be any contour beginning at z_0 and ending at z_1. Either all or none of the following three statements are true:

(a) $f(z)$ has a primitive $F(z)$ throughout $\mathcal{R}$;

(b) for all such contours $\boldsymbol{C}$, we have $\int_{\boldsymbol{C}} f(z)\, dz = F(z_1) - F(z_0)$ where $F(z)$ is the primitive in statement (a);

(c) for all such contours $\boldsymbol{C}$ that are closed contours (i.e., $z_0 = z_1$), we have $\int_{\boldsymbol{C}} f(z)\, dz = 0$.

Remark

Our approach will be to show $(a) \implies (b) \implies (c) \implies (a)$.

Proof $(\mathbf{a}) \implies (\mathbf{b})$.[14] Assume (a) is true. First, make the simplifying assumption that $\gamma \in \mathcal{R}$ is a smooth path between z_0 and z_1, parameterized by $\omega(t) : [a, b] \to \mathcal{R}$. That means $\omega(a) = z_0$ and $\omega(b) = z_1$. By assumption, $F'(z) = f(z)$, so application of the chain rules gives $\frac{d}{dt} F(\omega(t)) = F'(\omega(t))\omega'(t)$. Thus

$$
\begin{aligned}
\int_{\gamma} f(z)\, dz &= \int_a^b f(\omega(t))\omega'(t)\, dt \\
&= \int_a^b F'(\omega(t))\omega'(t)\, dt \\
&= \int_a^b \frac{d}{dt} F(\omega(t))\, dt \\
&= F(\omega(b)) - F(\omega(a)) \\
&= F(z_1) - F(z_0).
\end{aligned}
$$

Now assume the general case: the contour $\boldsymbol{C} \in \mathcal{R}$ is a piecewise smooth contour consisting of the smooth paths $\gamma_1, \gamma_2, ..., \gamma_n$. The paths are parameterized by $\omega_i : [a_i, b_i] \to \mathcal{R}$, where the endpoint of γ_k coincides with the start point of γ_{k+1}. In particular, $\omega_1(a_1) = z_0$ and $\omega_n(b_n) = z_1$. Then, using the same logic as above and applying telescoping, we have

$$
\begin{aligned}
\int_{\boldsymbol{C}} f(z)\, dz &= \sum_{k=1}^n \int_{\gamma_n} f(z)\, dz \\
&= \sum_{k=1}^n F(\omega(b_k)) - F(\omega(a_k)) \\
&= F(\omega_n(b_n)) - F(\omega_1(a_1)) \\
&= F(z_1) - F(z_0). \qquad \square
\end{aligned}
$$

Proof $(\mathbf{b}) \implies (\mathbf{c})$. Assume (b) is true. Because $z_0 = z_1$, we have $F(z_1) - F(z_0) = 0$, as required. $\quad\square$

Proof $(\mathbf{c}) \implies (\mathbf{a})$.[15] Assume (c) is true. We use our assumption to first show that integration of $f(z)$ in $\mathcal{R}$ is independent of path.

By assumption any closed contour $\boldsymbol{C} \subset \mathcal{R}$ with any endpoints $z_0 = z_1$ gives $\int_{\boldsymbol{C}} f(z)\,dz = 0$. Fix any other point $w \in \mathcal{R}$ and let $\boldsymbol{C}_1, \boldsymbol{C}_2 \in \mathcal{R}$ be any two contours beginning at z_0 and ending at w. Now create the closed contour $\boldsymbol{C} = \boldsymbol{C}_1 + (-\boldsymbol{C}_2)$. We have

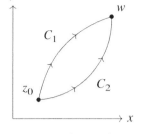

$$\int_{\boldsymbol{C}} f(z)\,dz = \int_{\boldsymbol{C}_1} f(z)\,dz + \int_{-\boldsymbol{C}_2} f(z)\,dz = 0$$

$$\int_{\boldsymbol{C}_1} f(z)\,dz = \int_{\boldsymbol{C}_2} f(z)\,dz,$$

Figure 5.2: Path Independence

showing integration between any two points in $\mathcal{R}$ is independent of path.

Now fix $z_0 \in \mathcal{R}$ and define

$$F(z) = \int_{z_0}^{z} f(w)\,dw$$

for all $z \in \mathcal{R}$. Let ϵ be small enough so that $\mathbf{D}_\epsilon(z) \subset \mathcal{R}$, and choose any $z + \Delta z \in \mathbf{D}_\epsilon(z)$. Then,

$$F(z + \Delta z) - F(z) = \int_{z_0}^{z+\Delta z} f(w)\,dw - \int_{z_0}^{z} f(w)\,dw$$

$$= \int_{z}^{z_0} f(w)\,dw + \int_{z_0}^{z+\Delta z} f(w)\,dw = \int_{z}^{z+\Delta z} f(w)\,dw,$$

where path independence allows us to choose the line segment $[z, z + \Delta z]$ for the last integral. Using that the derivative of z is 1 and the primitive of 1 is z, we can set $g(z) = 1$ and $G(z) = z$ and have

$$\int_{z}^{z+\Delta z} dw = \int_{z}^{z+\Delta z} g(w)\,dw = G(z + \Delta z) - G(z) = \Delta z,$$

so that

$$\frac{1}{\Delta z} \int_{z}^{z+\Delta z} dw = 1$$

$$f(z) \left(\frac{1}{\Delta z} \int_{z}^{z+\Delta z} dw \right) = f(z)$$

$$\frac{1}{\Delta z} \int_{z}^{z+\Delta z} f(z)\,dw = f(z).$$

Therefore

$$\frac{F(z + \Delta z) - F(z)}{\Delta z} - f(z) = \frac{1}{\Delta z} \int_{z}^{z+\Delta z} f(w)\,dw - \frac{1}{\Delta z} \int_{z}^{z+\Delta z} f(z)\,dw$$

$$= \frac{1}{\Delta z} \int_{z}^{z+\Delta z} [f(w) - f(z)]\,dw.$$

But f is continuous at z. Thus, for any $\epsilon > 0$ there is a $\delta > 0$ such that $|f(w) - f(z)| < \epsilon$ whenever $|w - z| < \delta$. That is, for $|\Delta z| < \delta$, we have by the ML inequality

$$\left| \frac{F(z + \Delta z) - F(z)}{\Delta z} - f(z) \right| < \frac{1}{|\Delta z|} \epsilon |\Delta z| = \epsilon.$$

We therefore have

$$\lim_{\Delta z \to 0} \frac{F(z + \Delta z) - F(z)}{\Delta z} = f(z),$$

which is to say $F'(z) = f(z)$, as required. $\qquad\square$

5.5 Supplemental Material

5.5.1 Exercises

> **Exercises 5.1**
>
> *Let $f(z) = z^2$ and parameterize two smooth paths, both beginning at 1 and ending at i:*
>
> - *Let the path L be parameterized by $\omega(t) = (1-t) + it, 0 \le t \le 1$ (a straight line from 1 to i).*
> - *Let the path **C** be parameterized by $\phi(t) = e^{it}, 0 \le t \le \pi/2$ (follows the unit circle in a counterclockwise direction from 1 to i).*
>
> *Show that*
> $$\int_L f(z)\,dz = \int_C f(z)\,dz = F(i) - F(1).$$

> **Remark**
>
> Answers to exercises are in Appendix A.

5.5.2 Examples

We present an important set of examples which, in some form, are included in all complex analysis textbooks. Our example functions either do (or do not) have a primitive in a given region, and therefore Theorem 5.4 either does (or does not) apply when integrating those functions. Studying these examples should also further our understanding of the complex logarithm.

To begin, we define two function. For $z \in \mathbb{C}\backslash\{0\}$ and $n \in \mathbb{Z}\backslash\{-1\}$, let

$$f(z) = z^n \quad \text{and} \quad F(z) = \frac{z^{n+1}}{(n+1)}$$

so that by Exercise 4.1(c), both are holomorphic in $\mathbb{C}\backslash\{0\}$, with

$$f'(z) = nz^{n-1} \quad \text{and} \quad F'(z) = z^n = f(z).$$

Due to the divide by zero, note that $F(z)$ and therefore $F'(z)$ is undefined for $n = -1$. For all other $n \in \mathbb{Z}$, we see that $F(z)$ is a primitive of $f(z)$.

We must look elsewhere to find a primitive for $1/z$. In fact, we have shown in Theorem 4.10 that the derivative of $\log(z)$ is $1/z$, but only in the slit plane $\mathbb{C}\backslash(-\infty, 0]$. In fact, no branch of $\log(z)$ is even continuous along the negative real axis. Thus, $1/z$ *does* have a primitive of $\log(z)$, but that primitive is only valid in the slit plane $\mathbb{C}\backslash(-\infty, 0]$.

Next, we set up several paths. All but two follows the unit circle in the "normal" counterclockwise direction.

Path	Parameterization	Interval	Description
C	$\phi(t) = e^{it}$	$0 \le t \le 2\pi$	Full counterclockwise circle
C^-	$\phi(t) = e^{-it}$	$0 \le t \le 2\pi$	Full clockwise circle
C_T	$\phi(t) = e^{it}$	$0 \le t \le \pi$	Half (top) counterclockwise circle
C_B	$\phi(t) = e^{it}$	$\pi \le t \le 2\pi$	Half (bottom) counterclockwise circle
C_B^-	$\phi(t) = e^{-it}$	$0 \le t \le \pi$	Half (bottom) clockwise circle

With our parameterizations, it is helpful to remember $(e^{at})' = e^{at} \cdot (at)' = ae^{at}$, using the chain rule. Working in the reverse direction, that means the primitive of e^{at} is e^{at}/a.

We use $f(z)$ and $F(z)$ as defined above. In these examples, we assume that $n \ne -1$ unless otherwise stated. There is substantial computational similarity in the five cases. We start with the full circle, moving counterclockwise:

$$\int_C z^n \, dz = \int_0^{2\pi} e^{it^n} \phi'(t) \, dt = \int_0^{2\pi} e^{int} i e^{it} \, dt = \int_0^{2\pi} i e^{i(n+1)t} \, dt = \left. \frac{e^{i(n+1)t}}{(n+1)} \right|_0^{2\pi} = \frac{1}{n+1} - \frac{1}{n+1} = 0.$$

This is as expected. Because $f(z) = z^n$ has $F(z)$ as a primitive, Theorem 5.4 applies and the integral over any closed contour is 0.

For C^-, brief inspection shows that you obtain the same result with the full circle moving clockwise. The only change is that t becomes $-t$, which makes no difference for a 2π periodic function.

Moving counterclockwise through the top half of the semi-circle, we have:

$$\int_{C_T} z^n \, dz = \int_0^{\pi} i e^{i(n+1)t} \, dt = \left. \frac{e^{i(n+1)t}}{(n+1)} \right|_0^{\pi} = 0 \text{ for } n \text{ odd}; \frac{-2}{n+1} \text{ for } n \text{ even.}$$

Similarly, moving counterclockwise through the bottom half of the semi-circle, we have:

$$\int_{C_B} z^n \, dz = \int_{\pi}^{2\pi} i e^{i(n+1)t} \, dt = \left. \frac{e^{i(n+1)t}}{(n+1)} \right|_{\pi}^{2\pi} = 0 \text{ for } n \text{ odd}; \frac{2}{n+1} \text{ for } n \text{ even.}$$

In both cases (n odd or even), combining the two half-circles adds up to zero, as expected. Also as expected, using $-t$ to move *clockwise* through both semi-circles yields a similar result.

Now we move to the heart of this example, the case where $n = -1$. We start by moving through the top half of the unit semi-circle *counterclockwise* and obtain:

$$\int_{C_T} z^n \, dz = \int_{C_T} \frac{1}{z} \, dz = \int_0^{\pi} \frac{1}{e^{it}} i e^{it} \, dt = \int_0^{\pi} i \, dt = i \int_0^{\pi} dt = i\pi.$$

Now moving *clockwise* through the bottom half of the unit semi-circle, we obtain:

$$\int_{C_B^-} z^n \, dz = \int_{C_B^-} \frac{1}{z} \, dz = \int_0^{\pi} \frac{1}{e^{-it}} \left(-i e^{it} \right) dt = \int_0^{\pi} -i \, dt = -i \int_0^{\pi} dt = -i\pi.$$

We can already see an issue. Integrating on two different paths with the same starting and ending points gives two different results. We immediately know that our function does not satisfy the requirements of the Fundamental Theorem of Calculus and therefore does not have a proper primitive in any region that includes our contour. Let's see what happens when we integrate over the full unit circle.

$$\int_C z^n\, dz = \int_0^{2\pi} \frac{1}{e^{it}} i e^{it}\, dt = \int_0^{2\pi} i\, dt = i \int_0^{2\pi} dt = 2\pi i.$$

As we thought. Even when the starting and ending points are the same, the integral is not zero. We again conclude that $f(z) = z^{-1}$ does not have a primitive throughout the entire region that includes our contour. So, what's going on here? We consider that question next.

5.5.3 Another Look at the Complex Logarithm

We introduced the complex logarithm in Section 1.8. We showed there that $\log(z)$ is a multi-valued function. We also showed that $\mathrm{Log}(z)$, the principal value of $\log(z)$, although single-valued, is discontinuous at each point on the nonpositive real axis.

On the other hand, on the slit plane $\mathbb{C} \setminus \{(-\infty, 0]\}$, the function $\mathrm{Log}\, z$ is holomorphic and single-valued. On the slit plane, we can use $\mathrm{Log}\, z$ as the primitive for $1/z$. For example, we can take the integral over a path C_ϵ counterclockwise around the unit circle starting at a point $(-1, -i\epsilon)$ just below the slit and ending at a point $(-1, i\epsilon)$ just above the slit. Then:

$$\lim_{\epsilon \to 0} \int_{C_\epsilon} \frac{1}{z}\, dz = \lim_{\epsilon \to 0} \mathrm{Log}\, z \Big|_{-1-i\epsilon}^{-1+i\epsilon} = i\pi - (-i\pi) = 2\pi i,$$

as expected.

So, while $\log z$ (or its principal value) is the only possible primitive for $1/z$, it cannot be a primitive in any region where it is multi-valued.

Now let's make one other change to our integration of $1/z$ over the unit circle. We leave the circle still centered at the origin, but change the radius to any real number r. That is, for our parameterization we have $\phi(t) = re^{it}, 0 \le t \le 2\pi$, so that:

$$\int_C \frac{1}{z}\, dz = \int_0^{2\pi} \frac{1}{re^{it}} rie^{it}\, dt = \int_0^{2\pi} i\, dt = i \int_0^{2\pi} dt = 2\pi i.$$

We see the radius term is cancelled out and the result remains the same: $2\pi i$. Let's try something else and evaluate the integral: $\int_C 1/(z - z_0)\, dz$ where C is a circle centered at z_0 of radius r. We parameterize the circle by $\phi(t) = z_0 + re^{it}, 0 \le t \le 2\pi$. Integrating, we have:

$$\int_C \frac{1}{z - z_0}\, dz = \int_0^{2\pi} \frac{1}{z_0 + re^{it} - z_0} \phi'(t)\, dt = \int_0^{2\pi} \frac{1}{re^{it}} rie^{it}\, dt = \int_0^{2\pi} i\, dt = i \int_0^{2\pi} dt = 2\pi i.$$

Note what is happening. The circle C is centered at z_0 and z gets its values from C. However, then the integral phase shifts back to the origin by subtracting z_0 from z. So we are back to traversing the slit plane, with the expected results.

Using the last example immediately above, we generalize it as follows. C is still a circle centered at z_0 of radius r parameterized by $\phi(t) = z_0 + re^{it}, 0 \le t \le 2\pi$. But now we evaluate the following integral:

$$\int_C (z - z_0)^n\, dz, \text{ for } n \in \mathbb{Z}, n \ne -1.$$

Using our standard approach, we have

$$\int_C (z - z_0)^n \, dz = \int_0^{2\pi} [(z_0 + re^{it}) - z_0]^n \phi'(t) \, dt = \int_0^{2\pi} [re^{it}]^n \, rie^{it} \, dt$$

$$= ir^{n+1} \int_0^{2\pi} e^{i(n+1)t} \, dt = 0,$$

as shown previously above.

Thus, for the circle parameterized by $\phi(t) = z_0 + re^{it}, 0 \le t \le 2\pi$, we have

$$\int_C (z - z_0)^n \, dz = \begin{cases} 0 & \text{for } n \in \mathbb{Z}, n \ne -1, \\ 2\pi i & \text{for } n = -1. \end{cases}$$

As will be seen, this is a very important result that is fundamental to complex function theory. Much of complex function theory depends on the fact that this integral is non-zero for $n = -1$.

Now another idea. We would like our integral path to avoid the slit plane. We know that $\operatorname{Log} z$ is single-valued if we avoid the slit plane. Let's integrate (*without* a phase shift) over a circle that resides wholly in the half-plane where $Re(z) > 0$. Our circle is centered at 2 with radius 1. Set $f(z) = 1/z$ and parameterize the circle by $\phi(t) = 2 + e^{it}, 0 \le t \le 2\pi$.

$$\int_C f(z) \, dz = \int_0^{2\pi} f(\phi(t)) \phi'(t) \, dt = \int_0^{2\pi} \frac{1}{2 + e^{it}} ie^{it} \, dt.$$

Now using u-substitution, let $u = \phi(t) = 2 + e^{it}$ so that $du = \phi'(t) \, dt = ie^{it} \, dt$. That means the limits of integration change to $\phi(0)$ and $\phi(2\pi)$, giving:

$$\int_0^{2\pi} \frac{1}{2 + e^{it}} ie^{it} \, dt = \int_{\phi(0)}^{\phi(2\pi)} \frac{du}{u}.$$

For multiple reasons, the final integral evaluates to 0. The integrand $1/u$ is holomorphic in $Re(u) > 0$, so any closed path beginning and ending in the right half-plane (and limited to the right half-plane) will evaluate to zero. We also have that $\operatorname{Log}(u)$ is a primitive for $1/u$ in the right half-plane and note that $\operatorname{Log}(\phi(2\pi)) - \operatorname{Log}(\phi(0)) = \operatorname{Log}(3) - \operatorname{Log}(3) = 0$.

Chapter 6

Infinite Sequences, Series and Products

Although we assume familiarity with real variable infinite sequences, series and products, we review basic principles here and then extend the theory to the complex domain.

6.1 Convergent Sequences

Definition 6.1

*Let $\{z_n\}$ be a sequence of complex numbers. The sequence is said to **converge** to a limit p if for every $\epsilon > 0$, there exists and $N \in \mathbb{N}$ such that for $n > N$, $|z_n - p| < \epsilon$. We write $\lim_{n \to \infty} z_n = p$. If no such limit exists, then the sequence is said to **diverge**.*

Theorem 6.1

Let $\{z_n\}$ be a sequence of complex numbers, with $z_n = x_n + iy_n$. Then $\{z_n\}$ converges if and only if both real sequences $\{x_n\}$ and $\{y_n\}$ converge. Further, if $\{z_n\}$ converges, then

$$\lim_{n \to \infty} z_n = \lim_{n \to \infty} (x_n + iy_n).$$

Proof. Assume $\{z_n\}$ converges to the point p. Fix $\epsilon > 0$ and choose N such that for $n > N$, $|z_n - p| < \epsilon$. Using that $|Re(z)| < |z|$, we have $|Re(z_n - p)| \leq |z_n - p| < \epsilon$, so that $|x_n - Re(p)| < \epsilon$ for $n > N$. Thus, $\lim_{n \to \infty} x_n = Re(p)$ and $\{x_n\}$ converge to $Re(p)$. For the same reason $\{y_n\}$ converge to $Im(p)$. Thus, $\lim_{n \to \infty} (x_n + iy_n) = Re(p) + iIm(p) = p = \lim_{n \to \infty} z_n$.

Next assume that $\{x_n\}$ and $\{y_n\}$ converge to p_x and p_y, respectively. Choose N large enough so that for $n > N$, both $|x_n - p_x|$ and $|y_n - p_y|$ are less than $\epsilon/2$. Let $p = p_x + ip_y$. We have

$$|z_n - p| = |(x_n + iy_n) - (p_x + ip_y)| = |(x_n - p_x) + i(y_n - p_y)|$$
$$\leq |x_n - p_x| + |y_n - p_y| < \epsilon/2 + \epsilon/2 = \epsilon,$$

showing that $\lim_{n \to \infty} z_n = p$. □

6.1.1 Convergent Sequences – The Cauchy Criterion

Definition 6.2

*Let $\{z_n\}$ be a sequence of complex numbers. The sequence is said to be a **Cauchy sequence** if for every $\epsilon > 0$, there exists and $N \in \mathbb{N}$ such that for all $m, n > N$, we have $|z_m - z_n| < \epsilon$.*

Equally, the sequence $\{z_n\}$ is a Cauchy sequence if for every $\epsilon > 0$, there exists an $N \in \mathbb{N}$ such that for all $n > N$ and all $p \geq 1$, we have $|z_{n+p} - z_n| < \epsilon$.

> **Theorem 6.2**
>
> *Let $\{z_n\}$ be a Cauchy sequence of complex numbers. Then, $\{z_n\}$ is bounded.*

Proof. For our Cauchy sequence $\{z_n\}$, choose N such that for $m, n > N$, we have $|z_m - z_m| < 1$. Thus, for all $n > N$,

$$|z_n| = |z_n - z_{N+1} + z_{N+1}| \leq |z_n - z_{N+1}| + |z_{N+1}| \leq 1 + |z_{N+1}|.$$

Therefore, for all $j \in \mathbb{N}$, $|z_j| \leq \max\{|z_1|, |z_2|, \cdots, |z_N|, 1 + |z_{N+1}|\}$, showing $|z_j|$ is less than or equal to the maximum of a finite set of numbers, and thus bounded. $\square$

> **Theorem 6.3**
>
> *Let $\{x_n\}$ be a Cauchy sequence of real numbers. Then, $\{x_n\}$ converges.*

Proof. By Theorem 6.2, our Cauchy sequence $\{x_n\}$ is bounded. Thus, by Theorem 2.6, or by Theorem 6.13, $\{x_n\}$ has a subsequence $\{x_{n_k}\}$ that converges to a point p. Fix ϵ. Choose N_1 such that for $k > N_1$, $|x_{n_k} - p| < \epsilon/2$. Using that $\{x_n\}$ is Cauchy, choose N_2 such that for $n, m > N_2$, $|x_m - x_n| < \epsilon/2$. For $m > \max(N_1, N_2)$, we have (noting that $n_m \geq m$)

$$\begin{aligned}
|x_m - p| &= |(x_m - x_{n_m}) + (x_{n_m} - p)| \\
&\leq |x_n - x_{n_m}| + |x_{n_m} - p| \\
&< \epsilon/2 + \epsilon/2 = \epsilon.
\end{aligned}$$

$\square$

> **Theorem 6.4**
>
> *Let $\{z_n\}$ be a sequence of complex numbers. Then, the following statements are equivalent:*
>
> *(a) The sequence $\{z_n\}$ converges.*
>
> *(b) The sequence $\{z_n\}$ is a Cauchy sequence.*

Proof (a). We assume $\{z_n\}$ converges to the point p. Fix $\epsilon > 0$ and choose N such that for $n > N$, $|z_n - p| < \epsilon/2$. For $m, n > N$, we have $|z_m - p| < \epsilon/2$ and $|z_n - p| < \epsilon/2$. Thus

$$\begin{aligned}
|z_m - z_n| &= |(z_m - z_n) + (p - p)| = |(z_m - p) - (z_n - p)| \\
&\leq |z_m - p| + |z_n - p| \\
&< \epsilon/2 + \epsilon/2 = \epsilon,
\end{aligned}$$

showing that $\{z_n\}$ is a Cauchy sequence. $\square$

Proof (b). We assume $\{z_n\}$ is a Cauchy sequence. Let $z_n = x_n + iy_n$. We have that

$$|x_m - x_n| = |Re(z_m - z_n)| \leq |z_m - z_n| \quad \text{and} \quad |y_m - y_n| = |Im(z_m - z_n)| \leq |z_m - z_n|.$$

Therefore, $\{x_n\}$ and $\{y_n\}$ are Cauchy sequences. By Theorem 6.3, $\{x_n\}$ and $\{y_n\}$ converge. Thus, by Theorem 6.1, $\{z_n\}$ converges. $\square$

6.2 Infinite Sums

Definition 6.3

Let $\{z_k\}$ be a sequence of complex numbers. Then the following expression

$$\sum_{k=0}^{\infty} z_k$$

*is called a **series** or sometimes an **infinite series**. The following expression*

$$S_n = \sum_{k=0}^{n} z_k$$

*is called the **nth partial sum** of the series, with $\{S_n\}$ forming a sequence of such partial sums.*

*If $\lim_{n\to\infty} S_n$ exists, we say the series is **convergent**, and we call that limit the **sum** of the series. If no such limit exists, we say the series is **divergent**.*

Remark

From the definition of a series, we have a convergent sum if and only if the sequence $\{S_n\}$ converges. Thus, we can restate the Cauchy criterion for sequences into a Cauchy criterion for series. It will be convenient to use the second criterion in Definition 6.2.

6.2.1 Infinite Sums – The Cauchy Criterion

Theorem 6.5

Let $\{z_k\}$ be a sequence of complex numbers. The series $\sum_{k=0}^{\infty} z_k$ is convergent if and only if for every $\epsilon > 0$, there exists and $N \in \mathbb{N}$ such that for all $n > N$ and all $p \geq 1$

$$\left| \sum_{k=n+1}^{n+p} z_k \right| < \epsilon. \tag{6.1}$$

Proof. Let $\{S_n\}$ be the sequence of partial sums of the series. For $n \in \mathbb{N}$ and $p \geq 1$, we have

$$|S_{n+p} - S_n| = \left| \sum_{k=0}^{n+p} z_k - \sum_{k=0}^{n} z_k \right| = \left| \sum_{k=n+1}^{n+p} z_k \right|. \tag{6.2}$$

If the series is convergent, then by Definition 6.3 the sequence $\{S_n\}$ is a Cauchy sequence. By equation (6.2), that means the conditions of the theorem in equation (6.1) are met.

Similarly, if the conditions of the theorem in equation (6.1) are met, then equation (6.2) shows that $\{S_n\}$ is a Cauchy sequence. Thus, the series is convergent. $\qquad\square$

6.3 Infinite Products

> **Definition 6.4**
>
> Let $\{z_k\}$ be a sequence of complex numbers. Then the following expression
>
> $$\prod_{k=1}^{\infty} z_k$$
>
> is called an **infinite product**. The following expression
>
> $$P_n = \prod_{k=1}^{n} z_k$$
>
> is called the **nth partial product**.

> **Definition 6.5**
>
> Let $\{z_k\}$ be a sequence of complex numbers, forming
>
> $$\text{the infinite product} \quad \prod_{k=1}^{\infty} z_k \quad \text{and the nth partial product} \quad P_n = \prod_{k=1}^{n} z_k.$$
>
> We consider several cases regarding the $z_i \in \{z_k\}$
>
> (a) $z_i = 0$ for an infinite number of such z_i. We say the product **diverges to zero**.
>
> (b) $z_i = 0$ for a finite number of such z_i. Then there exists an N such that $z_i \neq 0$ for $i > N$. If the infinite product $\prod_{i=N}^{\infty} z_i$ converges to a non-zero complex number, we say the full product **converges to zero**. Otherwise, we say the full product **diverges to zero**.
>
> (c) $z_i \neq 0$ for all such z_i. Let $P = \lim_{n \to \infty} P_n$. If P is a non-zero complex number, we say the product **converges**. If $P = 0$, we say the product **diverges to zero**. Otherwise, we say the product **diverges**.

Remark

We are only interested here in cases where none of the $z_i = 0$. Therefore, we assume here that all terms of the product are non-zero unless specifically stated otherwise.

Remark

Now consider the sequence $\{P_n\}$ of nth partial products, where P_n converges to some $P \neq 0$. Then we must have $P_n/P_{n-1} \to P/P = 1$. By definition, $P_n/P_{n-1} = z_n$. Therefore, for $\prod_{k=1}^{\infty} z_k$ to converge, a necessary (but not sufficient) condition is that $z_k \to 1$ as $k \to \infty$.

It is customary to write the infinite product as $\prod_{k=1}^{\infty}(1 + z_k)$, with convergence possible only if $z_k \to 0$ as $k \to \infty$. As will be seen, this form allows for more direct comparison between infinite series and infinite products.

Of course, when we use the $(1 + z_k)$ form, we assume $z_k \neq -1$.

6.3.1 Infinite Products – Three Simple Lemmas

We start with a simple real variable case.

Lemma 6.1

Let $\{x_n\}$ be a sequence of non-negative real numbers. Then $\sum_{n=1}^{\infty} x_n$ converges if and only if $\prod_{n=1}^{\infty}(1 + x_n)$ converges.

Proof. For all non-negative real numbers x, we have:

$$(1 + x) = 1 + \left(n \cdot \frac{x}{n}\right) \leq \left(1 + \frac{x}{n}\right)^n \leq \lim_{n\to\infty}\left(1 + \frac{x}{n}\right)^n = e^x.$$

Thus, for all n, the result is immediate from the following inequality

$$x_1 + x_2 + \ldots x_n \leq (1 + x_1) \cdot (1 + x_2) \cdots (1 + x_n) \leq e^{x_1} \cdot e^{x_2} \cdots e^{x_n} = e^{x_1 + x_2 + \ldots x_n}. \qquad \square$$

We use Lemma 6.1 to prove two simple complex variable cases.

Lemma 6.2

Let $\{z_n\}$ be a sequence of complex numbers. Then:

the sum $\sum_{n=1}^{\infty} |z_n|$ converges if and only if the product $\prod_{n=1}^{\infty}(1 + |z_n|)$ converges.

Proof. Because $|z_n|$ is real-valued, the result is immediate from Lemma 6.1. $\qquad \square$

Lemma 6.3

Let $\{z_k\}$ be a sequence of complex numbers. Then: $\left|\prod_{k=1}^{n}(1 + z_k) - 1\right| \leq \prod_{k=1}^{n}(1 + |z_k|) - 1$.

Proof. Our proof is by induction.

Base Case: $n = 1$. The inequality is obviously true for $n = 1$.

Assumed Case: $n = m$. We assume the inequality is true for $n = m$. Let $A = \prod_{k=1}^{m}(1 + z_k)$ and let $B = \prod_{k=1}^{m}(1 + |z_k|)$. Therefore $|A - 1| \leq B - 1$. By the triangle inequality we have $|A| - |1| \leq |A - 1|$ so that $|A| \leq |A - 1| + |1| \leq B - 1 + |1| \implies |A| \leq B$.

Induction Step: $n = m + 1$. For $z = z_{m+1}$, we must show $|A(1 + z) - 1| \leq B(1 + |z|) - 1$. Our approach will be to assume the inequality is false and look for a contradiction. We therefore assume

$$B(1 + |z|) - 1 < |A(1 + z) - 1|$$

so that

$$
\begin{aligned}
(B - 1) + B|z| &< |A - 1 + Az| \\
&< |A - 1| + |Az| && \text{by the triangle inequality} \\
&< (B - 1) + |Az| && |A - 1| \leq B - 1 \text{ is assumed in our } n = m \text{ case} \\
B|z| &< |Az|.
\end{aligned}
$$

And we have reached our contradiction because we were to assume $|A| \leq B$. $\qquad \square$

6.3.2 Infinite Products – The Cauchy Criterion

> **Theorem 6.6**
>
> *Let $\{z_k\}$ be a sequence of complex numbers, with $z_k \neq -1$. The infinite product $\prod_{k=1}^{\infty}(1 + z_k)$ converges if and only if (the Cauchy criterion) for every $\epsilon > 0$, there exists an $N \in \mathbb{N}$ such that for all $n > N$ and all $p \geq 1$*
>
> $$|(1 + z_{n+1})(1 + z_{n+2}) \cdots (1 + z_{n+p}) - 1| < \epsilon.$$

Proof. Fix $\epsilon < 1$ and let $P_n = \prod_{k=1}^{n}(1 + z_k)$.

Convergence $\Rightarrow$ Cauchy. Assume the infinite product converges, and let $\lim\limits_{n\to\infty} P_n = P \neq 0$. Because $\{P_n\}$ is a Cauchy sequence, there is an N such that for all $m, n > N$

$$|P_n| > \frac{|P|}{2} \quad \text{and} \quad |P_n - P_m| < \epsilon \frac{|P|}{2}.$$

Our Cauchy criterion is satisfied because for all $n > N$ and all $p \geq 1$, we set $m = n + p$ and have:

$$|(1 + z_{n+1})(1 + z_{n+2}) \cdots (1 + z_m) - 1| = \left| \frac{P_m}{P_n} - 1 \right|$$

$$= |P_n| \left| \frac{P_m}{P_n} - 1 \right| \frac{1}{|P_n|} = |P_m - P_n| \frac{1}{|P_n|}$$

$$< \epsilon \frac{|P|}{2} \cdot \frac{2}{|P|} = \epsilon.$$

Cauchy $\Rightarrow$ Convergence. Assume the Cauchy criterion. Thus, for our given ϵ there is an N such that for all $n > N$ and all $p \geq 1$

$$|(1 + z_{n+1})(1 + z_{n+2}) \cdots (1 + z_{n+p}) - 1| = \left| \frac{P_{n+p}}{P_n} - 1 \right| < \frac{\epsilon}{2}. \tag{6.3}$$

Fix $n > N$.

Define $b_p = P_{n+p}/P_n$ so that $|b_p - 1| < \epsilon/2$ from equation (6.3). From Theorem 1.1(d), we also have $1 - |b_p - 1| \leq |b_p| \leq 1 + |b_p - 1|$. Thus,

$$\frac{1}{2} < \left(1 - \frac{\epsilon}{2}\right) < |b_p| < \left(1 + \frac{\epsilon}{2}\right) < \frac{3}{2}. \tag{6.4}$$

Therefore, for $p_2 \geq p_1 \geq 1$

$$\frac{b_{p_2}}{b_{p_1}} = \frac{P_{n+p_2}}{P_n} \cdot \frac{P_n}{P_{n+p_1}} = \frac{P_{n+p_2}}{P_{n+p_1}} \quad \text{so that} \quad \left| \frac{b_{p_2}}{b_{p_1}} - 1 \right| < \frac{\epsilon}{2} \quad \text{and thus} \quad |b_{p_2} - b_{p_1}| < \frac{\epsilon}{2}|b_{p_1}| < \epsilon.$$

That means $\{b_p\}$ is a Cauchy sequence. But $b_{p_2}/b_{p_1} = P_{n+p_2}/P_{n+p_1}$, so $\{P_n\}$ must also be a Cauchy sequence. Hence, the sequence $\{P_n\}$ converges. From equation (6.4), we see that the "tail" of $\{P_n\}$, for all $n > N$, is $\geq 1/2$. By assumption, $(1 + z_k) \neq 0$ for all k. Thus, P_n converges to a non-zero complex number and therefore the infinite product converges. $\square$

6.3.3 Infinite Products – Convergence and the Logarithm

A common technique in complex analysis is to convert a product into a sum by taking the logarithm. That makes the following theorem quite useful.

Theorem 6.7

Let $\{z_k\}$ be a sequence of complex numbers, with $z_k \neq -1$. Assume the terms of $\log(1 + z_k)$ are from the principal branch of the logarithm. Then the series $\sum_{k=1}^{\infty} \log(1 + z_k)$ converges if and only if the product $\prod_{k=1}^{\infty}(1 + z_k)$ converges.

Proof. [16] Assume the series converges. Set $S_n = \sum_{k=1}^{n} \log(1 + z_k)$ and $P_n = \prod_{k=1}^{n}(1 + z_k)$. We have $P_n = e^{S_n}$ and have assumed $S_n \to S$ for some S. It follows that P_n tends to the limit $P = e^S \neq 0$. So, the convergence of the series assures the convergence of the product.

Now assume the product converges, with $P_n \to P \neq 0$. We do not claim that the series converges to the principal value of $\log P$, but we will show it converges to some value of $\log P$.

To begin, observe that for each n there exists and integer h_n such that

$$\text{Log}(P_n/P) = \text{Log}(P_n) - \text{Log}(P) = [S_n + h_n \cdot 2\pi i] - \text{Log}(P) = S_n - \text{Log}(P) + h_n \cdot 2\pi i. \quad (6.5)$$

Next, compute $\text{Log}(P_{n+1}/P) - \text{Log}(P_n/P)$ and rearrange terms to obtain

$$(h_{n+1} - h_n) \cdot 2\pi i = \text{Log}(P_{n+1}/P) - \text{Log}(P_n/P) - \text{Log}(1 + z_{n+1})$$

$$(h_{n+1} - h_n) \cdot 2\pi = \boxed{\text{Arg}(P_{n+1}/P) - \text{Arg}(P_n/P)} - \boxed{\text{Arg}(1 + z_{n+1})}. \quad (6.6)$$

Finally, assume large n and consider equation (6.6) and the two boxed terms. Product convergence means that $P_n/P \to 1$, and therefore $\log(P_n/P) \to 0$. Thus, the first boxed term $\to 0$. Convergence also means that $z_{n+1} \to 0$. With $|\text{Arg}(1 + z_{n+1})| \leq \pi$, the second boxed term must also $\to 0$.

Therefore, for some fixed large N and $n \geq N$, we must have $(h_{n+1} - h_n) = 0$ and thus $h_n = h_N$. It follows from equation (6.5) that $S_n \to \log P - h_N \cdot 2\pi i$. Hence, convergence of the product ensures the convergence of the series. $\qquad\square$

6.4 Absolute Convergence

Definition 6.6

Let $\{z_k\}$ be a sequence of complex numbers, with $z_k \neq -1$. Then the following expression

$$\prod_{k=1}^{\infty}(1 + z_k) \quad \text{is said to \textbf{converge absolutely} if} \quad \prod_{k=1}^{\infty}(1 + |z_k|) \quad \text{converges.}$$

Definition 6.7

Let $\{z_k\}$ be a sequence of complex numbers. Then the following expression

$$\sum_{k=1}^{\infty} z_k \quad \text{is said to \textbf{converge absolutely} if} \quad \sum_{k=1}^{\infty} |z_k| \quad \text{converges.}$$

Theorem 6.8

Let $\{z_k\}$ be a sequence of complex numbers, with $z_k \neq -1$. Then:

   (a) The infinite product $\prod_{k=1}^{\infty}(1 + z_k)$ converges absolutely if and only if the infinite series $\sum_{k=1}^{\infty} z_k$ converges absolutely.

   (b) If the product $\prod_{k=1}^{\infty}(1 + z_k)$ converges absolutely, then the product converges.

   (c) If the series $\sum_{k=1}^{\infty} z_k$ converges absolutely, then the series converges.

Proof (a). We are claiming that $\prod_{k=1}^{\infty}(1 + |z_k|)$ converges if and only if $\sum_{k=1}^{\infty}|z_k|$ converges. The result follows immediately from Lemma 6.2(a). □

Proof (b). Fix ϵ. Applying Theorem 6.6, choose N such that for $n > N$ and for all $p \geq 1$ we have

$$\prod_{k=n+1}^{n+p}(1 + |z_k|) - 1 = \left| \prod_{k=n+1}^{n+p}(1 + |z_k|) - 1 \right| < \epsilon.$$

We can then apply Lemma 6.3, giving

$$\left| \prod_{k=n+1}^{n+p}(1 + z_k) - 1 \right| \leq \prod_{k=n+1}^{n+p}(1 + |z_k|) - 1 < \epsilon.$$

We have obtained the Cauchy criterion of Theorem 6.6 for $\prod_{k=1}^{\infty}(1 + z_k)$, as required. □

Proof (c). Fix ϵ. Applying Theorem 6.5, choose N such that for $n > N$ and for all $p \geq 1$ we have

$$\sum_{k=n+1}^{n+p}|z_k| = \left| \sum_{k=n+1}^{n+p}|z_k| \right| < \epsilon.$$

By repeated application of the triangle inequality (Theorem 1.1(b)), we then have

$$\left| \sum_{k=n+1}^{n+p} z_k \right| \leq \sum_{k=n+1}^{n+p}|z_k| < \epsilon.$$

We have obtained the Cauchy criterion of Theorem 6.5 for $\sum_{k=1}^{\infty} z_k$, as required. □

Remark

We next show that the commutative laws apply to absolutely convergent infinite series and products. That is, every rearrangement of the terms $\{z_n\}$ is also absolutely convergent. Moreover, every such rearrangement converges to the same limit.

For a counter-example when a series that is not absolutely convergent, see Exercise 6.1(c). We show there that the series converges to a different value after rearrangement.

Theorem 6.9

Let $\{z_n\}$ be a sequence of complex numbers, with $z_n \neq -1$, and assume $\prod_{n=1}^{\infty}(1 + z_n)$ converges absolutely.

Define $\{k_n\}$ to be a sequence in which every positive integer appears exactly once, but in no particular pre-assumed order. So, given our sequence $\{z_n\}$ ($n = 1, 2, 3...$), we can rearrange that sequence into the order $\{z_{k_n}\}$. We have, for all such rearrangements:

(a) $\sum_{n=1}^{\infty} z_{k_n}$ *and* $\prod_{n=1}^{\infty}(1 + z_{k_n})$ *converge absolutely.*

(b) $\sum_{n=1}^{\infty} z_n = \sum_{n=1}^{\infty} z_{k_n}.$

(c) $\prod_{n=1}^{\infty}(1 + z_n) = \prod_{n=1}^{\infty}(1 + z_{k_n}).$

Proof Definitions. For our given rearrangement sequence $\{k_n\}$, and for any given $N \in \mathbb{N}$:
  · define $[N]$ to be the lowest positive whole number such that $\{1, 2, ..., N\} \subseteq \{k_1, k_2, ..., k_{[N]}\}$.
  · define $[N']$ to be the lowest positive whole number such that $\{k_1, k_2, ..., k_N\} \subseteq \{1, 2, ..., [N']\}$.

Proof (a). From Theorem 6.8(a), $\sum_{n=1}^{\infty} |z_n|$ converges to some $A \in \mathbb{R}$. Let

$$S_j = \sum_{n=1}^{j} |z_n| \quad \text{and} \quad SR_j = \sum_{n=1}^{j} |z_{k_n}|.$$

Both S_j and SR_j are monotone increasing. Clearly, then, all $S_j \leq A$. By definition, for all $N \in \mathbb{N}$ all terms of SR_N are included in $S_{[N']}$, so that $SR_N \leq S_{[N']} \leq A$. Because SR_j is monotone increasing and bounded above, $\sum_{n=1}^{\infty} |z_{k_n}|$ converges. We can then use Theorem 6.8 to conclude that both $\sum_{n=1}^{\infty} z_{k_n}$ and $\prod_{n=1}^{\infty}(1 + z_{k_n})$ converge absolutely. $\square$

Proof (b). We have from Theorem 6.8 that $\sum_{n=1}^{\infty} z_n$ converges. Let

$$S_j = \sum_{n=1}^{j} z_n \quad \text{and} \quad SR_j = \sum_{n=1}^{j} z_{k_n}.$$

Fix $\epsilon > 0$. Because S_j is a Cauchy sequence, we can apply Theorem 6.5. Thus, there is an N such that for $m > n \geq N$ we have $|\sum_{i=n}^{m} z_i| < \epsilon/2$. Now choose $n > [N]$. Then

$$|S_n - SR_n| = \left| \left(\sum_{j=1}^{N} z_j + \sum_{j=N+1}^{n} z_j \right) - \left(\sum_{j=1, k_j \leq N}^{n} z_{k_j} + \sum_{j=1, k_j > N}^{n} z_{k_j} \right) \right|$$

$$= \left| \left(\sum_{j=1}^{N} z_j + \sum_{j=N+1}^{n} z_j \right) - \left(\sum_{j=1}^{N} z_j + \sum_{j=1, k_j > N}^{n} z_{k_j} \right) \right| < \epsilon.$$

Both sums include all terms where the index z_j is $\leq N$. Those terms cancel, leaving only the tails, which can be made arbitrarily small. Therefore, both series converge to the same sum. $\square$

Proof (c). [17] From Theorem 6.8(b), $\prod_{n=1}^{\infty}(1 + z_n)$ converges to some $P \in \mathbb{C}$. Let

$$P_j = \prod_{n=1}^{j}(1 + z_n) \quad \text{and} \quad Q_j = \prod_{n=1}^{j}(1 + z_{k_n}).$$

From Theorem 6.6, there is an N such that for $m > n \geq N$ we have both $\left| \prod_{j=n+1}^{m} (1 + z_j) - 1 \right| < \delta$ and $\left| \prod_{j=n+1}^{m} (1 + |z_{k_j}|) - 1 \right| < \delta$. It follows that $|P_N - P| \leq \delta$.

Now choose $n > [N]$. Define $\{b_j\}$ as all members of $\{k_j\}$ where $k_j \leq n$. Define $\{c_j\}$ as all members of $\{k_j\}$ where $k_j \leq N$ Finally, define $\{d_j\}$ as all members of $\{k_j\}$ where $k_j > N$ and $j \leq n$. Note that $\{b_j\} = \{c_j\} + \{d_j\}$.

We have $Q_n = \prod_{j=1}^{n} (1 + z_{k_j}) = \prod_{\{b_j\}} (1 + z_{b_j})$. Next, $P_N = \prod_{j=1}^{N} (1 + z_j) = \prod_{\{c_j\}} (1 + z_{c_j})$. Finally, let $R_n = \prod_{\{d_j\}} (1 + z_{d_j})$. Then $Q_n = P_N \cdot R_n$. We now apply Lemma 6.3 and have

$$|R_n - 1| = \left| \prod_{\{d_j\}} (1 + z_{d_j}) - 1 \right| \leq \left| \prod_{\{d_j\}} (1 + |z_{d_j}|) - 1 \right| < \delta.$$

Now fix ϵ and set $\delta = \epsilon/2(|P| + 1)$, giving

$$|Q_n - P| \leq |Q_n - P_N| + |P_N - P| = |P_N \cdot R_n - P_N| + |P_N - P|$$
$$= |P_N| |R_n - 1| + |P_N - P|$$
$$< |P_N| |\delta| + |P_N - P| < \epsilon/2 + \epsilon/2 < \epsilon.$$

Thus, $Q_n \to P$, as required. $\qquad \square$

6.5   Function Series – Infinite Series of Functions

In this section, we consider the following question regarding *function series* (defined below): under what circumstances can the function series be integrated termwise, so that the integral of the sum is equal to the sum of the integrals? The answer involves the concept of *uniform converge* of function series, which we also define below.

> **Definition 6.8**
>
> *Let $\{f_n(z)\}$ be a sequence of complex functions. Then any series of the form*
>
> $$F(z) = \sum_{n=0}^{\infty} f_n(z)$$
>
> *is called a **function series**.*
>
> *Let Λ be the set of points which are in the domain of definition of all of the $f_n(z)$, and let $\Omega \subset \Lambda$ be the set of points for which the series $F(z)$ converges. Then Ω is called the **domain of convergence** of the series $F(z)$.*

Assume Ω is the domain of convergence of $F(z) = \sum_{n=0}^{\infty} f_n(z)$. That means, for a given $z_0 \in \Omega$ and fixed $\epsilon > 0$, there is an $N(\epsilon) \in \mathbb{N}$ such that for $n > N(\epsilon)$ and for any $p \in \mathbb{N}$ (i.e., for any finite number of sequential terms in the "tail"):

$$|f_{n+1}(z_0) + f_{n+2}(z_0) + \cdots + f_{n+p}(z_0)| < \epsilon.$$

It might be better to rename our $N(\epsilon)$ as $N(z_0, \epsilon)$ because our convergence assumption does not guarantee the same $N(\epsilon)$ will work for another point $z_1 \in \Omega$. For that, we need *uniform convergence*.

Definition 6.9

*Assume the function series $F(z) = \sum_{n=0}^{\infty} f_n(z)$ has a domain of convergence Ω. We say that the series **converges uniformly** in the domain $\Omega' \subset \Omega$ if, given $\epsilon > 0$, there exists an $N \in \mathbb{N}$ such that for all $z \in \Omega'$, all $n > N$ and all $p \in \mathbb{N}$, we have*

$$|f_{n+1}(z) + f_{n+2}(z) + \cdots + f_{n+p}(z)| < \epsilon.$$

Remark

In our definition, because we are within the domain of convergence, we can let $p \to \infty$ and have

$$\left| \sum_{k=n}^{\infty} f_k(z) \right| \leq \epsilon \qquad \text{for } n > N.$$

With our focus on uniform convergence, we begin with a very useful comparison test that can be used to determine whether a sequence of functions is uniformly convergent in a domain.

Theorem 6.10: Weierstrass M-test

Let $\{f_n(z)\}$ be a sequence of functions on a domain Ω and let $\{M_n\}$ be a convergent sequence of positive real numbers. Suppose there exists a set $\Omega' \subset \Omega$, a $K > 0$ and an $N \in \mathbb{N}$ such that $|f_n(z)| < K \cdot M_n$ for all $n > N$ and all $z \in \Omega'$. Then $\sum_{n=0}^{\infty} f_n(z)$ converges uniformly in Ω'.

Proof. Fix $\epsilon > 0$. Choose N such that $M_n + M_{n+1} + \cdots + M_{n+p} < \epsilon/2K$ for all $n > N$ and all $p \in \mathbb{N}$. We therefore have for all $z \in \Omega'$

$$\left| \sum_{n=N+1}^{N+1+p} f_n(z) \right| \leq \sum_{n=N+1}^{N+1+p} |f_n(z)| \leq \sum_{n=N+1}^{N+1+p} (K \cdot M_n) = K \sum_{n=N+1}^{N+1+p} M_n \leq K \cdot \epsilon/2K < \epsilon.$$

Applying Definition 6.9, our sequence of functions converges uniformly. □

Theorem 6.11

Let $\{f_n(z)\}$ be a sequence of functions, all continuous in the domain Ω. Let $\mathcal{D} \subset \Omega$ be a closed region. Assume the series $\sum_{n=0}^{\infty} f_n(z)$ is uniformly convergent in every such closed region $\mathcal{D}$ and let $F(z) = \sum_{n=0}^{\infty} f_n(z)$. Then

(a) The function $F(z)$ is continuous in Ω.

(b) Let $\gamma \subset \Omega$ be any simple path (and therefore a closed region in which the series is uniformly convergent). Then, integration of the series termwise along the path γ converges and

$$\sum_{n=0}^{\infty} \int_{\gamma} f_n(z) = \int_{\gamma} F(z).$$

Proof (a). [18] Let $\epsilon > 0$ and fix $z_0 \in \Omega$. Choose δ small enough so that the closed disk $\overline{\mathbf{D}}_\delta(z_0) \subset \Omega$

and therefore $\sum f_n(z)$ is uniformly convergent in $\overline{\mathbf{D}}_\delta(z_0)$. For $z \in \overline{\mathbf{D}}_\delta(z_0)$, define

$$A(z) = \sum_{n=0}^{N} f_n(z) \qquad \text{and} \qquad B(z) = \sum_{n=N+1}^{\infty} f_n(z),$$

where N is large enough so that $|B(z)| \leq \epsilon/3$.

Because $A(z)$ is sum of a finite number of continuous functions, $A(z)$ is continuous. Thus, there is a $\delta_1 < \delta$ such that, in the neighborhood $\mathbf{D}_{\delta_1}(z_0)$, we have $|A(z) - A(z_0)| < \epsilon/3$. So, for $z \in \mathbf{D}_{\delta_1}(z_0)$

$$|F(z) - F(z_0)| \leq |A(z) - A(z_0)| + |B(z)| + |B(z_0)| < \epsilon.$$

We have shown that $F(z)$ is continuous at z_0. But $z_0 \in \Omega$ was arbitrarily chosen, so $F(z)$ is continuous in Ω. $\qquad\square$

Proof (b). We have shown that $F(z)$ is continuous in Ω, so the integral of $F(z)$ exists.

Fix $\epsilon > 0$, let $L(\gamma)$ be the length of γ and let $A(z)$ and $B(z)$ be defined as in (a). The uniform convergence of $\sum f_n(z)$ along γ allows us to choose an N large enough so that $|B(z)| \leq \epsilon/2L(\gamma)$. We therefore have

$$\int_\gamma F(z) = \int_\gamma A(z) + \int_\gamma B(z)$$

$$= \sum_{n=0}^{N} \int_\gamma f_n(z) + \int_\gamma B(z)$$

$$\left| \int_\gamma F(z) - \sum_{n=0}^{N} \int_\gamma f_n(z) \right| = \left| \int_\gamma B(z) \right|.$$

Applying the ML inequality, we obtain our desired result:

$$\leq L(\gamma) \cdot \epsilon/2L(\gamma) < \epsilon. \qquad\square$$

6.6   The Geometric Series

We begin with the finite geometric sum

$$S_N = \sum_{n=0}^{N} z^n = 1 + z + z^2 + \cdots z^N.$$

For $z = 1$, we have $S_n = N$. For $z \neq 1$, we start with a few manipulations of S_N

$$zS_N = S_N + z^{N+1} - 1$$
$$1 - z^{N+1} = S_N - zS_N = S_N(1 - z),$$

giving

$$S_N = \frac{1 - z^{N+1}}{1 - z} \quad \text{for } z \neq 1.$$

We now consider the full (infinite) geometric series. For $|z| \geq 1$, the Nth term does not converge to 0, so the series diverges. For $|z| < 1$, we have

$$\lim_{N \to \infty} z^{N+1} = 0 \quad \text{and therefore} \quad \lim_{N \to \infty} S_N = \lim_{N \to \infty} \frac{1 - z^{N+1}}{1 - z} = \frac{1}{1 - z},$$

giving the final form of the full geometric series

$$\sum_{n=0}^{\infty} z^n = \frac{1}{1 - z} \quad \text{for } |z| < 1.$$

6.7 Supplemental Material

6.7.1 The Zeta Function

The Zeta function holds an important place in analytic number theory. It is a central player in Riemann's 1859 paper [12] and in the subsequent proof in 1896 of the Prime Number Theorem.

Definition 6.10

*The "basic" definition of the **Zeta function** (before analytic continuation) is*

$$\zeta(s) = \sum_{n=1}^{\infty} \frac{1}{n^s} \quad s \in \mathbb{C}, \, Re(s) > 1.$$

We will see below that the above form of the Zeta function only converges for $Re(s) > 1$. Although not proved here, it is interesting to note an equivalent product form of the Zeta function

$$\zeta(s) = \sum_{n=1}^{\infty} \frac{1}{n^s} = \prod_{p} \frac{1}{(1 - p^{-s})} \quad \text{for } Re(s) > 1 \text{ and } p \text{ an ordered list of all the primes.}$$

Theorem 6.12

For $\zeta(s)$, the Zeta function, we have

    (a) The sum $\zeta(1)$ diverges.

    (b) The sum $\zeta(2)$ converges.

    (c) For $x \in \mathbb{R}$, the sum $\zeta(x)$ converges for $x > 1$.

    (d) For $s \in \mathbb{C}$, the sum $\zeta(s)$ converges absolutely for $Re(s) > 1$.

Proof (a). For $N \in \mathbb{N}$, we have

$$\sum_{n=1}^{N} \frac{1}{n} = \sum_{n=1}^{N} \int_{n}^{n+1} \frac{1}{n} \, dx \geq \sum_{n=1}^{N} \int_{n}^{n+1} \frac{1}{x} \, dx = \int_{1}^{N+1} \frac{1}{x} \, dx = \log(N + 1) - \log(1) = \log(N + 1) - 0.$$

Therefore

$$\zeta(1) = \sum_{n=1}^{\infty} \frac{1}{n} = \lim_{N \to \infty} \sum_{n=1}^{N} \frac{1}{n} \geq \lim_{N \to \infty} \log(N + 1) \to \infty. \qquad \square$$

Proof (b). $\zeta(2)$ is the famous "Basel problem", posed by Pietro Mengoli in 1644 and solved by Leonard Euler in 1735. Euler showed:

$$\zeta(2) = \sum_{n=1}^{\infty} \frac{1}{n^2} = \frac{\pi^2}{6}.$$

We will not show a complete solution to the Basel problem. Instead, we will show that the series is bounded above. Because the terms are all non-negative, that bound is sufficient to show the series converges to *some* fixed number between 0 and the bounded amount.

$$\begin{aligned}
S_N &= \sum_{n=1}^{N} \frac{1}{n^2} = 1 + \sum_{n=2}^{N} \frac{1}{n^2} \\
&< 1 + \sum_{n=2}^{N} \frac{1}{n(n-1)} \\
&= 1 + \sum_{n=2}^{N} \left(\frac{1}{n-1} - \frac{1}{n} \right) \\
&= 1 + \left[\sum_{n=2}^{2} \frac{1}{n-1} + \sum_{n=3}^{N} \frac{1}{n-1} \right] - \sum_{n=2}^{N} \frac{1}{n} \\
&= 1 + \sum_{n=2}^{2} \frac{1}{n-1} + \left[\sum_{n=2}^{N-1} \frac{1}{n} - \sum_{n=2}^{N} \frac{1}{n} \right] \\
&= 1 + 1 - \frac{1}{N}.
\end{aligned}$$

Thus, $\lim_{N \to \infty} S_N < 2$, showing the series is bounded above and therefore converges. $\square$

Proof (c). Let $t \geq 1$ and $f(t) = \frac{1}{t^x}$ so that $\zeta(x) = \sum_{n=1}^{\infty} f(n)$. Because $x > 1, f(t)$ is continuous, positive and decreasing. Thus, by the integral test, $\zeta(x)$ converges if and only if $\int_1^{\infty} f(t)\, dt$ converges. We have for $x > 1$:

$$\int_1^a t^{-x}\, dt = \left(\frac{1}{-x+1} \right) \left(a^{-x+1} - 1 \right) = \left(\frac{-1}{x-1} \right) \left(\frac{1}{a^{x-1}} - 1 \right).$$

Taken to the limit, we have:

$$\begin{aligned}
\int_1^{\infty} f(t)\, dt &= \lim_{a \to \infty} \int_1^a t^{-x}\, dt = \lim_{a \to \infty} \left(\frac{-1}{x-1} \right) \left(\frac{1}{a^{x-1}} - 1 \right) \\
&= \left(\frac{-1}{x-1} \right) \lim_{a \to \infty} \left(\frac{1}{a^{x-1}} - 1 \right) = \left(\frac{-1}{x-1} \right) (0-1) = \left(\frac{1}{x-1} \right).
\end{aligned}$$

But that final fraction is finite for all $x > 1$, completing our proof. $\square$

Proof (d). For $\zeta(s)$, it is traditional to use $s = \sigma + it$ as the complex variable. To test for absolute convergence, we evaluate

$$\zeta(s) = \sum_{n=1}^{\infty} \frac{1}{|n^s|} \quad s = \sigma + it, \ \sigma > 1,$$

with $|n^s| = |e^{\sigma \log|n| + i\theta}| = e^{\sigma \log n} = n^{\sigma}$. Applying (c), the series converges absolutely for $\sigma > 1$. $\square$

6.7.2 Exercises

Exercises 6.1

(a) *To show that Lemma 6.1 does not always hold if the real-valued sequence $\{x_n\}$ includes negative numbers:*

    (1) for $x_n = (-1)^n \sqrt{\frac{2}{n+1}}$ show that the the sum converges but the product does not;

    (2) for $x_{2n-1} = \frac{1}{\sqrt{n}}$ and $x_{2n} = \left(\frac{1}{n} - \frac{1}{\sqrt{n}}\right)$ show that the product converges but the sum does not.

(b) *Show that following sequences are consistent with the results obtained in Lemma 6.1:*

    (1) $z_n = 1/n$;

    *(2) $z_n = -1/n$ (can you extend Lemma 6.1 to apply when **all** of the terms of the sequence are negative?);*

    (3) $z_n = -1/n^2$.

(c) *For the alternating series $\displaystyle\sum_{n=1}^{\infty} \frac{(-1)^{n+1}}{n}$*

    (1) Show that the above alternating series is not absolutely convergent;

    (2) Using the Taylor Series for $\log(1 + x)$, show that the above alternating series converges to $\log(2)$;

    (3) Rearrange the terms of the above alternating series in such a way that the rearranged series converges to $\log(2)/2$.

(d) *Prove: if the sum $\sum_{n=1}^{\infty} |z_n|$ converges, then the product $\prod_{n=1}^{\infty} |1 + z_n|$ converges.*

Remark

Answers to exercises are in Appendix A.

6.7.3 More on Cauchy Sequences

The following Theorem allows us to prove Theorem 6.3 without the Bolzano-Weierstrass Theorem.

Theorem 6.13

Let $\{x_n\}$ be a Cauchy sequence of real numbers. Without using Theorem 2.6 (the Bolzano-Weierstrass Theorem) show that $\{x_n\}$ has a convergent subsequence.

Proof. By Theorem 6.2, our Cauchy sequence $\{x_n\}$ is bounded. Thus, all elements are contained in some interval $[a_0, b_0]$. Set $d = b_0 - a_0$.

Because our sequence is Cauchy, we can choose an N_1 such that for $n, m \geq N_1$, $|x_m - x_n| < d/2^2$. Thus, there exists an interval $[a_1, b_1] \subset [a_0, b_0]$ with $b_1 - a_1 = d/2$ and $x_n \in [a_1, b_1]$ for $x_n \geq N_1$.

Continuing recursively, we can choose an $N_k > N_{k-1}$ such that for $n, m \geq N_k$, $|x_m - x_n| < d/2^{k+1}$, and there exists an interval $[a_k, b_k] \subset [a_{k-1}, b_{k-1}]$ with $b_k - a_k = d/2^k$ and $x_n \in [a_k, b_k]$ for $x_n \geq N_k$.

We then have a monotone increasing sequence $\{a_k\}$ and a monotone decreasing sequence $\{b_k\}$, with $\lim\limits_{n \to \infty} a_n \leq \lim\limits_{n \to \infty} b_n$. They must converge to the same limit (call it L), because

$$\lim_{k \to \infty} (b_k - a_k) = \lim_{k \to \infty} d/2^k = 0.$$

We can now construct a subsequence $\{x_{N_k}\}$. Each $x_{N_k} \in [a_k, b_k]$, and therefore $|x_{N_k} - L| < d/2^k$. For any fixed $\epsilon > 0$ and sufficiently large k, we have $|x_{N_k} - L| < \epsilon$ and thus $\{x_{N_k}\}$ converges to L. $\quad\square$

Cauchy's Integral Theorem

In Theorem 5.4 (the Fundamental Theorem of Calculus), we showed the *conditions* needed to allow evaluation of an integral over a path by reference only to the endpoints of the path (known as "path independence"). We show here the *circumstances* where those conditions are obtained. Cauchy's Integral Theorem essentially states that if $f(z)$ is holomorphic in the domain Ω and $\gamma \subset \Omega$ is a closed path, then $\int_\gamma f(z)\, dz = 0$.

We use a classic approach to prove Cauchy's Integral Theorem. We first prove it for a closed contour consisting of a triangle, following a proof known as Goursat's Theorem. Having established some key properties of polygons in Chapter 3, a very simple proof extends Goursat's Theorem to any closed polygon. Finally, to prove the case for any closed contour, we show that a polygon can be constructed whose integral value is arbitrarily close to the integral value of that closed contour.

7.1 Cauchy's Integral Theorem for Triangles

Theorem 7.1: Goursat's Theorem

Let $f(z)$ be holomorphic in the domain Ω. Let T be the boundary and T° the interior of a triangle (oriented in the positive direction), with $T \cup T^\circ \subset \Omega$. Then

$$\int_T f(z)\, dz = 0.$$

Proof. [19] Let S be the length of the longest side of T and let L be the overall length of the three sides of T. We proceed in steps.

Step 1. Set a point at the midpoint of each side of T and scribe lines connecting the three midpoints. We have transformed T into four equal triangles, all similar to T and all with longest side and overall length of $S/2$ and $L/2$, respectively. Orient the new triangles in the positive direction. Name the new triangles T_A, T_B, T_C, T_D.

Note (Figure 7.1) that all internal legs of the four new triangles are digons that cancel. That means

$$\int_T f(z)\, dz = \int_{T_A} f(z)\, dz + \int_{T_B} f(z)\, dz + \int_{T_C} f(z)\, dz + \int_{T_D} f(z)\, dz.$$

Next, choose any one of the new triangles that obtains the maximum in

$$\max_{j=A,B,C,D} \left| \int_{T_j} f(z)\, dz \right|.$$

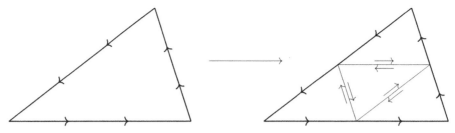

Figure 7.1: Subdivide Triangle

Call that triangle T_1 and call $\blacktriangledown^1$ the boundary plus interior or T_1. We then have the following inequality with respect to the integral over T

$$\left|\int_T f(z)\,dz\right| \le 4\left|\int_{T_1} f(z)\,dz\right|.$$

Step 2. We proceed exactly as in the prior step, except the starting triangle is T_1. At the end of this step, we have T_2 and $\blacktriangledown^2$. The longest side of T_2 is $S/(2^2)$ and the overall length is $L/(2^2)$. We also have the following inequality with respect to the integral over T

$$\left|\int_T f(z)\,dz\right| \le 4^2\left|\int_{T_2} f(z)\,dz\right|.$$

Step n. Continuing as before, by the nth step the starting triangle is $T_{(n-1)}$. At the end of this step, we have T_n and $\blacktriangledown^n$. The longest side of T_n is $S/(2^n)$ and the overall length is $L/(2^n)$. We also have the following inequality with respect to the integral over T

$$\left|\int_T f(z)\,dz\right| \le 4^n\left|\int_{T_n} f(z)\,dz\right|.$$

After n Steps. We have created the nested compact sets

$$\blacktriangledown^1 \supset \blacktriangledown^2 \supset \blacktriangledown^3 \supset \dots \supset \blacktriangledown^n \supset \dots$$

whose length goes to 0. By Lemma 2.2, there exists a unique point z_0 that belongs to all of the $\blacktriangledown^n$.

For some $r > 0$, $f(z)$ is holomorphic in the neighborhood $\mathbf{D}_r(z_0)$ of z_0. Define $h(z)$ as

$$h(z) = \frac{f(z) - f(z_0)}{z - z_0} - f'(z_0),$$

so that $\lim\limits_{z \to z_0} h(z) = 0$ and

$$f(z) = f(z_0) + f'(z_0)(z - z_0) + h(z)(z - z_0). \tag{7.1}$$

Fix $\epsilon > 0$. Then there is a $0 < \delta < r$ such that for $z \in \mathbf{D}_\delta(z_0)$, we have $h(z) < \epsilon$. Because our $\blacktriangledown^n$ nest to the point z_0, with $L/(2n) \to 0$, there must be an n such that for $n > N$ we have $\blacktriangledown^n \subset \mathbf{D}_\delta(z_0)$. From this point forward, we assume our chosen n satisfies $n > N$.

Using equation (7.1), we have

$$\int_{T_n} f(z)\,dz = \int_{T_n} f(z_0)\,dz + \int_{T_n} f'(z_0)(z - z_0)\,dz + \int_{T_n} h(z)(z - z_0)\,dz.$$

CHAPTER 7. CAUCHY'S INTEGRAL THEOREM

But $f(z_0)$ (a constant) and $f'(z_0)(z - z_0)$ both have primitives. Thus, by Theorem 5.4, their integrals over closed paths equal 0, leaving

$$\int_{T_n} f(z)\,dz = \int_{T_n} h(z)(z - z_0)\,dz.$$

We have $h(z) < \epsilon$, $|z - z_0| \le S/(2^n)$ and the overall length of $T_n \le L/(2^n)$. By the ML inequality

$$\left| \int_{T_n} f(z)\,dz \right| = \left| \int_{T_n} h(z)(z - z_0)\,dz \right| \le \epsilon \cdot S/(2^n) \cdot L/(2^n) = 4^{-n} \cdot \epsilon \cdot S \cdot L.$$

But that means

$$\left| \int_T f(z)\,dz \right| \le 4^n \left| \int_{T_n} f(z)\,dz \right| \le 4^n \cdot 4^{-n} \cdot \epsilon \cdot S \cdot L = \epsilon \cdot S \cdot L.$$

We can make ϵ as small as we like, completing the proof. $\qquad\square$

> **Remark**
>
> With Goursat's Theorem, we are well on our way to proving Cauchy's Integral Theorem. Next, we slightly extend Goursat's Theorem. In this version, $f(z)$ is holomorphic in Ω except at a finite set of isolated points $\{p_j\}$. We assume only that f is continuous at the points $\{p_j\}$.

> **Theorem 7.2**
>
> Let Ω be a domain and let $\{p_j\} \subset \Omega$ be a finite set of isolated points. Let T be the boundary and T° the interior of a triangle (oriented in the positive direction), with $\blacktriangledown = T \cup T^\circ \subset \Omega$. Assume $f(z)$ is continuous in Ω and holomorphic in $\Omega \backslash \{p_j\}$. Then
>
> $$\int_T f(z)\,dz = 0.$$

Proof - Introduction. We will initially assume that $\{p_j\}$ consists of just a single point p. Based on that assumption, we prove the theorem for all three possible cases: (1) $p \notin T \cup T^\circ$, (2) $p \in T$, and (3) $p \in T^\circ$. As case (4), we return to the initial assumption that $\{p_j\}$ is a finite set of isolated points. $\quad\square$

Proof (1): $p \notin \blacktriangledown = T \cup T^\circ$. For each $z \in T$, let the disk $\mathbf{D}_{r(z)}(z)$ have radius $r(z)$ small enough so that $\mathbf{D}_{r(z)}(z) \subset \Omega$ and $p \notin \mathbf{D}_{r(z)}(z)$. For the compact set $\blacktriangledown$, let

$$S = \left[\bigcup_{z \in T} \mathbf{D}_{r(z)}(z) \right] \cup T^\circ$$

be an open cover of $\blacktriangledown$.

Then $S \subset \Omega$ is a domain. Because $p \notin S$, by assumption $f(z)$ is holomorphic in S. With $T \subset S$, we can apply Theorem 7.1 and have $\int_T f(z)\,dz = 0$. $\quad\square$

Proof (2): $p \in T$. Fix $\epsilon > 0$. Our goal is to show that $\int_T f(z)\,dz < \epsilon$.

Label the vertices of T as A, B, C. If p is not already at a vertex, assume it is on the leg of the triangle between vertices A and B. Draw a line from p to vertex C. This puts p at a vertex of the two resulting triangles, and we have reduced this case to one where p is at vertex A of T.

Now consider a disk centered at p. Let r_1 be small enough such that $\mathbf{D}_{r_1}(p) \subset \Omega$. Let $r_2 \leq r_1$ be small enough such that r_2 is less than the length of the shorter of leg AB and leg AC. Let $r_3 \leq r_2$ be small enough such that the part of the disk's arc that scribes the interior angle of T at A (beginning at leg AB and ending at leg AC) is wholly in the interior of T.

Using that $f(z)$ is continuous in Ω, let $r_4 \leq r_3$ be small enough such that, for $z \in \mathbf{D}_{r_4}(p)$, we have $|f(p) - f(z)| < 1$. By the triangle inequality, we have

$$|f(z)| = |(f(z) - f(p)) + (f(p)| \leq |(f(z) - f(p))| + |f(p)| \leq 1 + |f(p)|.$$

Setting $M = |f(p)| + 1$, we therefore have $|f(z)| \leq M$ for $z \in \mathbf{D}_{r_4}(p)$.

Finally, set $\delta = \min(r_4, \epsilon/4M)$ and let δ be the final radius of our disk $\mathbf{D}_\delta(p)$.

Let b' be the point where $\mathbf{D}_\delta(p)$ intersects leg AB and let c' be the point where $\mathbf{D}_\delta(p)$ intersects leg AC. Draw a line from b' to c' and a line from b' to C. We now have three triangles: $T_1 = Ac'b'$, $T_2 = b'c'C$ and $T_3 = b'CB$, with p only on T_1. We orient our three triangles in the positive direction. All internal legs are digons that cancel, so we have

$$\int_T f(z)\, dz = \int_{T_1} f(z)\, dz + \int_{T_2} f(z)\, dz + \int_{T_3} f(z)\, dz$$
$$= \int_{T_1} f(z)\, dz + 0 + 0$$
$$= \int_{T_1} f(z)\, dz.$$

Basic trigonometry tells us that the length of the boundary of T_1 is less than 4δ. Thus, using the ML inequality, we have our desired result:

$$< M \cdot 4\delta \leq M \cdot 4 \cdot \frac{\epsilon}{4M} = \epsilon. \qquad \square$$

Proof (3): $p \in T^\circ$. For any triangle, we can convert this to *Case 2* as follows. Label the vertices of the triangle A, B, C. Draw a line from vertex A, through p to the leg between vertices B and C. Now draw a line from p to B and from p to C. If we orient all four triangles in the positive direction, all of the interior legs are digons that cancel and we have

$$\int_T f(z)\, dz = \int_{T_1} f(z)\, dz + \int_{T_2} f(z)\, dz + \int_{T_3} f(z)\, dz + \int_{T_4} f(z)\, dz = 0. \qquad \square$$

Proof (4): $\{p_j\} \in \Omega$. We can use the technique of Theorem 7.1 to cut T into finitely many smaller triangles that are as small as we need. Here we assume they are small enough so that no more than one p_j is inside or on any one triangle. With that, the proofs for cases (1) through (3) apply, and we have our desired result. $\qquad \square$

7.2 Cauchy's Integral Theorem for Rectangles

The following corollary could be proved using the same nesting approach as Theorem 7.1. But, with that proof already in hand, the result is essentially immediate.

Corollary 7.1

Let Ω be a domain and let $\{p_j\} \subset \Omega$ be a finite set of isolated points. Let R be the boundary and $R°$ the interior of a rectangle (oriented in the positive direction), with $R \cup R° \subset \Omega$. Assume $f(z)$ is continuous in Ω and holomorphic in $\Omega \backslash \{p_j\}$. Then

$$\int_R f(z)\, dz = 0.$$

Proof. Choose any one corner of R and denote that point z_0. Let z_1 denote the point at the only remaining corner of R that is not adjacent to z_0. Let L be the diagonal line that connects z_0 and z_1. We now have two triangles, T_0 and T_1. If we orient the boundaries of our two triangles in the positive direction, their common hypotenuse will have opposite orientations that cancel each other, leaving only R. Using the results of Theorem 7.2, we therefore have

$$\int_R f(z)\, dz = \int_{T_0} f(z)\, dz + \int_{T_1} f(z)\, dz = 0. \qquad \square$$

7.3 Cauchy's Integral Theorem for Polygons

By combining Theorems 3.3 and 3.4, we can decompose any closed polygon into a finite number of digons and triangles. We can then apply Goursat's Theorem (Theorem 7.1) on triangles and obtain the following important theorem.

Theorem 7.3

Let Ω be a domain and let $\{p_j\} \subset \Omega$ be a finite set of isolated points. Let $P \subset \Omega$ be a closed polygon (not necessarily simple). Assume $f(z)$ is continuous in Ω and holomorphic in $\Omega \backslash \{p_j\}$. Then

$$\int_P f(z)\, dz = 0.$$

Proof. Under Theorem 3.3, every closed polygon P can be decomposed into a finite number of simple closed polygons and a finite number of digons. The digons self-cancel, so it is only necessary to prove the theorem for a simple closed polygon.

By Theorem 3.4, any simple closed polygon P can be decomposed into triangles (all oriented in the same direction as P) by means of digons in the interior of P.

Now suppose our P is decomposed into n such triangles, denoted as T_1 through T_n. By Theorem 7.1, for each such T_k, we have $\int_{T_k} f(z)\, dz = 0$. Thus

$$\int_P f(z)\, dz = \sum_{k=1}^{n} \int_{T_k} f(z)\, dz = 0. \qquad \square$$

7.4 Cauchy's Integral Theorem for Closed Contours

We can now present our final version of Cauchy's Integral Theorem, applicable not just to triangles, rectangles and polygons, but to any closed contour.

Theorem 7.4: Cauchy's Integral Theorem

Let Ω be a domain and let $\{p_j\} \subset \Omega$ be a finite set of isolated points. Let $\mathbf{C} \subset \Omega$ be a closed contour. Assume $f(z)$ is continuous in Ω and holomorphic in $\Omega \backslash \{p_j\}$. Then

$$\int_{\mathbf{C}} f(z)\, dz = 0.$$

Proof. [20] Fix $\epsilon > 0$. Our goal is to find a suitable closed polygon P such that

$$\left| \int_{\mathbf{C}} f(z)\, dz - \int_P f(z)\, dz \right| < \epsilon. \tag{7.2}$$

Then, applying Theorem 7.3, we would have

$$\left| \int_{\mathbf{C}} f(z)\, dz \right| < \epsilon,$$

and our proof would be complete.

Because f is continuous in Ω, and holomorphic except on on a set of measure zero, f is Riemann integrable in Ω. We can therefore use Riemann sums to estimate our integral. Let $\mathbf{C}$ be parameterized by[21] the continuous function $\omega : [a, b] \to \Omega$. Our integral is approximated by subdividing the interval $[a, b]$ into subintervals $a = x_0 < x_1 < x_2 < ... < x_n = b$ of equal width and evaluating the expression

$$J_n = \sum_{k=1}^{n} f(\omega(x_k)) \Delta \omega_k \quad \text{where} \quad \Delta \omega_k = \omega(w_k) - \omega(w_{k-1}).$$

The integral is then the limit of this Riemann sum as the lengths of the subintervals approach zero.

$$\int_{\mathbf{C}} f(z)\, dz = \lim_{n \to \infty} J_n = \lim_{n \to \infty} \sum_{k=1}^{n} f(\omega(x_k)) \left[\omega(w_k) - \omega(w_{k-1}) \right].$$

So, with large enough n, we can get J_n as close as we like to our integral. We now apply three criteria to the size of n.

Criteria N_1. For our given ϵ, we require N_1 large enough so that, for $n > N_1$:

$$\left| \int_{\mathbf{C}} f(z)\, dz - J_n \right| < \epsilon/2.$$

Criteria N_2. Using Theorem 3.1, choose r such that, for all $z \in \mathbf{C}$, $\mathbf{D}_r(z) \subset \Omega$. We require N_2 large enough so that for $n > N_2$ the lengths of all path segments $\Delta \omega_k$ are less than $r/4$.

Criteria N_3. Let L be the length of our contour $\mathbf{C}$ and let z_1 and z_2 be any two points either on $\mathbf{C}$ or at a distance of at most $r/4$ from $\mathbf{C}$ (where r is as described immediately above). We require N_3 large enough so that for $n > N_3$ the lengths of all path segments $\Delta \omega_k$ are less than δ, where δ is a number such that $|f(z_1) - f(z_2)| < \epsilon/2L$ for $|z_1 - z_2| < \delta$. The existence of δ follows from the fact that f is uniformly continuous on the closed set $K = \{z \in \mathbb{C} : |z - w| \leq r/2, w \in \mathbf{C}\}$. Then we have $\mathbf{C}$ in the interior of K and K in the interior of Ω. Since f is continuous in Ω and K is closed and bounded ($\mathbf{C}$ has finite length), f is uniformly continuous in K by Theorem 4.11.

Now let $N = \max(N_1, N_2, N_3)$ and assume $n > N$. Further, let $0 \leq k \leq n$ and let P be the closed oriented polygon $[\omega(x_0), \omega(x_1) \cdots \omega(x_n)]$, where the x_k are the subinterval points of the interval $[a, b]$

above. We have from Criteria N_2 that the line segments $[\omega(x_k), \omega(x_{k+1})] \subset \Omega$, and we have from Criteria N_3 that $|\omega(w_k) - \omega(w_{k-1})| < \delta$ so that $|f(\omega(w_k)) - f(\omega(w_{k-1}))| < \epsilon/2L$.

Putting it all together, we have

$$
\begin{aligned}
\left| \int_P f(z)\,dz - J_n \right| &= \left| \sum_{k=1}^{n} \int_{\omega(x_{k-1})}^{\omega(x_k)} f(z)\,dz - \sum_{k=1}^{n} f(\omega(x_k)) \int_{\omega(x_{k-1})}^{\omega(x_k)} 1\,dz \right| \\
&= \left| \sum_{k=1}^{n} \int_{\omega(x_{k-1})}^{\omega(x_k)} [f(z) - f(\omega(x_k))]\,dz \right| \\
&\leq \left| \sum_{k=1}^{n} \int_{\omega(x_{k-1})}^{\omega(x_k)} |f(z) - f(\omega(x_k))|\,|dz| \right| \\
&< \frac{\epsilon}{2L} \sum_{k=1}^{n} \int_{\omega(x_{k-1})}^{\omega(x_k)} 1\,|dz| \\
&\leq \frac{\epsilon}{2L} \cdot L \\
&= \frac{\epsilon}{2}.
\end{aligned}
$$

Consequently,

$$
\begin{aligned}
\left| \int_C - \int_P \right| &= \left| \left(\int_C - J_n \right) - \left(\int_P - J_n \right) \right| \\
&\leq \left| \int_C - J_n \right| + \left| \int_P - J_n \right| \\
&< \frac{\epsilon}{2} + \frac{\epsilon}{2} = \epsilon.
\end{aligned}
$$

We have satisfied the requirements of equation (7.2), completing the proof. □

7.5 Principle of Deformation of Paths

Theorem 7.5

Let $f(z)$ be holomorphic in the region $\mathcal{R}$. Let C_1 and C_2 be positively oriented simple closed contours, with C_2 lying entirely in the interior of C_1, and let the region K consist of all points in $\mathbb{C}$ that lie both in the interior of C_1 and in the exterior of C_2. Assume $C_1 \cup C_2 \cup K \subset \mathcal{R}$. Then

$$
\int_{C_1} f(z)\,dz = \int_{C_2} f(z)\,dz.
$$

Remark

We *do not assume* that all points in the interior of C_2 belong to $\mathcal{R}$.

Proof.[22] Connect C_1 and C_2 by two simple and non-intersecting subpaths (γ_1 and γ_2) that remain in K, as shown by the dotted lines in Figure 7.2. The (path connected) region K is now decomposed into

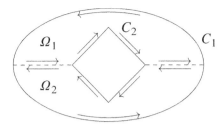

Figure 7.2: Deformed Path

two (simply connected) domains, call them Ω_1 and Ω_2, with $\Omega_1 \cup \partial\Omega_1 \subset \mathscr{R}$ and $\Omega_2 \cup \partial\Omega_2 \subset \mathscr{R}$. By Theorem 7.4, orienting $\partial\Omega_1$ and $\partial\Omega_2$ in the positive direction, we have that

$$\int_{\partial\Omega_1} f(z)\,dz = \int_{\partial\Omega_2} f(z)\,dz = 0 \quad \text{so that} \quad \int_{\partial\Omega_1} f(z)\,dz + \int_{\partial\Omega_2} f(z)\,dz = 0.$$

With the positive orientation of both $\partial\Omega_1$ and $\partial\Omega_2$: (1) they form canceling orientations across the subpaths γ_1 and γ_2, and (2) they form a negative orientation along C_2. Therefore

$$\int_{\partial\Omega_1 + \partial\Omega_2} f(z)\,dz = \int_{C_1 - C_2} f(z)\,dz = 0 \quad \text{so that} \quad \int_{C_1} f(z)\,dz = \int_{C_2} f(z)\,dz. \qquad \square$$

| Remark |

The above theorem is known as the *principle of deformation of paths* since it tells us that if C_1 is continuously deformed into C_2, always passing through points at which $f(z)$ is holomorphic, then the value of the integral of $f(z)$ never changes.

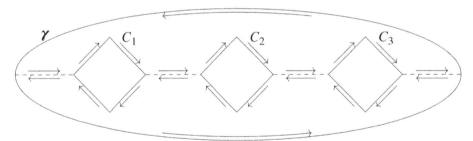

Figure 7.3: Deformed Path (Multiple Internal Contours)

| Theorem 7.6 |

Let $f(z)$ be holomorphic in the region $\mathscr{R}$. Let γ and $C_1, C_2, \cdots, C_n$ be positively oriented simple closed contours, with $C_1, C_2, \cdots, C_n$ not only lying entirely in the interior of γ but also entirely in the exterior of each other. Let the region K consist of all points in $\mathbb{C}$ that lie both in the interior of γ and in the exterior of all C_j. Assume $\gamma \cup C_1 \cup C_2 \cdots \cup C_n \cup K \subset \mathscr{R}$. Then

$$\int_{\gamma} f(z)\,dz = \sum_{j=1}^{n} \int_{C_j} f(z)\,dz.$$

CHAPTER 7. CAUCHY'S INTEGRAL THEOREM

Proof. Connect contours γ and $C_1, C_2, \cdots, C_n$ by means of $n+1$ simple and non-intersecting subpaths $(\gamma_1, \gamma_2, \cdots, \gamma_{n+1})$ that remain in K, as shown by the dotted lines in Figure 7.3.

The (path connected) region K is now decomposed into two (simply connected) domains, call them Ω_1 and Ω_2, with $\Omega_1 \cup \partial\Omega_1 \subset \mathcal{R}$ and $\Omega_2 \cup \partial\Omega_2 \subset \mathcal{R}$.

By Theorem 7.4, orienting $\partial\Omega_1$ and $\partial\Omega_2$ in the positive direction, we have that

$$\int_{\partial\Omega_1} f(z)\,dz = \int_{\partial\Omega_2} f(z)\,dz = 0 \quad \text{so that} \quad \int_{\partial\Omega_1} f(z)\,dz + \int_{\partial\Omega_2} f(z)\,dz = 0.$$

With the positive orientation of both $\partial\Omega_1$ and $\partial\Omega_2$: (1) they form canceling orientations across the subpaths $\gamma_1, \gamma_2, \cdots, \gamma_{n+1}$, and (2) they form a negative orientation along each of the C_j's. Therefore

$$\int_{\partial\Omega_1 + \partial\Omega_2} f(z)\,dz = \int_\gamma f(z)\,dz - \sum_{j=1}^n \int_{C_n} f(z)\,dz = 0 \quad \text{so that} \quad \int_\gamma f(z)\,dz = \sum_{j=1}^n \int_{C_n} f(z)\,dz. \qquad \square$$

7.6   Supplemental Material

Assume $f(z)$ is holomorphic in the domain Ω. In Cauchy's Integral Theorem we showed that, for any closed contour $C \subset \Omega$, we have $\int_C f(z)\,dz = 0$. By that result, we can use condition (c) of Theorem 5.4 to prove that the Fundamental Theorem of Calculus (path independence) applies to $\int_\gamma f(z)\,dz$ for *any* contour (closed or not) where $\gamma \subset \Omega$.

Below we use a different technique to show that the Fundamental Theorem of Calculus applies. Assume $f(z)$ is holomorphic in the open disk $\mathbf{D}_R(z_0)$. By proving that $f(z)$ has a primitive in the disk, we can use condition (a) of Theorem 5.4 to show that the Fundamental Theorem of Calculus applies to $\int_\gamma f(z)\,dz$ for *any* contour γ in the disk.

Theorem 7.7

Let $f(z)$ be holomorphic in an open disk $\mathbf{D}_R(z_0)$. Then $f(z)$ has a primitive in that disk.

Proof. [23] We could always make the change of variable $w = (z - z_0)$ to center the disk at the origin, so we can (and will) assume $z_0 = 0$. Thus, we assume $f(z)$ is holomorphic for $z \in \mathbf{D}_R(0)$.

Fix $z \neq 0 \in \mathbf{D}_R(0)$ and let $\mathbf{D}_\epsilon(z)$ be a neighborhood of z small enough such that: (1) $\mathbf{D}_\epsilon(z) \subset \mathbf{D}_R(0)$, (2) if z is not on the real or imaginary axis, $\mathbf{D}_\epsilon(z)$ remains in the same quadrant as z, and (3) if z is on the real or imaginary axis, $\mathbf{D}_\epsilon(z)$ remains in the same half-plane as z.

Fix $z_0 \in \mathbf{D}_\epsilon(z)$ and let $\Delta z = z_0 - z$ so that $z_0 = z + \Delta z$.

Define $P(w)$ to be a polygon traversing from 0 to w as follows: (1) a horizontal line (if needed) from 0 to $Re(w)$ and then (2) a vertical line (if needed) from $Re(w)$ to w. The convexity of $\mathbf{D}_R(0)$ ensures that both $P(z)$ and $P(z + \Delta z) \subset \mathbf{D}_R(0)$. Define

$$F(z) = \int_{P(z)} f(w)\,dw.$$

We will show that F is holomorphic in $\mathbf{D}_R(0)$ and that $F'(z) = f(z)$. We have

$$F(z + \Delta z) - F(z) = \int_{P(z+\Delta z)} f(w)\,dw - \int_{P(z)} f(w)\,dw.$$

Because $f(z)$ is holomorphic for $z \in \mathbf{D}_R(0)$, integrals of $f(z)$ over digons (by definition), triangles (by Theorem 7.1) and rectangles (by Corollary 7.1) all resolve to zero. Thus, using Theorem 3.5, the integral over $P(z + \Delta z) - P(z)$ is equal to the integral over the line segment from z to $(z + \Delta z)$.

Let γ be the straight line segment from z to $(z + \Delta z)$, giving

$$F(z + \Delta z) - F(z) = \int_{P(z+\Delta z)} f(w)\, dw - \int_{P(z)} f(w)\, dw = \int_\gamma f(w)\, dw.$$

For our fixed z, let $M = f(z)$. Because f is holomorphic (and thus continuous) in $\mathbf{D}_R(0)$, we have in a neighborhood of z a continuous function $\phi(w)$ such that $f(w) = M + \phi(w)$, with $\lim_{w \to z} \phi(w) = 0$.

We therefore have

$$F(z + \Delta z) - F(z) = \int_\gamma M\, dw + \int_\gamma \phi(w)\, dw = M \int_\gamma dw + \int_\gamma \phi(w)\, dw.$$

The integral $\int_\gamma dw$ has a constant of 1 as its integrand and a primitive of w. Thus, we can use Theorem 5.4 to see that $M \int_\gamma dw = M \cdot [(z + \Delta z) - z] = M \cdot \Delta z = f(z) \cdot \Delta z$.

Using the ML inequality

$$\left| \int_\gamma \phi(w)\, dw \right| \leq \max_{w \in \gamma} |\phi(w)| |\Delta z|$$

$$\lim_{\Delta z \to 0} \left| \int_\gamma \phi(w)\, dw \right| \leq \lim_{\Delta z \to 0} \max_{w \in \gamma} |\phi(w)| |\Delta z|,$$

and noting that $\max_{w \in \gamma} |\phi(w)| \to 0$ as $\Delta z \to 0$, we can disregard the $\phi(w)$ term of the integral and have

$$\lim_{\Delta z \to 0} [F(z + \Delta z) - F(z)] = \lim_{\Delta z \to 0} (f(z) \cdot \Delta z)$$

$$\lim_{\Delta z \to 0} \frac{F(z + \Delta z) - F(z)}{\Delta z} = f(z).$$

The last equation above shows that F is holomorphic and is a primitive for f in $\mathbf{D}_R(0)$. $\square$

In the next theorem, we use Cauchy's Integral Theorem to extend Theorem 6.11 to holomorphic functions.

Theorem 7.8

Let $\{f_n(z)\}$ be a sequence of functions, all holomorphic in the domain Ω. Let $\mathcal{D} \subset \Omega$ be a closed region. Assume the series $\sum_{n=0}^{\infty} f_n(z)$ is uniformly convergent in every such closed region $\mathcal{D}$ and let $F(z) = \sum_{n=0}^{\infty} f_n(z)$. Then the function $F(z)$ is holomorphic in Ω.

Proof. Choose any simple closed contour $\mathbf{C} \subset \Omega$, so that $\sum f_n(z)$ is uniformly convergent for all $z \in \mathbf{C}$. From Theorem 6.11(b), we have

$$\int_{\mathbf{C}} F(z)\, dz = \int_{\mathbf{C}} \left[\sum_{n=0}^{\infty} f_n(z) \right] dz = \sum_{n=0}^{\infty} \int_{\mathbf{C}} f_n(z)\, dz.$$

But $f_n(z)$ is holomorphic, so by Cauchy's Integral Theorem the right hand side of the last equation equals zero. Thus, the integral of $F(z)$ over any closed contour in Ω is zero. We can therefore apply Theorem 5.4, to conclude $F(z)$ has a primitive and thus is holomorphic in Ω. $\square$

Chapter 8

Cauchy's Integral Formula

Cauchy's Integral Formula follows almost directly from Cauchy's Integral Theorem. It is a remarkable result at the very center of complex function theory. Assume $f(z)$ is holomorphic in a domain Ω, with $\gamma \subset \Omega$ a simple closed contour. Cauchy's Integral Formula tells us that the value of $f(z)$ at any point in the interior of γ can be determined by knowing only the values of $f(z)$ on γ.

Many important results follow from Cauchy's Integral Formula, such as the Identity Theorem, the Residue Theorem and the Power Series development of holomorphic function. In this chapter, we use the Formula to prove that holomorphic functions have derivatives of all orders.

8.1 Cauchy's Integral Formula

Lemma 8.1

Let Ω be a domain, with $\partial\Omega$ a positively oriented simple closed contour. For $z_0 \notin \partial\Omega$, we have

$$\int_{\partial\Omega} \frac{dz}{z - z_0} = \begin{cases} 0 & \text{if } z_0 \notin \overline{\Omega} = \Omega \cup \partial\Omega \\ 2\pi i & \text{if } z_0 \in \Omega. \end{cases}$$

Proof (1): $z_0 \notin \overline{\Omega}$. Fix z_0. For each point $z \in \partial\Omega$, let the open disk $\mathbf{D}_{r(z)}(z)$ have a radius $r(z)$ small enough so that $z_0 \notin \mathbf{D}_{r(z)}(z)$. Define

$$\Lambda = \left[\bigcup_{z \in \partial\Omega} \mathbf{D}_{r(z)}(z) \right] \cup \Omega \qquad \text{and} \qquad f(z) = \frac{1}{z - z_0}.$$

Then Λ is a domain. Because $z_0 \notin \Lambda$, f is holomorphic in Λ. With $\partial\Omega \subset \Lambda$, we can apply Cauchy's Integral Theorem and our integral evaluates to 0, as required. $\qquad\square$

Proof (2): $z_0 \in \Omega$. Choose δ small enough so that $\mathbf{C} = \partial\mathbf{C}_\delta(z_0) \subset \Omega$. We parameterize the circle by $\omega(\theta) = z_0 + \delta e^{i\theta}, 0 \leq \theta \leq 2\pi$, so that $dz = i\delta e^{i\theta} d\theta$. Thus

$$\int_{\mathbf{C}} \frac{dz}{z - z_0} = \int_0^{2\pi} \frac{1}{(z_0 + \delta e^{i\theta}) - z_0} i\delta e^{i\theta} d\theta = \int_0^{2\pi} \frac{1}{\delta e^{i\theta}} i\delta e^{i\theta} d\theta = \int_0^{2\pi} i d\theta = i \int_0^{2\pi} d\theta = 2\pi i.$$

By Theorem 7.5, the integral over $\partial\Omega$ has the same value as the integral over $\mathbf{C}$. That is,

$$\int_{\partial\Omega} \frac{dz}{z - z_0} = \int_{\mathbf{C}} \frac{dz}{z - z_0} = 2\pi i. \qquad\square$$

Lemma 8.2

Let $f(z)$ be holomorphic in the domain Ω and let $\boldsymbol{C} \subset \Omega$ be a positively oriented simple closed contour. Then, if z_0 is a point in the interior of $\boldsymbol{C}$, we have

$$\int_{\boldsymbol{C}} \frac{f(z) - f(z_0)}{z - z_0} \, dz = 0.$$

Proof #1. Let

$$g(z) = \frac{f(z) - f(z_0)}{z - z_0}.$$

Because $f(z)$ is holomorphic in Ω, $g(z)$ is holomorphic in $\Omega \backslash z_0$. To see $g(z)$ is continuous at z_0, define $g(z_0) = f'(z_0)$. For the disk $\mathbf{D}_r(z_0)$, choose r small enough so that $\mathbf{D}_r(z_0) \subset \Omega$. For $n \in \mathbb{N}$, let $r_n = r/n$. We form a sequence $\{z_n\}$ by letting z_n be any point such that $z_n \in \mathbf{D}_{r_n}(z_0)$. Clearly, $\lim_{n \to \infty} z_n = z_0$. To see that $g(z)$ is continuous at z_0, we must show that $\lim_{n \to \infty} g(z_n) = g(z_0)$. But that result is immediate based on the definition of the complex derivative of $f(z)$ at z_0 (the left equation below) and the definition of $g(z)$ (the right equation below):

$$f'(z_0) = \lim_{z \to z_0} \frac{f(z) - f(z_0)}{z - z_0} \quad and \quad \lim_{n \to \infty} g(z_n) = \lim_{z_n \to z_0} \frac{f(z_n) - f(z_0)}{z_n - z_0} = f'(z_0).$$

Having shown that $g(z)$ is holomorphic in $\Omega \backslash z_0$ and continuous at z_0, we can then apply Cauchy's Integral Theorem to obtain

$$\int_{\boldsymbol{C}} \frac{f(z) - f(z_0)}{z - z_0} \, dz = 0. \qquad \square$$

Proof #2. Because f is holomorphic in Ω it is continuous at z_0. Thus, for every $\epsilon > 0$ there exists a $\delta > 0$ such that if $z \in \mathbf{D}_\delta(z_0)$ then $f(z) \in \mathbf{D}_\epsilon(f(z_0))$. We assume that δ is small enough so that the closed disk $\overline{\mathbf{D}}_\delta(z_0) \subset \Omega$. Let ∂D be the boundary of $\overline{\mathbf{D}}_\delta(z_0)$. Fix ϵ and choose the necessary δ. Now use the ML inequality, giving

$$\left| \int_{\partial D} \frac{f(z) - f(z_0)}{z - z_0} \, dz \right| \leq \int_{\partial D} \left| \frac{f(z) - f(z_0)}{z - z_0} \right| \, dz \leq \frac{\epsilon}{\delta} \cdot \boldsymbol{L}(\partial D) = \frac{\epsilon}{\delta} \cdot 2\pi\delta = 2\pi\epsilon.$$

Because the integral is less than an arbitrarily small positive number, it must equal 0. By Theorem 7.5, the integral over ∂D has the same value as the integral over $\boldsymbol{C}$. Therefore

$$\int_{\boldsymbol{C}} \frac{f(z) - f(z_0)}{z - z_0} \, dz = 0. \qquad \square$$

Theorem 8.1: Cauchy's Integral Formula

Let $f(z)$ be holomorphic in the domain Ω and let $\boldsymbol{C} \subset \Omega$ be a positively oriented simple closed contour. Then, if z is a point in the interior of $\boldsymbol{C}$, we have

$$f(z) = \frac{1}{2\pi i} \int_{\boldsymbol{C}} \frac{f(w)}{w - z} \, dw.$$

Proof. From Lemma 8.1:

$$\frac{1}{2\pi i} \int_C \frac{f(z)}{w-z} \, dw = \frac{f(z)}{2\pi i} \int_C \frac{1}{w-z} \, dw = \frac{f(z)}{2\pi i} \cdot 2\pi i = f(z). \tag{8.1}$$

From Lemma 8.2:

$$\frac{1}{2\pi i} \int_C \frac{f(w) - f(z)}{w - z} \, dw = 0. \tag{8.2}$$

Combining equations (8.1) and (8.2), we have

$$\frac{1}{2\pi i} \int_C \frac{f(w)}{w-z} \, dw = \frac{1}{2\pi i} \int_C \frac{f(w) - f(z)}{w-z} \, dw + \frac{1}{2\pi i} \int_C \frac{f(z)}{w-z} \, dw = 0 + f(z) = f(z). \qquad \square$$

> **Remark**
>
> Recall the Mean Value Theorem in real variable calculus. For a function continuous on a closed interval $[a, b]$ and differentiable in the open interval (a, b), the mean value is attained at some point on the interval.
>
> A much more powerful statement can be made here. For $f(z)$ holomorphic in a domain containing a point z_0 and a circle centered at z_0, the value of $f(z_0)$ is equal to the average value (arithmetic mean) of $f(z)$ on the circle.

Corollary 8.1: Gauss's Mean Value Theorem

Let $f(z)$ be holomorphic in the domain Ω and let $\mathbf{C}_R(z_0) \subset \Omega$ be a positively oriented circle of radius $R > 0$, centered at z_0. Then

$$f(z_0) = \frac{1}{2\pi} \int_0^{2\pi} f(z_0 + Re^{i\theta}) \, d\theta.$$

Proof. By Cauchy's Integral Formula (Theorem 8.1):

$$f(z_0) = \frac{1}{2\pi i} \int_{\mathbf{C}_R(z_0)} \frac{f(w)}{w - z_0} \, dw$$

Now parameterize the circle by $w = z_0 + Re^{i\theta}$ so that $dw = iRe^{i\theta} \, d\theta$, giving

$$= \frac{1}{2\pi i} \int_0^{2\pi} \frac{f(z_0 + Re^{i\theta})}{Re^{i\theta}} iRe^{i\theta} \, d\theta$$

$$= \frac{1}{2\pi} \int_0^{2\pi} f(z_0 + Re^{i\theta}) \, d\theta. \qquad \square$$

8.2 Cauchy's Integral Formula for Derivatives

We begin this section with two technical lemmas. After that, the proof of Cauchy's Integral Formula for Derivatives follows almost immediately.

Lemma 8.3

*Let **C** be a contour and let $g(z)$ be continuous along **C**. Define*

$$f(z) = \frac{1}{2\pi i} \int_{\mathbf{C}} \frac{g(w)}{w - z}\, dw.$$

Let $\mathcal{R}$ be a region, with $\mathbf{C} \cap \mathcal{R} = \emptyset$. Then $f(z)$ is holomorphic in $\mathcal{R}$, with derivative

$$f'(z) = \frac{1}{2\pi i} \int_{\mathbf{C}} \frac{g(w)}{(w - z)^2}\, dw.$$

Proof.[24] Clearly, $f(z)$ is well-defined for $z \in \mathcal{R}$. Fix $z \in \mathcal{R}$. Let δ be small enough so that $\mathbf{D}_\delta(z) \subset \mathcal{R}$. Further, let $\{z_n\} \subset \mathbf{D}_\delta(z)$ be a sequence with $\lim_{n \to \infty} z_n = z$. To complete our proof, we must show that

$$\lim_{n \to \infty} A_n = 0 \qquad \text{for} \qquad A_n = \left[\frac{f(z_n) - f(z)}{z_n - z} - \frac{1}{2\pi i} \int_{\mathbf{C}} \frac{g(w)}{(w - z)^2}\, dw \right].$$

Using our definition of $f(z)$, we have

$$\frac{f(z_n) - f(z)}{z_n - z} = \frac{1}{2\pi i} \int_{\mathbf{C}} \frac{g(w)}{(z_n - z)} \left[\frac{1}{w - z_n} - \frac{1}{w - z} \right] dw$$

$$= \frac{1}{2\pi i} \int_{\mathbf{C}} \frac{g(w)}{(w - z)(w - z_n)}\, dw \quad \text{(after some algebraic manipulation).}$$

This allows us to restate A_n as

$$A_n = \left[\frac{1}{2\pi i} \int_{\mathbf{C}} \frac{g(w)}{(w - z)(w - z_n)}\, dw \right] - \left[\frac{1}{2\pi i} \int_{\mathbf{C}} \frac{g(w)}{(w - z)^2}\, dw \right]$$

$$= \frac{1}{2\pi i} \int_{\mathbf{C}} g(w) \left[\frac{1}{(w - z)(w - z_n)} - \frac{1}{(w - z)^2} \right] dw$$

$$= \frac{z_n - z}{2\pi i} \int_{\mathbf{C}} \frac{g(w)}{(w - z)^2(w - z_n)}\, dw \qquad \text{(after some algebraic manipulation).}$$

Let $M = \{\max(|g(w)|) : w \in \mathbf{C}\}$. For our fixed z, let $D = \{\min(|w - z|) : w \in \mathbf{C}\}$, the minimum distance between z and $\mathbf{C}$. Also, let $L = L(\mathbf{C})$, the length of $\mathbf{C}$. For our sequence $\{z_n\}$, choose n large enough so that $|z - z_n| < D/2$. Then by the ML inequality

$$|A_n| \le \left| \frac{z_n - z}{2\pi i} \right| \cdot M \cdot L \cdot \frac{1}{D^2 \cdot D/2} = |z_n - z| \cdot \frac{ML}{\pi D^3}.$$

Because $\lim_{n \to \infty} |z - z_n| = 0$, we have $\lim_{n \to \infty} |A_n| = 0$, as required. $\qquad \square$

We have shown that the derivative of $f(z)$, as defined above, can be obtained by differentiation (with respect to z) under the integral sign. That is

$$\frac{d}{dz}f(z) = \frac{d}{dz}\left[\frac{1}{2\pi i}\int_{\boldsymbol{C}}\frac{g(w)}{w-z}\,dw\right] = \frac{1}{2\pi i}\int_{\boldsymbol{C}}\frac{d}{dz}\left[\frac{g(w)}{w-z}\right]\,dw.$$

The next theorem shows that we can repeat the same process and obtain derivatives of any higher order for $f(z)$.

Lemma 8.4

Let $\boldsymbol{C}$ be a contour and let $g(z)$ be continuous along $\boldsymbol{C}$. For $n \in \mathbb{N}$, define

$$F_n(z) = \int_{\boldsymbol{C}}\frac{g(w)}{(w-z)^n}\,dw.$$

Let $\mathscr{R}$ be a region, with $\boldsymbol{C} \cap \mathscr{R} = \emptyset$. Then $F_n(z)$ is holomorphic in $\mathscr{R}$, and its derivative can be obtained by differentiating under the integral sign, giving

$$F_n'(z) = \frac{d}{dz}F_n(z) = \frac{d}{dz}\left[\int_{\boldsymbol{C}}\frac{g(w)}{(w-z)^n}\,dw\right] = \int_{\boldsymbol{C}}\frac{d}{dz}\left[\frac{g(w)}{(w-z)^n}\right]\,dw = nF_{n+1}(z).$$

Proof. [25] Fix n and fix $z \in \mathscr{R}$. Let δ be small enough so that $\mathbf{D}_\delta(z) \subset \mathscr{R}$. To ensure a minimum distance away from $\boldsymbol{C}$, we further restrict the radius of our disk to $\mathbf{D}_{\delta/2}(z)$. Let $\{z_k\} \subset \mathbf{D}_{\delta/2}(z)$ be a sequence with $\lim_{k\to\infty} z_k = z$. Note that $|w - z_k| > \delta/2$ for $w \in \boldsymbol{C}$. Let $M = \{\max(|g(w)|) : w \in \boldsymbol{C}\}$ and let $L = L(\boldsymbol{C})$, the length of $\boldsymbol{C}$.

We state an easily verified algebraic formula that will be used in what follows:

$$\frac{1}{(w-z_k)^n} - \frac{1}{(w-z)^n} = \left[\frac{1}{w-z_k} - \frac{1}{w-z}\right]\sum_{j=1}^{n}\frac{1}{(w-z_k)^{n-j}}\frac{1}{(w-z)^{j-1}}$$

$$= \left[(z_k - z)\frac{1}{(w-z_k)(w-z)}\right]\sum_{j=1}^{n}\frac{1}{(w-z_k)^{n-j}}\frac{1}{(w-z)^{j-1}}$$

$$= (z_k - z)\left[\sum_{j=1}^{n}\left(\frac{1}{(w-z_k)^{n+1-j}}\cdot\frac{1}{(w-z)^{j}}\right)\right]. \tag{8.3}$$

We begin by showing that F_n is continuous at our fixed $z \in \mathscr{R}$, and therefore continuous in $\mathscr{R}$. We use equation (8.3) and the ML inequality to have

$$F_n(z_k) - F_n(z) = \int_{\boldsymbol{C}}g(w)\left[\frac{1}{(w-z_k)^n} - \frac{1}{(w-z)^n}\right]\,dw$$

$$= (z_k - z)\int_{\boldsymbol{C}}g(w)\left[\sum_{j=1}^{n}\left(\frac{1}{(w-z_k)^{n+1-j}}\cdot\frac{1}{(w-z)^{j}}\right)\right]\,dw \tag{8.4}$$

$$|F_n(z_k) - F_n(z)| \le |(z_k - z)|\cdot ML\cdot n\cdot\left(\frac{2}{\delta}\right)^{n+1}.$$

Thus, (for our fixed n) $\lim_{k \to \infty} |F_n(z_k) - F_n(z)| = 0$, proving that $F_n(z)$ is continuous for $z \in \mathscr{R}$. For the same reason, we can conclude that the integrand is continuous and bounded because: (1) $g(w)$ is continuous on $\mathbf{C}$, (2) $g(w)$ is bounded (by M) on $\mathbf{C}$, and (3) for our fixed z and n, the finite number of terms in the denominator are bounded below by $\delta/2$. We therefore have the conditions necessary to conclude that the limit of the integral is equal to the integral of the limit.

With that, we can now obtain the value of $F'_n(z)$. Dividing both sides of equation (8.4) by $(z_k - z)$, we have the form of our complex derivative:

$$\frac{F_n(z_k) - F_n(z)}{(z_k - z)} = \int_{\mathbf{C}} g(w) \left[\sum_{j=1}^{n} \left(\frac{1}{(w - z_k)^{n+1-j}} \cdot \frac{1}{(w - z)^j} \right) \right] dw.$$

Taken to the limit

$$
\begin{aligned}
F'_n(z) = \lim_{k \to \infty} \frac{F_n(z_k) - F_n(z)}{(z_k - z)} &= \lim_{k \to \infty} \int_{\mathbf{C}} g(w) \left[\sum_{j=1}^{n} \left(\frac{1}{(w - z_k)^{n+1-j}} \cdot \frac{1}{(w - z)^j} \right) \right] dw \\
&= \int_{\mathbf{C}} g(w) \left[\lim_{k \to \infty} \sum_{j=1}^{n} \left(\frac{1}{(w - z_k)^{n+1-j}} \cdot \frac{1}{(w - z)^j} \right) \right] dw \\
&= \int_{\mathbf{C}} g(w) \left[\sum_{j=1}^{n} \left(\frac{1}{(w - z)^{n+1}} \right) \right] dw = n \int_{\mathbf{C}} \frac{g(w)}{(w - z)^{n+1}} dw \\
&= n F_{n+1}(z).
\end{aligned}
$$

Theorem 8.2: Cauchy's Integral Formula for Derivatives

Let $f(z)$ be holomorphic in the domain Ω and let $\mathbf{C} \subset \Omega$ be a positively oriented simple closed contour. Then, if z is a point in the interior of $\mathbf{C}$, $f(z)$ possesses derivatives in Ω of every order, as follows

$$f^{(n)}(z) = \frac{n!}{2\pi i} \int_{\mathbf{C}} \frac{f(w)}{(w - z)^{n+1}} dw.$$

Proof. From Theorem 8.1, we have

$$f(z) = \frac{1}{2\pi i} \int_{\mathbf{C}} \frac{f(w)}{w - z} dw.$$

Applying Lemma 8.3, we obtain

$$f'(z) = \frac{1}{2\pi i} \int_{\mathbf{C}} \frac{f(w)}{(w - z)^2} dw.$$

If we now define

$$F_n(z) = \int_{\mathbf{C}} \frac{f(w)}{(w - z)^n} dw,$$

we can apply Lemma 8.4 so that, for all n, $F_n(z)$ is holomorphic in Ω, and $F'_n(z) = n F_{n+1}(z)$.

But $f(z) = F_1(z)$ and $f'(z) = F'_1(z)$. Thus, Lemma 8.4 shows that $f(z)$ has a derivative of every order, each holomorphic in Ω. For each such order, the expression for the derivative can be obtained by iteratively applying $F'_n(z) = n F_{n+1}(z)$, giving

$$f^{(n)}(z) = \frac{n!}{2\pi i} \int_{\mathbf{C}} \frac{f(w)}{(w - z)^{n+1}} dw.$$

8.3 Supplemental Material

> **Remark**
>
> We present here important and useful theorems that follow from Cauchy's Integral Formula. In *Liouville's Theorem*, we learn that if an entire function is bounded, it is a constant function. For a non-constant function $f(z)$ holomorphic in a domain, The *Maximum Modulus Principle* tells us that $|f(z)|$ has no maximum value in that domain.

8.3.1 Cauchy's Inequality and Liouville's Theorem

> **Theorem 8.3: Cauchy's Inequality**
>
> Let $f(z)$ be holomorphic in the domain Ω and let $\mathbf{C}_R(z_0)$ be a positively oriented circle of radius $R > 0$, centered at z_0, with $\mathbf{C}_R(z_0) \subset \Omega$. Let $M = \{\max(|f(z)|) : z \in \mathbf{C}_R(z_0)\}$. Then
> $$\left| f^{(n)}(z_0) \right| \leq \frac{n!}{R^n} \cdot M \quad \text{for } n \geq 0.$$

Proof. From Theorem 8.2, we have

$$\left| f^{(n)}(z_0) \right| = \left| \frac{n!}{2\pi i} \int_{\mathbf{C}_R(z_0)} \frac{f(w)}{(w - z_0)^{n+1}} \, dw \right|$$

Now parameterize the circle by $w = z_0 + Re^{i\theta}$ so that $dw = iRe^{i\theta} d\theta$, giving

$$= \left| \frac{n!}{2\pi i} \int_0^{2\pi} \frac{f(z_0 + Re^{i\theta})}{(Re^{i\theta})^{n+1}} iRe^{i\theta} \, d\theta \right|$$

$$= \left| \frac{n!}{2\pi} \int_0^{2\pi} \frac{f(z_0 + Re^{i\theta})}{R^n e^{i\theta n}} \, d\theta \right|$$

$$= \frac{n!}{R^n} \cdot \frac{1}{2\pi} \cdot \left| e^{-i\theta n} \right| \cdot \left| \int_0^{2\pi} f(z_0 + Re^{i\theta}) \, d\theta \right|$$

$$\leq \frac{n!}{R^n} \cdot \frac{1}{2\pi} \cdot [2\pi \cdot M]$$

$$= \frac{n!}{R^n} \cdot M. \qquad \square$$

> **Theorem 8.4: Liouville's Theorem**
>
> Let $f(z)$ be an entire function. If f is bounded, then f is constant.

Proof. Fix z_0 and let M be the bound for f. For any $R > 0$, let $\mathbf{C}_R(z_0)$ be a circle of radius R, centered at z_0. Because f is entire, the conditions of Theorem 8.3 apply and $|f'(z_0)| \leq M/R$. Because this is true for all $R > 0$, we can let $R \to \infty$ and conclude $f'(z_0) = 0$. But z_0 was arbitrarily chosen, so we must have $f'(z) = 0$ for all $z \in \mathbb{C}$. With a derivative of zero everywhere, $f(z)$ must be constant. $\qquad \square$

8.3.2 The Maximum (and Minimum) Modulus Principle

> **Lemma 8.5**
>
> Let $f(z)$ be holomorphic in the open disk $\mathbf{D}_R(z_0)$. If $|f(z)| \leq |f(z_0)|$ for all $z \in \mathbf{D}_R(z_0)$, then $f(z)$ is constant in $\mathbf{D}_R(z_0)$.

Proof. Fix any point $w \in \mathbf{D}_R(z_0)$ and let $r = |w - z_0|$, so that $w \in \mathbf{C}_r(z_0)$. By Corollary 8.1 (Gauss's Mean Value Theorem):

$$f(z_0) = \frac{1}{2\pi} \int_0^{2\pi} f(z_0 + re^{i\theta})\, d\theta,$$

which calculates $f(z_0)$ as the average of $f(z)$ on the circle. By assumption, no such $|f(z)| > |f(z_0)|$. We claim that average can only be obtained if all $f(z) = f(z_0)$. To see that, we have

$$|f(z_0)| = \left| \frac{1}{2\pi} \int_0^{2\pi} f(z_0 + re^{i\theta})\, d\theta \right| \qquad \text{from the equation just above}$$

$$\leq \frac{1}{2\pi} \int_0^{2\pi} \left| f(z_0 + re^{i\theta}) \right| d\theta \qquad \text{from the triangle inequality}$$

$$\leq \frac{1}{2\pi} \int_0^{2\pi} \left| f(z_0) \right| d\theta \qquad \text{using that } \left| f(z_0 + re^{i\theta}) \right| \leq |f(z_0)|$$

$$= |f(z_0)|.$$

The final equality means that all inequalities in the above equations are actually equalities. Therefore

$$|f(z_0)| = \frac{1}{2\pi} \int_0^{2\pi} \left| f(z_0 + re^{i\theta}) \right| d\theta$$

$$0 = |f(z_0)| - \frac{1}{2\pi} \int_0^{2\pi} \left| f(z_0 + re^{i\theta}) \right| d\theta$$

$$= \frac{1}{2\pi} \int_0^{2\pi} |f(z_0)|\, d\theta - \frac{1}{2\pi} \int_0^{2\pi} \left| f(z_0 + re^{i\theta}) \right| d\theta$$

$$= \frac{1}{2\pi} \int_0^{2\pi} \left[|f(z_0)| - \left| f(z_0 + re^{i\theta}) \right| \right] d\theta.$$

The last integrand is a continuous function of θ and, by assumption, $|f(z_0)| - \left| f(z_0 + re^{i\theta}) \right| \geq 0$. With the integral 0, we must have $|f(z_0)| = \left| f(z_0 + re^{i\theta}) \right|$; that is $|f(z_0)| = |f(z)|$ for all $z \in \mathbf{C}_r(z_0)$.

To see that $f(z_0) = f(z)$, assume $f(z_0) = A$. If $A = 0$ we are done so assume $A \neq 0$. The continuity of $f(z)$ ensures that $f(z)$ is fixed at either A or $-A$ on $\mathbf{C}_r(z_0)$.

But w was arbitrarily chosen. Therefore, we have shown $f(z)$ is constant (either A or $-A$) on any circle $\mathbf{C}_r(z_0)$ for $0 < r < R$. Thus, $f(z)$ equals either A or $-A$ at every point in $\mathbf{D}_R(z_0)$. Because $f(z)$ is continuous in $\mathbf{D}_R(z_0)$ and $A \neq 0$, there can be no point in $\mathbf{D}_R(z_0)$ where $f(z)$ "jumps" from A to $-A$ (or vice versa). In particular, $f(z)$ must equal A in some very small neighborhood close to z_0. Thus $f(z)$ must equal A in all of $\mathbf{D}_R(z_0)$. $\qquad \square$

Theorem 8.5: Maximum Modulus Principle

Let $f(z)$ be holomorphic in the domain Ω. If there exists some $z_0 \in \Omega$ with $|f(z)| \leq |f(z_0)|$ for all $z \in \Omega$, then $f(z)$ is constant in Ω.

Proof. [26] Assume there exists a $z_0 \in \Omega$ with $|f(z)| \leq |f(z_0)|$ for all $z \in \Omega$.

Fix any $w \in \Omega$ with $w \neq z_0$. By Theorem 3.2, there is a polygon $P \in \Omega$ joining z_0 and w. Using Theorem 3.1, choose $r > 0$ such that for all $z \in P$ we have $\mathbf{D}_r(z) \subset \Omega$.

Let $z_0, z_1, \cdots, z_n$ be a finite sequence of points following an ordered traversal of P from z_0 to $z_n = w$. For $k > 0$, we require that each point satisfy $|z_k - z_{k-1}| < r$. Next, define the disks $D_k = \mathbf{D}_r(z_k) \subset \Omega$. For all but z_0, we have $z_k \in D_{k-1}$.

By our assumption, we have from Lemma 8.5 that $f(z) = f(z_0)$ for all $z \in D_0$. Because $z_1 \in D_0$, we have $f(z_0) = f(z_1)$. Therefore, by our assumption, $|f(z)| \leq |f(z_1)|$ for all $z \in \Omega$. Noting that $z_2 \in D_1$, we again apply Lemma 8.5 and have $f(z_1) = f(z_2)$. The same logic applies for all D_n and all z_n. In particular, $f(w) = f(z_0)$. But w was arbitrarily chosen, so $f(z)$ is constant in Ω. $\square$

Theorem 8.6

Let $f(z)$ be continuous in the domain Ω and let $G \subset \Omega$ be a compact set, with $f(z)$ holomorphic in the interior of G. Then

(a) there exists an $M > 0$ such that $|f(z)| \leq M$ for $z \in G$; and

(b) the maximum value for $|f(z)|$ on G is obtained on the boundary of G.

Proof (a). Assume $f : G \mapsto H \subset \mathbb{C}$. We first show that H is compact.

Let $\{w_n\}$ be a sequence in H. Then, for each $w_j \in H$ there is some $z_j \in G$ such that $w_j = f(z_j)$. We therefore have a sequence $\{z_n\} \in G$. Because G is compact, $\{z_n\}$ has a convergent subsequence $\{z_{n_m}\}$ whose limit is some $p \in G$. Since f is continuous

$$\lim_{m \to \infty} w_{n_m} = \lim_{m \to \infty} f(z_{n_m}) = f(p).$$

Because $p \in G$, $f(p) \in H$. Therefore, $\{w_n\}$ has a convergent subsequence $\{w_{n_m}\}$ whose limit is $f(p) \in H$. We have shown that every sequence in H has a convergent subsequence whose limit is also in H. By Theorem 2.7, that makes H compact.

We have shown that H is compact and therefore bounded. That gives us an $M > 0$ such that $|w| \leq M$ for $w \in H$, or equally $|f(z)| \leq M$ for $z \in G$, as required. $\square$

Proof (b). From Theorem 8.5, if a maximum value is actually obtained by $|f(z)|$ on G, then it cannot be obtained in the interior of G. It remains only to show the maximum value is actually obtained on the boundary of G.

Now let $M = \sup\{f(z) : z \in \partial G\}$. For $n \in \mathbb{N}$, define $M_n = M - 1/n$. By the continuity of $f(z)$ and the definition of supremum, there is a $z \in G$ with $M_n < f(z) = w_n \leq M$. We use that to build a sequence $\{w_n\} \in H$, where H is the compact set obtained in proof (a). Because H is compact, $\{w_n\}$ has a convergent subsequence $\{w_{n_k}\}$, which by our definition must have a limit of M. Because H is compact, we can use Lemma 2.1 to see $M \in H$. That means there is a $z \in \partial G$ with $f(z) = M$, as required. $\square$

> **Theorem 8.7: Minimum Modulus Principle**
>
> *Let $f(z)$ be continuous in the domain Ω and let $f(z)$ be holomorphic, non-constant and non-zero in the bounded domain Λ, with $\overline{\Lambda} \subset \Omega$. Then, the minimum value for $|f(z)|$ on $\overline{\Lambda}$ is obtained on $\partial \Lambda$.*

Proof. Because f has no zeros in Λ, $1/f$ is holomorphic in Λ and continuous on $\partial \Lambda$. (See Exercise 4.1(d)). Therefore, by Theorem 8.6, $|1/f(z)|$ obtains its maximum on $\partial \Lambda$. Thus, there is some $w \in \partial \Lambda$ such that $|1/f(z)| \leq |1/f(w)|$ and therefore $|f(z)| \geq |f(w)|$ for all $z \in \overline{G}$, as required. $\square$

8.3.3 Restating Cauchy's Integral Theorem

By Theorem 8.2, we now know that holomorphic functions have derivatives of all orders. That allows us to restate Cauchy's Integral Theorem, now with two results. Result (a) below is just the result we originally obtained in Cauchy's Integral Theorem (Theorem 7.4). We can now add result (b). That is, under the conditions of the theorem, $f(z)$ is in fact holomorphic in all of Ω.

> **Theorem 8.8**
>
> *Let Ω be a domain and let $\{p_j\} \subset \Omega$ be a finite set of isolated points. Let $\mathbf{C} \subset \Omega$ be a closed contour. Assume $f(z)$ is continuous in Ω and holomorphic in $\Omega \backslash \{p_j\}$. Then*
>
> *(a) $\int_{\mathbf{C}} f(z)\, dz = 0$, and*
>
> *(b) The function $f(z)$ is holomorphic in all of Ω.*

Proof (a). This is the exact statement of Cauchy's Integral Theorem (Theorem 7.4). $\square$

Proof (b). From Cauchy's Integral Theorem, the integral over any closed contour $\mathbf{C} \subset \Omega$ is 0. Thus, from Theorem 5.4, $f(z)$ has a primitive $F(z)$ throughout Ω, with $F'(z) = f(z)$ for all $z \in \Omega$. That means $F(z)$ is holomorphic in Ω. Applying Theorem 8.2, that means $F(z)$ has derivatives all orders in Ω. But that means $f(z)$ has derivatives all orders in Ω. Thus, $f(z)$ is holomorphic in Ω. $\square$

> **Remark**
>
> After our study of isolated singularities in Chapter 12, we will be able to weaken the assumptions of Cauchy's Integral Theorem even further. For our finite set of isolated points $\{p_j\}$, we can assume: (1) $f(z)$ is holomorphic in $\Omega \backslash \{p_j\}$, and (2) for each isolated point p_j, $f(z)$ is bounded in a neighborhood of p_j. With those assumptions, the point p_j is a "removable singularity" of $f(z)$. If we define $f(p_j) = \lim_{z \to p_j} f(z)$, then $f(z)$ is holomorphic in Ω.

Chapter 9

Power Series

Up to this point, our focus has been on holomorphic (complex differentiable) functions. In this chapter, we study analytic functions (functions that can be represented by a power series). In later chapters, we will find that the power series contributes greatly to the development of complex function theory. Importantly, We will also show here that a function is holomorphic in a domain if and only if it is analytic in that domain. That allows us to combine the best features of both holomorphic and analytic functions.

9.1   Power Series

We begin with the definition and basic properties of power series.

Definition 9.1

For variable z and fixed c, let $\{a_n\}$ be a sequence where a_n may be dependent on n but not on z. Then any series of the form

$$\sum_{n=0}^{\infty} a_n (z - c)^n \qquad z, c, a_n \in \mathbb{C}$$

*is called a **power series** with center c and **coefficients** a_n.*

Remark

If we define

$$f(z) = \sum_{n=0}^{\infty} a_n (z - c)^n \quad \text{and} \quad g(w) = \sum_{n=0}^{\infty} a_n w^n$$

for the identical coefficients a_n, we see that f is obtained from g by a change of variable $w = z - c$ so that $f(z) = g(w)$. Thus, properties of the series for $f(z)$ can be obtained by use of the series for $g(w)$. We therefore can (and often will) assume our power series is centered at the origin.

Remark

We include here a brief reminder of the meaning of limit superior. For a given real-valued series $\{b_n\}$, the limit superior of the series is

$$\limsup_{n \to \infty} b_n = \lim_{n \to \infty} \left(\sup_{m \geq n} b_m \right).$$

So, it is the smallest real number K such that, for any $\epsilon > 0$ there exists an $N \in \mathbb{N}$ such that $b_n < K + \epsilon$ for all $n > N$. That is, for any $\epsilon > 0$, only a finite number of $b_n > K + \epsilon$.

> ### Theorem 9.1: Power Series
>
> Let $\sum_{n=0}^{\infty} a_n z^n$ be a power series. For $R \geq 0$, let
>
> $$\frac{1}{R} = \limsup_{n \to \infty} |a_n|^{1/n} \qquad (or,\ equally) \qquad R = \frac{1}{\limsup_{n \to \infty} |a_n|^{1/n}}.$$
>
> Then
>
> (a) if $|z| < R$, the series converges absolutely, and converges uniformly on any $|z| \leq r < R$;
>
> (b) if $|z| > R$, the series diverges.
>
> (c) If $R = 0$, the series diverges for all $z \neq 0$. If $R = \infty$, the series converges uniformly for all $z \in \mathbb{C}$.

Proof (a). [27] Fix z, with $|z| < R$. Choose any r_1 and r_2 with $|z| < r_1 < r_2 < R$. By the definition of limit superior, and using that $1/r_1 > 1/r_2 > 1/R$, there is some $N \in \mathbb{N}$ such that for all $n > N$ we have $|a_n|^{1/n} < 1/r_2$. Therefore, for $n > N$:

$$|a_n| < \frac{1}{(r_2)^n} \qquad \text{which means} \qquad |a_n z^n| < \left(\frac{|z|}{r_2}\right)^n \leq \left(\frac{r_1}{r_2}\right)^n = \frac{1}{(r_2/r_1)^n},$$

so that

$$\sum_{n=0}^{\infty} |a_n z^n| = \sum_{n=0}^{N} |a_n z^n| + \sum_{n=N+1}^{\infty} |a_n z^n|$$
$$\leq \sum_{n=0}^{N} |a_n z^n| + \sum_{n=N+1}^{\infty} \frac{1}{(r_2/r_1)^n}.$$

Taking the absolute value of each term, our power series equals a finite number of terms plus a convergent sum, showing absolute convergence for each $|z| < R$. The convergent sum is a geometric series, so by the Weierstrass M-test (setting $r = r_1$) the power series converges uniformly on any $|z| \leq r < R$. □

Proof (b). Now fix z, with $|z| > R$. Choose any r with $|z| > r > R$. By the definition of limit superior, and using that $1/r < 1/R$, there are infinitely many arbitrarily large n such that $|a_n|^{1/n} > 1/r$, or equally, $|a_n| > 1/r^n$. Thus, $|a_n z^n| > (|z|/r)^n$ for infinitely many n. Because $(|z|/r) > 1$, those terms are unbounded and the series diverges. □

Proof (c). We now discuss the special cases where $R = 0$ or $R = \infty$. Here we use the convention that $1/0 = \infty$ and $1/\infty = 0$.

For $R = \infty$, we must have $\limsup_{n \to \infty} |a_n|^{1/n} = 0$. Thus, proof (a) above for $|z| < R$ applies equally to $|z| < R = \infty$. We can choose any $r > 0$ and the series converges uniformly for all $|z| \leq r$. Therefore, the series converges uniformly for all $z \in \mathbb{C}$.

For $R = 0$, we must have $\limsup_{n \to \infty} |a_n|^{1/n}$ diverges. Thus, proof (b) above for $|z| > R$ applies equally to $|z| > R = 0$, so the series diverges for $|z| > 0$. Note that *all* power series converge at their center point. To see that, set $z = 0$ and our given series equals a_0. □

Definition 9.2

*The number R obtained in Theorem 9.1 is called the **radius of convergence** of the power series, and the domain $|z| < R$ is called the **disk of convergence**.*

Theorem 9.2

Let $\{a_n\}$ be a sequence and let $R > 0$ be the radius of convergence for the function

$$f(z) = \sum_{n=0}^{\infty} a_n z^n.$$

For the same sequence $\{a_n\}$, define

$$G(z) = \sum_{n=1}^{\infty} n a_n z^{n-1}.$$

Then

(a) $G(z)$ is a power series, with the same radius of convergence R.

(b) The derivative $f'(z)$ can be obtained by termwise differentiation, giving $f'(z) = G(z)$.

(c) Derivatives of $f(z)$ of all orders can likewise be obtained by termwise differentiation. For all such derivatives, the radius of convergence remains at R. The formula for the kth derivative is given in equation (9.1) on page 101.

(d) The function $f(z)$ is holomorphic in the open disk $\mathbf{D}_R(0)$.

Proof (a). [28] Let $\{b_n\}$ be a sequence with $b_n = (n+1)a_{n+1}$. Then $G(z) = \sum_{n=0}^{\infty} b_n z^n$ and is therefore a power series.

If $\limsup |a_n|^{1/n} = \limsup |n a_n|^{1/n}$, then the radius of convergence of $G(z)$ is equal to the radius of convergence of $f(z)$. That means it is sufficient to prove $\lim_{n\to\infty} n^{1/n} = 1$. Set $n^{1/n} = 1 + \delta_n$. Clearly $\delta_n > 0$. We then have (using the binomial theorem)

$$n^{1/n} = 1 + \delta_n$$

$$n = (1 + \delta_n)^n = \sum_{k=0}^{n} \binom{n}{k} (\delta_n)^k = \binom{n}{0}(\delta_n)^0 + \binom{n}{1}(\delta_n)^1 + \binom{n}{2}(\delta_n)^2 + + \cdots + \binom{n}{n}(\delta_n)^n$$

$$n > \binom{n}{0}(\delta_n)^0 + \binom{n}{2}(\delta_n)^2 = 1 + \frac{n(n-1)}{2}(\delta_n)^2$$

$$(n-1) > \frac{n(n-1)}{2}(\delta_n)^2$$

$$\frac{2}{n} > (\delta_n)^2.$$

With the last, we see $\lim_{n\to\infty}(\delta_n)^2 \to 0$, proving that $\left[n^{1/n} = 1 + \delta_n\right] \to 1$, as required. $\qquad\square$

Proof (b). Fix $z \in \mathbf{D}_R(0)$ and let λ be small enough so that $\mathbf{D}_\lambda(z) \subset \mathbf{D}_R(0)$. Therefore, we can choose

---

a $K < R$ with $|w| < K$ for $w \in \mathbf{D}_\lambda(z)$. Let $\{z_m\}$ be a sequence with $z \neq z_m$ and $z_m \in \mathbf{D}_{\lambda/(2+m)}(z)$. We then have $|z_m| < K$ and $\lim_{m\to\infty} z_m = z$.

We define several expressions whose usefulness will soon become apparent. Define

$$A_n(z) = \sum_{k=0}^{n-1} a_k z^k \qquad \text{and} \qquad D_n(z) = \sum_{k=n}^{\infty} a_k z^k$$

$$\mathcal{A}_n = \left| \frac{(A_n(z) - A_n(z_m))}{z - z_m} - A_n'(z_m) \right|$$

$$\mathcal{D}_n = \left| \frac{D_n(z) - D_n(z_m)}{z - z_m} \right|$$

$$\mathcal{G}_n = |A_n'(z_m) - G(z_m)|.$$

Note that $f(z) = A_n(z) + D_n(z)$ and $G(z) = \lim_{n\to\infty} A_n'(z)$.

To show $f'(z) = G(z)$, we evaluate the following equations and then take n to the limit.

$$\frac{f(z) - f(z_m)}{z - z_m} - G(z_m) = \frac{[A_n(z) - A_n(z_m)] + [D_n(z) - D_n(z_m)]}{z - z_m} - G(z_m)$$

$$= \left(\frac{A_n(z) - A_n(z_m)}{z - z_m} - A_n'(z_m) \right) + \frac{[D_n(z) - D_n(z_m)]}{z - z_m} + (A_n'(z_m) - G(z_m))$$

$$\left| \frac{f(z) - f(z_m)}{z - z_m} - G(z_m) \right| \leq \mathcal{A}_n + \mathcal{D}_n + \mathcal{G}_n.$$

Fix $\epsilon > 0$. We must show there is an $N \in \mathbb{N}$ with $(\mathcal{A}_n + \mathcal{D}_n + \mathcal{G}_n) < \epsilon$ for $n > N$ and sufficiently large m.

We start with $\mathcal{A}_n$.

$$\mathcal{A}_n = \left| \frac{(A_n(z) - A_n(z_m))}{z - z_m} - A_n'(z_m) \right|.$$

Let n be given. $A_n(z)$ is a polynomial that can be differentiated termwise. By the definition of the complex derivative, there is a $\delta(n)$ such that for $z_m \in \mathbf{D}_{\delta(n)}(z)$ we have $\mathcal{A}_n < \epsilon/3$. Choose $M(n) \in \mathbb{N}$ such that $\lambda/(2 + M(n)) < \delta(n)$. Then, for $m > M(n)$, $z_m \in \mathbf{D}_{\lambda/(2+m)}(z) \subset \mathbf{D}_{\delta(n)}(z)$. Thus, for any n we can set $m = M(n) + 1$ and have $\mathcal{A}_n < \epsilon/3$.

Next, we consider $\mathcal{D}_n$.

$$\mathcal{D}_n = \left| \frac{D_n(z) - D_n(z_m)}{z - z_m} \right| \leq \sum_{k=n}^{\infty} |a_k| \left| \frac{z^k - z_m^k}{z - z_m} \right|.$$

Using $a^n - b^n = (a-b)(a^{n-1} + a^{n-2}b + \cdots + ab^{n-2} + b^{n-1})$, combined with $|z| < K$ and $|z_m| < K$

$$\leq \sum_{k=n}^{\infty} |a_k| n K^{n-1}.$$

For our given $\{a_n\}$, the last expression is the vanishing tail of an absolutely convergent series since K is less than the radius of convergence of $G(z)$. Therefore, for large enough N_1, we have for $n > N_1$

$$\left| \frac{D_n(z) - D_n(z_j)}{z - z_j} \right| < \epsilon/3.$$

Finally, we consider $\mathscr{G}_n$.

$$\mathscr{G}_n = |A'_n(z_m) - G(z_m)|.$$

With $G(z) = \lim_{n \to \infty} A'_n(z)$, there is an N_2 such that $|A'_n(z_m) - G(z_m)| < \epsilon/3$ for $n > N_2$.

Combining our results, let $N = \max(N_1, N_2)$. Then, for any $n > N$, we can choose $m = M(n) + 1$ and have $(\mathscr{A}_n + \mathscr{D}_n + \mathscr{G}_n) < \epsilon$, as required. □

Proof (c). Once we have proved (a) and (b), above, (c) follows immediately by repeated application of those results. Specifically, we have

$$f'(z) = a_1 + 2a_2 z + 3a_3 z^2 + \cdots$$
$$f^{(2)}(z) = 2a_2 + 6a_3 z + 12a_4 z^2 + \cdots,$$

with the following equation giving the formula for the kth derivative:

$$f^{(k)}(z) = \sum_{n=k}^{\infty} a_n k! \binom{n}{k} z^{n-k} = \sum_{n=k}^{\infty} a_n \frac{n!}{(n-k)!} z^{n-k}. \tag{9.1}$$

We have therefore shown that $f(z)$ has derivatives of all orders. □

Proof (d). We have shown that $f(z)$ is complex differentiable at every point in the open disk $\mathbf{D}_R(0)$. By definition, that means $f(z)$ is holomorphic in the disk. □

> **Remark**
>
> By setting $z = 0$ and looking at the first term of the kth-order derivative, we can use the formula in *Proof (c)* to see that $a_k = f^k(0)/k!$, which allows us to restate the power series:
>
> $$f(z) = \sum_{n=0}^{\infty} \left[\frac{f^{(n)}(0)}{n!} \right] z^n.$$
>
> We have obtained the well-known Taylor (Maclaurin) series for our power series.

> **Definition 9.3**
>
> *Let $f(z)$ be defined on a domain Ω. Then f is **analytic** (or has a power series expansion) at a point $z_0 \in \Omega$ if there exists a power series $\sum a_n(z - z_0)^n$ centered at z_0 and with positive radius of convergence, such that*
>
> $$f(z) = \sum_{n=0}^{\infty} a_n(z - z_0)^n \qquad \text{for all } z \text{ in some neighborhood of } z_0.$$
>
> *If $f(z)$ has a power series expansion at every point in Ω, we say that $f(z)$ is **analytic** in Ω.*

> **Remark**
>
> The next theorem tells us that any power series expansion is unique.

Theorem 9.3

Let
$$f(z) = \sum_{n=0}^{\infty} a_n(z - z_0)^n \qquad and \qquad g(z) = \sum_{n=0}^{\infty} b_n(z - z_0)^n$$

be two power series, centered at z_0, both with a positive radius of convergence of at least $R > 0$. Let $K \subset \mathbf{D}_R(z_0)$ be the set of points in $\mathbf{D}_R(z_0)$ where $f(z) = g(z)$.

Assume there exists an infinite set of distinct points $\{w_n\} \subset K$ such that $w_n \neq z_0$ and $\{w_n\}$ has the limit point z_0. Then $f(z)$ and $g(z)$ are identical in $\mathbf{D}_R(z_0)$.

Proof.[29] Our proof is by induction. We will prove that $a_n = b_n$ for $n < 1$. We will assume that $a_n = b_n$ for $n < N$ and must prove $a_n = b_n$ for $n < (N + 1)$. In other words, we must prove that $a_N = b_N$.

For $z = z_0$, the limit point at z_0 implies $a_0 = b_0$, giving our proof for $n < 1$. We now inductively assume the equality for $n < N$. Thus, for all points $z \in \{w_n\}$ (because $f(z) = g(z)$)

$$\sum_{n=N}^{\infty} a_n(z - z_0)^n = \sum_{n=N}^{\infty} b_n(z - z_0)^n$$

$$(z - z_0)^{-N} \sum_{n=N}^{\infty} a_n(z - z_0)^n = (z - z_0)^{-N} \sum_{n=N}^{\infty} b_n(z - z_0)^n$$

$$a_N + \sum_{n=N+1}^{\infty} a_n(z - z_0)^{n-N} = b_N + \sum_{n=N+1}^{\infty} b_n(z - z_0)^{n-N}.$$

Now let $z \to z_0$ via the points in $\{w_n\}$. Using that both power series are continuous, we must have $a_N = b_N$, completing our proof. $\qquad\square$

9.2 Holomorphic Functions and Power Series

In this section we show that any function holomorphic in a domain can be *locally* expanded into a power series in some neighborhood of each point in the domain.

Theorem 9.4

Let $f(z)$ be holomorphic in the domain Ω and let $z_0 \in \Omega$. Choose any $R > 0$ such that the path $\gamma = \mathbf{C}_R(z_0) \subset \Omega$ and therefore $\mathbf{D}_R(z_0) \subset \Omega$. Then for all $z \in \mathbf{D}_R(z_0)$, $f(z)$ has a power series expansion at z_0, given by

$$f(z) = \sum_{n=0}^{\infty} a_n(z - z_0)^n \qquad where \qquad a_n = \frac{f^{(n)}(z_0)}{n!}.$$

Proof.[30] Fix $z \in \mathbf{D}_R(z_0)$. By Cauchy's Integral Formula (Theorem 8.1), we have

$$f(z) = \frac{1}{2\pi i} \int_{\gamma} \frac{f(w)}{w - z} \, dw. \tag{9.2}$$

For our fixed z and some $r > 0$, we have $|z - z_0| = r < R$. Thus, for $w \in \gamma$, we have

$$\left| \frac{z - z_0}{w - z_0} \right| = \frac{r}{R} < 1.$$

That allows a uniformly convergent geometric series expansion by the Weierstrass M-test (Theorem 6.10):

$$\frac{1}{w-z} = \frac{1}{(w-z_0)-(z-z_0)} = \frac{1}{(w-z_0)} \cdot \frac{1}{1-\left(\frac{z-z_0}{w-z_0}\right)} = \sum_{n=0}^{\infty} \frac{(z-z_0)^n}{(w-z_0)^{n+1}}. \tag{9.3}$$

If $K = \max(f(w))$ for $w \in \gamma$, then we can again use the Weierstrass M-test (with an additional factor of K) to see that the series

$$\sum_{n=0}^{\infty} \frac{f(w)(z-z_0)^n}{(w-z_0)^{n+1}} \tag{9.4}$$

is uniformly convergent.

Combining equations (9.2) and (9.3), and using that equation (9.4) is uniformly convergent, we have

$$f(z) = \frac{1}{2\pi i} \int_{\gamma} \left[\sum_{n=0}^{\infty} \frac{f(w)(z-z_0)^n}{(w-z_0)^{n+1}} \right] dw.$$

By Theorem 6.11, The uniform convergence of the series of functions allows us to integrate termwise and obtain

$$f(z) = \sum_{n=0}^{\infty} \left(\left[\frac{1}{2\pi i} \int_{\gamma} \frac{f(w)}{(w-z_0)^{n+1}} \, dw \right] \cdot (z-z_0)^n \right).$$

Substituting for the expression in square brackets above with the value obtained in Theorem 8.2:

$$= \sum_{n=0}^{\infty} \left(\left[\frac{f^{(n)}(z_0)}{n!} \right] \cdot (z-z_0)^n \right)$$

$$= \sum_{n=0}^{\infty} a_n (z-z_0)^n \quad \text{where} \quad a_n = \frac{f^{(n)}(z_0)}{n!}. \qquad \square$$

Remark

Two notes regarding Theorem 9.4:

- The power series expansion centered at z_0 has a radius of convergence equal to the largest R such that $\mathbf{D}_R(z_0) \subset \Omega$.
- Theorem 9.3 tells us that the power series expansion at z_0 is unique.

Remark

An important takeaway from this chapter: every analytic function is holomorphic (by Theorem 9.2) and every holomorphic function is analytic (by Theorem 9.4).

9.3 Supplemental Material

9.3.1 Exercises

Exercises 9.1

(a) *Expand $\frac{2z+3}{z+1}$ into a power series centered at $z = 1$ and determine the radius of convergence. Hint: restate $f(z)$ so that it includes a geometric series.*

(b) *Let $f(z) = \sum_{n=0}^{\infty} a_n z^n$ and $g(z) = \sum_{n=0}^{\infty} b_n z^n$. Assume there exists some $N \in \mathbb{N}$ such that $a_n = b_n$ for $n > N$. Show that $f(z)$ and $g(z)$ have the same radius of convergence.*

(c) *Let $\sum_{n=0}^{\infty} a_n (z - c)^n$ be a power series with radius of convergence R. Show that $R = \lim_{n \to \infty} |a_n / a_{n+1}|$, so long as the limit exists (this is the "ratio test").*

(d) *Using the ratio test of (c) just above, determine the radius of convergence of a power series with coefficients: (i) $a_n = 1/n^2$, (ii) $a_n = 1/n$, (iii) $a_n = 1$, (iv) $a_n = n$, and (v) $a_n = 1/n!$.*

Remark

Answers to exercises are in Appendix A.

9.3.2 Boundary of Radius of Convergence

For our power series $\sum_{n=0}^{\infty} a_n z^n$ with radius of convergence R, we showed in Theorem 9.1 that the power series converges for $|z| < R$ and diverges for $|z| > R$. The convergence or divergence of the power series on the boundary $|z| = R$ is left unstated in the theorem. In fact, there is no general rule for the behavior of a power series on its boundary. Consider the following two examples.

We proved in Exercise 9.1(d)(iii) that a coefficient of $a_n = 1$ has a radius of convergence of 1. Of course, this is not surprising because this is the geometric series $\sum_{n=0}^{\infty} z^n$. We showed in Section 6.6 that the geometric series diverges for $|z| \geq 1$. Thus, this power series diverges on the boundary of its radius of convergence.

Compare the above example with the power series having coefficients of $a_n = 1/n^2$. We proved in Exercise 9.1(d)(i) that this power series has a radius of convergence of 1. For $|z| = 1$, we can use the Weierstrass M-Test (Theorem 6.10) and compare to the series $\sum_{n=0}^{\infty} 1/n^2$, which we showed convergent in Theorem 6.12(b). Thus, this power series converges on the boundary of its radius of convergence.

Chapter 10

Zeros and the Identity Theorem

This is a good point to highlight our progress in developing the theory of holomorphic functions. In Chapter 4, we learned that holomorphic functions satisfy the Cauchy-Riemann equations and therefore belong to the class of very well behaved harmonic functions. In Chapter 7, we showed that functions holomorphic in a domain satisfy the Fundamental Theorem of Calculus, allowing path independent evaluation of integrals. Then, in Chapter 8, we developed Cauchy's Integral Formula and learned that, for functions holomorphic in a domain, the value of the function at any point in the interior of a closed contour can be determined by knowing only the values on the contour. Finally, in Chapter 9, we showed that holomorphic functions have a power series expansion in a neighborhood of each point.

We advance the theory of holomorphic functions much further here. We will show that the values of a holomorphic function *at all points in a domain* are fully determined once we know the values along any path in the domain, no matter how small. And that means that any two holomorphic functions that are equal along that same path must be equal everywhere in their common domains.

> **Remark**
>
> We showed in Chapter 9 that a function is holomorphic in a domain if and only if it is analytic in that domain. In the remainder of this book, we will be relying primarily on properties associated with analytic functions. For that reason, from this point forward, it will be more natural to refer to such functions as analytic rather than holomorphic.

10.1 Zeros of Analytic Functions

Definition 10.1
Let $f(z)$ be analytic in the domain Ω. A point z_0 is called a **zero** of the function if $f(z_0) = 0$.

Theorem 10.1

Let $f(z)$ be a non-constant function analytic in the domain Ω and let $z_0 \in \Omega$ be a zero of the function. Then there is a unique positive integer n such that the function

$$g(z) = \frac{f(z)}{(z - z_0)^n}$$

is analytic in a neighborhood of z_0 and can be expanded into a power series with non-zero first coefficient.

Proof.[31] Consider the power series expansion

$$f(z) = \sum_{n=0}^{\infty} a_k(z - z_0)^n.$$

At z_0, we have $(z-z_0)^0 = 1$ and $(z-z_0)^n = 0$ for all $n \geq 1$, so we must have $a_0 = 0$. The assumption that $f(z)$ is non-constant (here meaning not identically 0) means that not all coefficients are zero. Assume a_n is the first non-zero coefficient. Then, setting $b_k = a_{(k+n)}$, we have

$$f(z) = \sum_{k=n}^{\infty} a_k(z - z_0)^k \quad \text{so that} \quad g(z) = \sum_{k=n}^{\infty} a_k(z - z_0)^{k-n} = \sum_{k=0}^{\infty} b_k(z - z_0)^k.$$

Because $b_k = a_{(k+n)}$, the power series for $g(z)$ has the same radius of convergence as $f(z)$ at z_0 (for the reasons explained in *Proof (a)* of Theorem 9.2). Also, $b_0 = a_n$, so $g(z)$ has a non-zero first coefficient. Of course, as the first non-zero coefficient, n is unique. $\square$

Definition 10.2

*For $f(z)$, z_0 and n as stated in Theorem 10.1, n is called the **order** of the zero at z_0. We might also say the zero is a **zero of order n**, or a **zero of multiplicity n**.*

> **Remark**
>
> For a zero of order N at z_0, we can apply Theorem 9.2 and have
>
> $$f(z_0) = f'(z_0) = \cdots = f^{(N-1)}(z_0) = 0 \quad \text{and} \quad f^{(N)}(z_0) \neq 0.$$

Definition 10.3

*We restate here a definition included in Definition 2.7. Let A be a set of points. Then $z_0 \in A$ is an **isolated point** of A if there exists a neighborhood of z_0 containing no other points of A.*

Definition 10.4

*The point w is an **accumulation point** of the sequence $\{z_n\}$ if there exists a subsequence $\{z_{n_k}\}$ such that $\lim_{k\to\infty} z_{n_k} = w$. Stated differently, for all $\epsilon > 0$ there exists a $K \in \mathbb{N}$ such that for $k > K$ we have $z_{n_k} \in \mathbf{D}_\epsilon(w)$. Note that w cannot be an isolated point because there are points in the sequence $\{z_n\}$ that are arbitrarily close to w.*

Theorem 10.2

Let $f(z)$ be analytic in the domain Ω and let $\mathcal{A} = \{z \in \Omega : f(z) = 0\}$. Assume that $\mathcal{A} \neq \Omega$ (i.e., $f(z)$ is not identically zero) and $\mathcal{A} \neq \emptyset$ (i.e., $f(z) = 0$ for some $z \in \Omega$). Then, for each $z_0 \in \mathcal{A}$, there is a $\delta > 0$ such that $z \notin \mathbf{D}_\delta(z_0)$ for $z \in \mathcal{A}\backslash\{z_0\}$. That is, the zeros of $f(z)$ are isolated points.

Proof.[32] Let $\Lambda_1 = \{z \in \Omega : f^{(m)}(z) = 0 \text{ for all } m \geq 0\}$ and let $\Lambda_2 = \Omega\backslash\Lambda_1$ so that $\Omega = \Lambda_1 \cup \Lambda_2$ and $\Lambda_1 \cap \Lambda_2 = \emptyset$. Note that $\Lambda_2 = \{z \in \Omega : f^{(m)}(z) \neq 0 \text{ for some } m \geq 0\}$. Fix $z_0 \in \mathcal{A}$.

Because $f(z)$ is analytic, we can apply Theorem 9.4. Thus, $f(z)$ has a power series expansion, centered at z_0, with a positive radius of convergence (which we assume to be r) as follows:

$$f(z) = \sum_{n=0}^{\infty} a_n (z - z_0)^n = \sum_{n=0}^{\infty} \frac{f^{(n)}(z_0)}{n!} (z - z_0)^n.$$

Assume $z_0 \in \Lambda_1$. Then, for all n and for all $z \in \mathbf{D}_r(z_0)$, $a_n = f^{(n)}(z_0)/n! = 0$ and $f(z) = 0$. Thus, the open set $\mathbf{D}_r(z_0) \subset \Lambda_1$. That means Λ_1 is a union of open sets and hence must be open.

Now assume $z_0 \in \Lambda_2$. Then, for some n and for all $z \in \mathbf{D}_r(z_0)$, $a_n = f^{(n)}(z_0)/n! \neq 0$. Thus, the open set $\mathbf{D}_r(z_0) \subset \Lambda_2$. That means Λ_2 is a union of open sets and hence must be open.

Since $\Omega = \Lambda_1 \cup \Lambda_2$ and Ω is open and simply connected, either Λ_1 or Λ_2 must be empty [a simply connected open set cannot be formed from the union of two open and non-empty disjoint sets]. If Λ_2 is empty, then $\Omega = \Lambda_1$ and $f(z) = 0$ for all $z \in \Omega$, contrary to assumption. Thus, Λ_1 is empty, $\Omega = \Lambda_2$, and the power series centered at every zero of $f(z)$ has an $a_n \neq 0$, making that zero of finite order.

For our fixed z_0, assume a_N is the first non-zero coefficient, so that $f(z_0)$ a zero of order N. Define $g(z)$ as in Theorem 10.1. Then $g(z_0) \neq 0$ and $g(z)$ is analytic at z_0. Using the continuity of $g(z)$ in a neighborhood of z_0, we can choose $\delta > 0$ small enough so that $g(z) \neq 0$ for $z \in \mathbf{D}_\delta(z_0)$. But that means $f(z) = (z - z_0)^N g(z) \neq 0$ for $z \in \mathbf{D}_\delta(z_0) \setminus \{z_0\}$. For our given zero z_0, we have shown the required δ distance to any other zero of $f(z)$, as required. $\qquad \square$

10.2 Identity Theorem

Using Theorem 10.2, we obtain with no difficulty the following very important theorem.

Theorem 10.3: Identity Theorem

Let $f(z)$ and $g(z)$ be analytic in the domain Ω. Assume any one of the following is true:

(a) There is a sequence $\{z_n\} \subset \Omega$ with an accumulation point $w \in \Omega$ and with $f(z) = g(z)$ for all $z \in \{z_n\}$; or

(b) there is a smooth path γ of non-zero length in Ω with $f(z) = g(z)$ for $z \in \gamma$; or

(c) for some $z_0 \in \Omega$ and some $\epsilon > 0$, $f(z) = g(z)$ for $z \in \mathbf{D}_\epsilon(z_0) \subset \Omega$.

Then $f(z) = g(z)$ for all $z \in \Omega$.

Proof. Define $h(z) = f(z) - g(z)$. Because $h(z)$ is the difference of two analytic functions in Ω, $h(z)$ is analytic in Ω. If we can show there is a zero of $h(z)$ in Ω that is not an isolated point, then we can apply Theorem 10.2 and have $h(z) = 0$ for all $z \in \Omega$; that is, $f(z) = g(z)$ for all $z \in \Omega$. Thus, all that remains is to show, for (a), (b) and (c), there is a zero of $h(z)$ that is not an isolated point.

The result is immediate for (b) and (c) because the smooth path γ and the open disk $\mathbf{D}_\epsilon(z_0)$ are simply connected and therefore have no isolated points.

In (a), we consider the accumulation point w. The continuity of $f(z)$ and $g(z)$, along with $f(z) = g(z)$ for all $z \in \{z_n\}$, ensures that $f(w) = g(w)$ and therefore $h(w) = 0$. Because w is an accumulation point of $\{z_n\}$, for any $\epsilon > 0$, there is a $z_n \in \mathbf{D}_\epsilon(w)$. Therefore, w cannot be an isolated point. $\qquad \square$

10.3 Analytic Continuance

Suppose $f(z)$ is analytic in a domain Ω. Under what circumstances can we extend the analytic reach of $f(z)$ beyond Ω? And if that is possible, are the values obtained in the extended domain unique?

With the Identity Theorem in hand, we have answers to those questions. An almost immediate consequence of the Identity Theorem is the principle of **analytic continuation**, which we discuss below[33].

Theorem 10.4: Analytic Continuation (Intersecting Sets)

Let $f_1(z)$ be analytic in the domain Ω_1 and let $f_2(z)$ be analytic in the domain Ω_2. Assume there is a domain $\Lambda \neq \emptyset$, with $\Lambda = \Omega_1 \cap \Omega_2$ and $f_1(z) = f_2(z)$ for $z \in \Lambda$. Then, $f_2(z)$ is the only possible function, that is both analytic in Ω_2 and equal to $f_1(z)$ in Λ.

Proof. By the Identity Theorem, a function analytic in Ω_2 is wholly defined by its values in Λ. Thus, $f_2(z)$ is the only possible function that meets the criteria of the theorem. $\qquad\square$

Theorem 10.5: Analytic Continuation (Subset)

Let $f_1(z)$ be analytic in the domain Ω_1 and let $f_2(z)$ be analytic in the domain Ω_2. Assume $\Omega_1 \subset \Omega_2$ and $f_1(z) = f_2(z)$ for $z \in \Omega_1$. Then, $f_2(z)$ is the only possible function, that is both analytic in Ω_2 and equal to $f_1(z)$ in Ω_1.

Proof. By the Identity Theorem, a function analytic in Ω_2 is wholly defined by its values in Ω_1. Thus, $f_2(z)$ is the only possible function that meets the criteria of the theorem. $\qquad\square$

Definition 10.5

Let $f_1(z)$, $f_2(z)$, Ω_1 and Ω_2 be as given in Theorems 10.4 or 10.5. Then, we say that $f_2(z)$ is an **analytic continuation** of $f_1(z)$ to the domain Ω_2.

In the case of intersecting sets (Theorem 10.4), if we further define

$$F(z) = \begin{cases} f_1(z) & \text{for } z \in \Omega_1 \\ f_2(z) & \text{for } z \in \Omega_2 \backslash \Lambda, \end{cases}$$

then $F(z)$ is analytic in $\Omega_1 \cup \Omega_2$. We also say that $F(z)$ is an **analytic continuation** of $f_1(z)$, or equally $f_2(z)$, to the domain $\Omega_1 \cup \Omega_2$.

10.3.1 Example – Intersecting Sets

Using the definition of $F(z)$ (for intersecting sets) in Definition 10.5, note that both functions $f_1(z)$ and $f_2(z)$ are analytic continuations of each other within the combined domain $\Omega_1 \cup \Omega_2$. Moreover, both are *partial representations* of the combined function $F(z)$. In the typical case, $F(z)$ can only be defined by its partial representations. However, in some cases, a closed form of $F(z)$ may be known that applies throughout the combined domains. We give an example of the latter next.

Define

$$f_1(z) = \sum_{n=0}^{\infty} z^n \qquad\qquad \text{for } \Omega_1 = \{z \in \mathbb{C} : |z| < 1\},$$

$$f_2(z) = \frac{1}{1-i} \sum_{n=0}^{\infty} \left(\frac{z-i}{1-i}\right)^n = \frac{1}{1-i} \sum_{n=0}^{\infty} w^n \qquad \text{for } \Omega_2 = \{z \in \mathbb{C} : |z-i| < \sqrt{2}\} \text{ and } w = \left(\frac{z-i}{1-i}\right).$$

The sums in $f_1(z)$ and $f_2(z)$ are geometric series, convergent for $|z| < 1$ and $|w| < 1$, respectively.

Clearly, $f_1(z)$ is convergent in Ω_1. To evaluate $f_2(z)$, we must determine when $|w| < 1$. Before we do that, we evaluate $|1 - i|$ using Euclidean distance. We have

$$|1 - i| = |(1 + i0) - (0 - i1)| = \sqrt{(1-0)^2 + (0+1)^2} = \sqrt{2}$$

$$|w| = \left|\frac{z-i}{1-i}\right| = \left|\frac{z-i}{\sqrt{2}}\right| \quad \text{so that} \quad |w| < 1 \implies |z - i| < \sqrt{2}.$$

Thus, $f_2(z)$ is convergent in Ω_2. Using the rules of geometric series, we can determine a closed form for both functions in their domains of convergence.

$$f_1(z) = \sum_{n=0}^{\infty} z^n = \frac{1}{1-z}$$

$$f_2(z) = \frac{1}{1-i} \sum_{n=0}^{\infty} \left(\frac{z-i}{1-i}\right)^n = \left(\frac{1}{1-i}\right) \frac{1}{1 - \left(\frac{z-i}{1-i}\right)} = \frac{1}{(1-i) - (z-i)} = \frac{1}{1-z}.$$

Thus, $f_1(z) = f_2(z)$ in the region $\Omega_1 \cap \Omega_2 = \mathbf{D}_1(0) \cap \mathbf{D}_{\sqrt{2}}(i)$. Both functions are analytic continuations of each other within the combined domain $\Omega_1 \cup \Omega_2$. Moreover, both are partial representations of the combined function $F(z)$, which is analytic in $\Omega_1 \cup \Omega_2$. In this case, $F(z)$ has a single closed form of $1/(1-z)$.

10.3.2 Example – Subset

Here we give an example of the subset version of analytic continuation. Of course, the formula for $f_2(z)$ holds throughout the combined domains. Define

$$f_1(z) = \sum_{n=0}^{\infty} z^n \quad \text{for } \Omega_1 = \{z \in \mathbb{C} : |z| < 1\},$$

$$f_2(z) = \frac{1}{1-z} \quad \text{for } \Omega_2 = \mathbb{C}\backslash\{1\}.$$

It is immediately clear that $f_2(z)$ is the analytic continuation of $f_1(z)$ throughout the entire complex plane, excluding only the single point $z = 1$.

We briefly mention (without proof) probably the most famous example of the subset version of analytic continuation. (In this case, it is traditional to use s rather than z as the complex variable).

$$f_1(s) = \sum_{n=0}^{\infty} \frac{1}{n^s} \qquad\qquad \text{for } \Omega_1 = \{z \in \mathbb{C} : Re(s) > 1\},$$

$$f_2(s) = \frac{\Gamma(1-s)}{-2\pi i} \int_{\mathbf{C}} \frac{-z^{s-1}}{e^z - 1} \, dz \quad \text{for } \Omega_2 = \mathbb{C}\backslash\{1\} \text{ and } \mathbf{C} \text{ a "Hankel contour".}$$

In this example, $f_1(s)$ is the traditional form of $\zeta(s)$, the Zeta function, as known before Bernhard Riemann's 1859 paper, and $f_2(s)$ is the analytic continuation of $\zeta(s)$ to the full complex plane, with a simple pole at $s = 1$. For more on this (and Riemann's paper), see Murphy [10].

10.3.3 The Exponential and Trigonometric Functions

Returning to the Identity Theorem, suppose there is a path γ and a function $f_1(z)$ defined and continuous along γ. Next suppose that Ω is any domain that contains γ. Then we know that either: (a) there is *no* function analytic in Ω and equal to $f_1(z)$ along γ, or (b) there is *exactly one* such function. That is, by the Identity Theorem, any such function in Ω is *wholly determined* by its values along γ.

Here we consider a special case. The path γ is a line segment along the real axis and the function $f_1(x)$ is therefore a function of a real variable (whose values may be real or complex). Suppose a function $f_2(z)$ and a domain Ω exist with $f_2(z)$ analytic in Ω, $\gamma \subset \Omega$, and $f_2(x) = f_1(x)$ for $x \in \gamma$. Then we say that we have continued the real variable function $f_1(x)$ *into the complex domain*. And we know by the Identity Theorem that $f_2(z)$ is unique.

Now consider the real variable exponential function e^x and the trigonometric functions $\sin(x)$ and $\cos(x)$, defined by

$$e^x = \sum_{n=0}^{\infty} \frac{x^n}{n!} \qquad = 1 + x + \frac{x^2}{2!} + \cdots \frac{x^n}{n!} + \cdots$$

$$\sin x = \sum_{n=0}^{\infty} (-1)^n \frac{x^{2n+1}}{(2n+1)!} \qquad = x - \frac{x^3}{3!} + \frac{x^5}{5!} - + \cdots$$

$$\cos x = \sum_{n=0}^{\infty} (-1)^n \frac{x^{2n}}{(2n)!} \qquad = 1 - \frac{x^2}{2!} + \frac{x^4}{4!} - + \cdots.$$

It is a simple matter of replacing the x with z to obtain

$$e^z = \sum_{n=0}^{\infty} \frac{z^n}{n!} \qquad = 1 + z + \frac{z^2}{2!} + \cdots \frac{z^n}{n!} + \cdots$$

$$\sin z = \sum_{n=0}^{\infty} (-1)^n \frac{z^{2n+1}}{(2n+1)!} \qquad = x - \frac{z^3}{3!} + \frac{z^5}{5!} - + \cdots$$

$$\cos z = \sum_{n=0}^{\infty} (-1)^n \frac{z^{2n}}{(2n)!} \qquad = 1 - \frac{z^2}{2!} + \frac{z^4}{4!} - + \cdots.$$

We now have three complex-valued power series, each with an infinite radius of convergence, and each therefore analytic in the entire complex plane. The functions are equal to their real variable versions on the real axis. They are therefore *the only* continuations of their real variable counterparts to the complex domain. Thus, they are the *only possible* complex variable versions of the exponential, sine and cosine functions.

10.4   Supplemental Material

> **Remark**
>
> We showed in Theorem 10.2 that the zeros of a non-constant analytic function are isolated. It is quite remarkable how that one theorem reduces the proof of the Identity Theorem and of Analytic Continuation to just a few lines. Continuing that theme, you will find the four exercises below can be proved in just a few lines.

10.4.1   Exercises

> **Exercises 10.1**
>
> *In the following, assume $f(z)$ is a non-constant function analytic in the domain Ω.*
>
> (a) *Let $G \subset \Omega$ be a compact set. Show that $f(z)$ has a finite number of zeros in G.*
>
> (b) *Fix $z_0 \in \Omega$. Using Theorem 10.2, show that there is an $\epsilon > 0$ such that $f(z_0) \neq f(w)$ for all $w \in \mathbf{D}_\epsilon(z_0) \backslash \{z_0\}$. The last is a "punctured disk", denoted by $\mathbf{D}_\epsilon^\circ(z_0)$.*
>
> (c) *Use excercise (a) to show (b) above.*
>
> (d) *Show that $f(z)$ has a countable number of zeros in Ω.*

> **Remark**
>
> Answers to exercises are in Appendix A.

Chapter 11

Laurent Series

11.1 Laurent Series

In this chapter we develop the theory of Laurent series, an "extended power series" which allows the development of functions analytic in an annulus. The practical use of Laurent series will not be seen until Chapter 12 (Isolated Singularities), where the inner "hole" of the annulus is a single point.

11.1.1 The Foundational Idea

For some radius of convergence $R > 0$, a power series expansion centered at z_0 represents an analytic function within the open disk $\mathbf{D}_R(z_0)$. We would like to turn that idea on its head. Using what we will informally call a *negative power series*, we will demonstrate circumstances when an analytic function can be represented by a series that is convergent *outside* the closed disk $\overline{\mathbf{D}}_R(z_0)$.

To keep focus on the concept, and without loss of generality, we will assume our disk is centered at the origin. Thus, instead of convergence for $|z| < R$, we wish to represent an analytic function by a series that converges for $|z| > R$.

Consider a function $f(z)$ with a power series expansion

$$f(z) = \sum_{n=0}^{\infty} a_n z^n$$

and a radius of convergence of $R > 0$, so that the sum converges for $|z| < R$. Let $w = z^{-1}$, so that

$$f(z) = \sum_{n=0}^{\infty} a_n z^n = \sum_{n=0}^{-\infty} a_{-n} \left(\frac{1}{z}\right)^n = \sum_{n=0}^{-\infty} a_{-n} w^n.$$

The LHS converges for $|z| < R$ and thus the RHS converges for $|w| > 1/R$.

With this in mind, assume a function $f(z)$ is analytic in an annular region (centered at z_0) between a larger circle of radius R and a smaller circle of radius r. The goal of this chapter is to show that $f(z)$ can be represented by a series expansion which converges and equals $f(z)$ for all z in the annular region $r < |z - z_0| < R$.

> **Definition 11.1**
>
> *For variable z, fixed c and $n \in \mathbb{Z}$, let $\{a_n\}$ be a sequence where a_n may be dependent on n but not on z. Then any series of the form*
>
> $$\sum_{n=-\infty}^{\infty} a_n (z - c)^n \qquad z, c, a_n \in \mathbb{C}$$
>
> *is called a **Laurent series** with center c and coefficients a_n.*

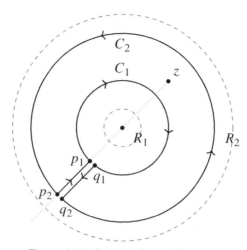

Figure 11.1: Laurent Series Expansion

11.1.2   Deriving the Laurent Series

Theorem 11.1: Laurent Series Expansion

For $0 \leq R_1 < r_1 < r_2 < R_2 \leq \infty$ and for the center point z_0, define the annular region $\Omega = \{z \in \mathbb{C} : R_1 < |z - z_0| < R_2\}$ and define the closed annular region $\overline{G} = \{z \in \mathbb{C} : r_1 \leq |z - z_0| \leq r_2\}$, so that $\overline{G} \subset \Omega$ and $\overline{G}$ has as its boundary the circles $C_1 = \mathbf{C}_{r_1}(z_0)$ and $C_2 = \mathbf{C}_{r_2}(z_0)$. Let $f(z)$ be analytic in Ω. Then $f(z)$ has a series expansion

$$f(z) = \sum_{n=-\infty}^{\infty} a_n (z - z_0)^n$$

that converges absolutely in Ω and converges uniformly in $\overline{G}$. The coefficients of the series are given by

$$a_n = \frac{1}{2\pi i} \int_{C_2} \frac{f(w)}{(w - z_0)^{n+1}} \, dw \quad \text{for } n \geq 0 \qquad (11.1)$$

$$a_n = \frac{1}{2\pi i} \int_{C_1} \frac{f(w)}{(w - z_0)^{n+1}} \, dw \quad \text{for } n < 0, \qquad (11.2)$$

where: (1) the coefficients are independent of the particular r_1, r_2 (and thus) C_1, C_2 chosen, and (2) C_1 and C_2 have positive orientations.

Proof: Develop Series.[34]   Fix any $z \in \Omega$. Set $r_1 = (R_1 + |z - z_0|)/2$ and $r_2 = (R_2 + |z - z_0|)/2$. We then have z in the interior of $\overline{G}$.

Now define four points (two on C_1 and two on C_2) as follows. Scribe a straight "guiding line" starting at z, then through z_0, then to a point p_1 on C_1 and then to a point p_2 on C_2. Next, from p_1, traverse C_1 in the positive direction for a length of ϵ to form a point q_1 on C_1; finally, from p_2, traverse C_2 in the positive direction for a length of ϵ to form a point q_2 on C_2.

We can now define our contour $\Gamma(\epsilon)$. Begin at q_2 and do a positive traversal of C_2 until reaching

p_2; then traverse from p_2 to p_1; then do a negative traversal of C_1 until reaching q_1; finally, traverse from q_1 to q_2. $\Gamma(\epsilon)$ is a simple closed contour, with $z \in \Gamma(\epsilon)$. We have $\lim_{\epsilon \to 0} \Gamma(\epsilon) = C_2 - C_1$ and can use Cauchy's Integral Formula:

$$f(z) = \lim_{\epsilon \to 0} \left[\frac{1}{2\pi i} \int_{\Gamma(\epsilon)} \frac{f(w)}{w - z} \, dw \right] = \boxed{\frac{1}{2\pi i} \int_{C_2} \frac{f(w)}{w - z} \, dw} - \boxed{\frac{1}{2\pi i} \int_{C_1} \frac{f(w)}{w - z} \, dw}. \tag{11.3}$$

We now use the same technique as in Theorem 9.4 for the two boxed integrals.

Equation (11.3) – *the First Boxed Integral.* Because w is a point on C_2

$$\left| \frac{z - z_0}{w - z_0} \right| < 1.$$

That allows a uniformly convergent geometric series expansion by the Weierstrass M-test (Theorem 6.10):

$$\frac{1}{w - z} = \frac{1}{(w - z_0) - (z - z_0)} = \frac{1}{(w - z_0)} \cdot \frac{1}{1 - \left(\frac{z - z_0}{w - z_0} \right)} = \sum_{n=0}^{\infty} \frac{(z - z_0)^n}{(w - z_0)^{n+1}} \tag{11.4}$$

If $K = \max(f(w))$ for $w \in C_2$, then we can again use the Weierstrass M-test to see that the series

$$\sum_{n=0}^{\infty} \frac{f(w)(z - z_0)^n}{(w - z_0)^{n+1}} \tag{11.5}$$

is uniformly convergent.

Equation (11.3) – *the Second Boxed Integral.* Because w is a point on C_1

$$\left| \frac{w - z_0}{z - z_0} \right| < 1.$$

For the same reasons as above, that allows a uniformly convergent geometric series expansion

$$\frac{1}{w - z} = \frac{1}{(w - z_0) - (z - z_0)} = \frac{-1}{(z - z_0)} \cdot \frac{1}{1 - \left(\frac{w - z_0}{z - z_0} \right)} = -\sum_{n=0}^{\infty} \frac{(w - z_0)^n}{(z - z_0)^{n+1}}, \tag{11.6}$$

and the uniformly convergent series (using $K = \max(f(w))$ for $w \in C_1$)

$$-\sum_{n=0}^{\infty} \frac{f(w)(w - z_0)^n}{(z - z_0)^{n+1}}. \tag{11.7}$$

Because of the uniform convergence of the above series for both boxed integrals, we can integrate term by term, giving (it will be clear shortly why we use k in the second integral)

$$f(z) = \sum_{n=0}^{\infty} \frac{1}{2\pi i} \int_{C_2} \frac{f(w)}{(w - z_0)^{n+1}} (z - z_0)^n \, dw + \sum_{k=0}^{\infty} \frac{1}{2\pi i} \int_{C_1} \frac{f(w)}{(z - z_0)^{k+1}} (w - z_0)^k \, dw \tag{11.8}$$

$$= \sum_{n=0}^{\infty} \frac{1}{2\pi i} \int_{C_2} \frac{f(w)}{(w - z_0)^{n+1}} (z - z_0)^n \, dw + \sum_{k=0}^{\infty} \frac{1}{2\pi i} \int_{C_1} \frac{f(w)}{(w - z_0)^{-k}} (z - z_0)^{-(k+1)} \, dw$$

In the second integral set $n = (-k - 1)$

$$= \sum_{n=0}^{\infty} \frac{1}{2\pi i} \int_{C_2} \frac{f(w)}{(w - z_0)^{n+1}} (z - z_0)^n \, dw + \sum_{n=-1}^{-\infty} \frac{1}{2\pi i} \int_{C_1} \frac{f(w)}{(w - z_0)^{n+1}} (z - z_0)^n \, dw. \tag{11.9}$$

Now setting

$$a_n = \frac{1}{2\pi i} \int_{C_2} \frac{f(w)}{(w-z_0)^{n+1}} \, dw \quad \text{for } n \geq 0,$$

$$a_n = \frac{1}{2\pi i} \int_{C_1} \frac{f(w)}{(w-z_0)^{n+1}} \, dw \quad \text{for } n < 0,$$

we have

$$f(z) = \sum_{n=-\infty}^{\infty} a_n (z-z_0)^n.$$

The coefficients a_n remain the same, even under a change in the contours C_1 and/or C_2, so long as any such change in the contours meets the requirements of Theorem 7.5 (principle of deformed paths). $\square$

Proof: Series Unique. To see that the Laurent expansion is unique, assume that

$$f(z) = \sum_{n=-\infty}^{\infty} a_n (z-z_0)^n = \sum_{n=-\infty}^{\infty} c_n (z-z_0)^n.$$

For $k \in \mathbb{N}$, we define $g_k(z)$:

$$g_k(z) = f(z)(z-z_0)^{-k-1} = \sum_{n=-\infty}^{\infty} a_n (z-z_0)^{n-k-1} = \sum_{n=-\infty}^{\infty} c_n (z-z_0)^{n-k-1}.$$

Define the closed contour $\boldsymbol{C}$ as a positively oriented circle centered at z_0 and lying inside the annular region Ω. We can then choose r_1 and r_2 such that $g_k(z)$ is uniformly convergent on $\boldsymbol{C}$. Now integrate $g_k(z)$ termwise along $\boldsymbol{C}$, giving

$$\sum_{n=-\infty}^{\infty} a_n \int_{\boldsymbol{C}} (z-z_0)^{n-k-1} \, dz = \sum_{n=-\infty}^{\infty} c_n \int_{\boldsymbol{C}} (z-z_0)^{n-k-1} \, dz.$$

Evaluating the integral, we have

$$\int_{\boldsymbol{C}} (z-z_0)^{n-k-1} \, dz = \begin{cases} 0 & \text{if } n \neq k, \\ 2\pi i & \text{if } n = k. \end{cases}$$

Therefore, for all $k \in \mathbb{N}$, we have $2\pi i a_k = 2\pi i c_k$, so that $a_k = c_k$, as required. $\square$

Proof: Series Convergence. We have developed a Laurent series expansion giving

$$f(z) = \sum_{n=-\infty}^{\infty} a_n (z-z_0)^n$$

in the annular region $\Omega = \{z \in \mathbb{C} : R_1 < |z-z_0| < R_2\}$. It is helpful to think of the component parts of the Laurent series. If we define

$$f_1(z) = \sum_{n=0}^{\infty} a_n (z-z_0)^n \quad \text{and} \quad f_2(z) = \sum_{n=-1}^{-\infty} a_n (z-z_0)^n, \tag{11.10}$$

then $f(z) = f_1(z) + f_2(z)$.

It is clear from the construction of $f(z)$ that $f_1(z)$ is analytic *inside* the open disk $\mathbf{D}_{R_2}(z_0)$ and $f_2(z)$ is analytic *outside* the closed disk $\overline{\mathbf{D}}_{R_1}(z_0)$. That is, $f_1(z)$ is a standard power series and $f_2(z)$ is a series of the type discussed in Section 11.1.1.

These two component parts are shown in equation (11.9), and are in the form we need in equation (11.8). We first show absolute convergence of both parts of equation (11.8). Let $L(C_1)$ and $L(C_2)$ be the lengths of C_1 and C_2, respectively. Let $F_1 = \{\max(f(w)) : w \in C_1\}$ and $F_2 = \{\max(f(w)) : w \in C_2\}$.

We have

$$f(z) = \sum_{n=0}^{\infty} \frac{1}{2\pi i} \int_{C_2} \frac{f(w)}{(w-z_0)^{n+1}} (z-z_0)^n \, dw + \sum_{k=0}^{\infty} \frac{1}{2\pi i} \int_{C_1} \frac{f(w)}{(z-z_0)^{k+1}} (w-z_0)^k \, dw$$

$$|f(z)| \leq \sum_{n=0}^{\infty} \frac{1}{2\pi i} \int_{C_2} \left| \frac{f(w)}{(w-z_0)^{n+1}} (z-z_0)^n \right| dw + \sum_{k=0}^{\infty} \frac{1}{2\pi i} \int_{C_1} \left| \frac{f(w)}{(z-z_0)^{k+1}} (w-z_0)^k \right| dw$$

Apply the ML inequality, this gives

$$|f(z)| \leq \left[\frac{L(C_2) \cdot F_2}{2\pi i} \right] \cdot \sum_{n=0}^{\infty} \left| \frac{(z-z_0)^n}{(w-z_0)^{n+1}} \right| + \left[\frac{L(C_1) \cdot F_1}{2\pi i} \right] \cdot \sum_{k=0}^{\infty} \left| \frac{(w-z_0)^k}{(z-z_0)^{k+1}} \right|.$$

From equations (11.4) and (11.6), both sums are uniformly convergent. Thus, the Laurent series expansion converges absolutely in Ω.

Regarding Uniform convergence in $\overline{G}$, we consider separately the $f_1(z)$ and $f_2(z)$ components of the Laurent series. The $f_1(z)$ component is an ordinary power series, so uniform convergence in $\overline{G}$ follows immediately from Theorem 9.1. For the $f_2(z)$ component, we can also apply Theorem 9.1 after we make the transformation to an ordinary power series as described in Section 11.1.1. $\qquad \square$

> **Definition 11.2**
>
> *The component parts of the Laurent series expansion are given in equation (11.10). The terms in $f_2(z)$ (over the negative values of n) are called the **principal part** of the Laurent series expansion.*

Remark

Regarding the component parts of the Laurent series expansion, why doesn't the $f_2(z)$ component have an a_0 term? Without the a_0 term, we say that $f_2(z)$ has been "normalized" because $\lim_{z \to \infty} f_2(z) = 0$. If $f_2(z)$ had an a_0 term, that limit would equal a_0.

Normalization is necessary to ensure the Laurent series expansion is unique. Otherwise, the current value of a_0 in $f_1(z)$ could be shared by $f_1(z)$ and $f_2(z)$ in any way such that their two a_0 terms add up to the current value of a_0 in $f_1(z)$.

Remark

We mentioned at the beginning of this chapter that Laurent series are used in studying isolated singularities of otherwise analytic functions. Once you have the theory of isolated singularities in hand, you will see in Chapter 13 (The Residue Calculus) the importance of Laurent series to the residue calculus.

11.2 Supplemental Material

11.2.1 Exercises

Exercises 11.1

For these exercises, assume

$$f(z) = \frac{1}{(z-1)(z-2)} \quad \text{and} \quad g(z) = \frac{(1-iz)}{(1+iz)}.$$

We see that $f(z)$ has singularities at $z = 1$ and $z = 2$ and is analytic in the following three regions:

$$\Omega_1 = |z| < 1 \qquad \Omega_2 = 1 < |z| < 2 \qquad \Omega_3 = 2 < |z| < \infty,$$

with a power series expansion in the disk Ω_1 and Laurent series expansions in the annuli Ω_2 and Ω_3.

The function $g(z)$ has a singularity at $z = i$, is analytic in $\mathbb{C}\backslash\{i\}$ and has a Laurent series expansion centered at i.

(a) *Show the power series expansion for $f(z)$ in Ω_1, centered at 0.*

(b) *Show the Laurent series expansion for $f(z)$ in Ω_2, centered at 0.*

(c) *Show the Laurent series expansion for $f(z)$ in Ω_3, centered at 0.*

(d) *Show the Laurent series expansion for $g(z)$, centered at i.*

Remark

Answers to exercises are in Appendix A.

Chapter 12

Isolated Singularities

12.1 The Punctured Disk

In Chapter 11, we developed the theory of Laurent series. A function represented by a Laurent series is analytic in an annulus. In this chapter, we restrict ourselves to a special kind of Laurent series (the *punctured disk*) and study functions that have an isolated singularity at the center of that disk.

> **Definition 12.1**
> *For the point w and the radius r > 0, the **punctured disk** is the open disk (excluding its center point) given by $\{z \in \mathbb{C} : 0 < |z - w| < r\}$. We denote the punctured disk by $\mathbf{D}_r^{\odot}(w)$.*

Remark

Our focus here is on the center point of the punctured disk.

> **Definition 12.2**
> *A function f has an **isolated singularity** at w if f is analytic in a punctured disk $\mathbf{D}_r^{\odot}(w)$.*

Given a function $f(z)$ analytic in a punctured disk $\mathbf{D}_r^{\odot}(w)$, consider the component parts of the Laurent series for $f(z)$, as discussed in Chapter 11:

$$f(z) = f_1(z) + f_2(z) \quad \text{where} \quad f_1(z) = \sum_{n=0}^{\infty} a_n(z-w)^n \quad \text{and} \quad f_2(z) = \sum_{n=-1}^{-\infty} a_n(z-w)^n. \quad (12.1)$$

For our punctured disk, $f_1(z)$ is a standard power series, analytic in the open disk $\mathbf{D}_r(w)$, and $f_2(z)$ is analytic in $\mathbb{C} \backslash w$.

It turns out that the properties of the isolated singularity at w are determined by the coefficients a_n of $f_2(z)$. That is the topic of our next section.

12.2 Classification of Isolated Singularities

Using $f(z) = f_1(z) + f_2(z)$ as described above, let $f(z)$ be a function analytic in a punctured disk $\mathbf{D}_r^{\odot}(w)$. The isolated singularity w of $f(z)$ is one of three types:

- A **removable singularity** if $a_n = 0$ for all coefficients of $f_2(z)$.
- A **pole** if only a finite number of the coefficients of $f_2(z)$ are non-zero.
- An **essential singularity** if an infinite number of the coefficients of $f_2(z)$ are non-zero.

We now provide formal definitions (unrelated to the coefficients of $f_2(z)$) for each of the three types of isolated singularities. In the following sections, we will further discuss each type of isolated singularity and show that the definitions below match the statements above regarding the coefficients of $f_2(z)$.

Definition 12.3

*Let $f(z)$ be analytic in a punctured disk $\mathbf{D}_r^\circ(w)$. The point w is called a **removable singularity** of $f(z)$ if there exists a function $g(z)$, analytic in the open disk $\mathbf{D}_r(w)$, with $g(z) = f(z)$ in the punctured disk $\mathbf{D}_r^\circ(w)$.*

Definition 12.4

*Let $f(z)$ be analytic in a punctured disk $\mathbf{D}_r^\circ(w)$. The point w is called a **pole** of $f(z)$ if there exists an integer $n \geq 1$ that is the smallest integer such that the function $g(z) = f(z)(z-w)^n$ is analytic in $\mathbf{D}_r(w)$. Using that smallest n, we say the $f(z)$ has a **pole of order n**. If $n = 1$, we say that $f(z)$ has a **simple pole**. If $n = 2$, we say that $f(z)$ has a **double pole**.*

Definition 12.5

*Let $f(z)$ be analytic in a punctured disk $\mathbf{D}_r^\circ(w)$. The point w is called an **essential singularity** of $f(z)$ if w is neither a removable singularity nor a pole of $f(z)$.*

12.2.1 Removable Singularities

Following is Riemann's theorem on removable singularities. Note that statement (a) in the theorem is just a restatement of Definition 12.3.

Theorem 12.1

Let $f(z)$ be analytic in the punctured disk $\mathbf{D}_r^\circ(w)$. If any one of the following statements is true, then so are the others:

(a) *The function $f(z)$ can be extended to an analytic function at w.*

(b) *The function $f(z)$ can be extended to a continuous function at w.*

(c) *For some $\epsilon > 0$, $f(z)$ is bounded on the open disk $\mathbf{D}_\epsilon(w)$.*

(d) $\lim\limits_{z \to w} (z-w)f(z) = 0$.

Proof # 1.[35] The three cases $(a) \implies (b) \implies (c) \implies (d)$ are immediate. We need only show that $(d) \implies (a)$.

Let

$$g(z) = \begin{cases} (z-w)^2 f(z) & \text{if } z \neq w, \\ 0 & \text{if } z = w, \end{cases}$$

so that $g(z)$ is analytic in the punctured disk $\mathbf{D}_r^\circ(w)$. We then have

$$g'(w) = \lim_{z \to w} \frac{(z-w)^2 f(z) - 0}{z - w} = \lim_{z \to w}(z-w)f(z) = 0,$$

using the assumption stated in (d). But that means $g(z)$ is analytic at w and therefore analytic in the entire open disk $\mathbf{D}_r(w)$. Therefore, $g(z)$ has a power series expansion about w:

$$g(z) = \sum_{n=0}^{\infty} a_n (z - w)^n.$$

The coefficient $a_0 = g(w) = 0$ and $a_1 = g'(w) = 0$. Hence

$$g(z) = \sum_{n=2}^{\infty} a_n (z - w)^n.$$

By our definition of $g(z)$, for $z \neq w$ we have

$$f(z) = \frac{g(z)}{(z-w)^2} = \sum_{n=0}^{\infty} a_{n+2} (z - w)^n.$$

The RHS of the last equation is analytic in the entire open disk $\mathbf{D}_r(w)$ and therefore extends $f(z)$ to an analytic function at w. $\quad\square$

Proof # 2. [36] Another approach is to use the boundedness assumption in (c) to obtain (a). Assume $|f(z)| < M$ in the punctured disk $\mathbf{D}_\epsilon^\odot(w)$ and assume $0 < r < \epsilon$. Expand $f(z)$ into a Laurent series. To compute the negative coefficients of the Laurent series, use the ML estimate on the formula for the negative coefficients, as given in Theorem 11.1:

$$a_n = \frac{1}{2\pi i} \int_{C_1} \frac{f(w)}{(w - z_0)^{n+1}} \, dw \quad \text{for } n < 0,$$

$$|a_n| \leq \frac{1}{2\pi} \frac{M}{r^{n+1}} \cdot 2\pi r = \frac{M}{r^n}.$$

Because r can be as small as we like, we must have $a_n = 0$ for $n < 0$. What remains is a power series analytic in $\mathbf{D}_r(w)$, showing that the singularity at w is removable. $\quad\square$

> **Remark**
>
> Now consider the component parts of the Laurent series, $f(z) = f_1(z) + f_2(z)$. As promised, for a removable singularity we have shown that $a_n = 0$ for all coefficients of $f_2(z)$. In other words, $f(z) = f_1(z)$, giving a standard power series that is analytic in all of the open disk $\mathbf{D}_r(w)$.

As an example, consider the function $f(z) = \sin z / z$, which has an isolated singularity at $z = 0$. In this case, the isolated singularity results from the indeterminate form of the function. At $z = 0$, the function evaluates to $0/0$. However, if we use the Taylor Series expansion for the sine function, we obtain

$$f(z) = \frac{\sin z}{z} = g(z) = \frac{1}{z} \left(\sum_{k=0}^{\infty} \frac{(-1)^k z^{2k+1}}{(2k+1)!} \right) = 1 - \frac{z^2}{3!} + \frac{z^4}{5!} - \frac{z^6}{7!} + \cdots$$

Clearly, $g(z)$, the expansion of $f(z)$, is an entire function (and therefore continuous at $z = 0$), with $g(0) = 1$. Also, $g(z) = f(z)$ on the punctured disk $\mathbf{D}_r^\odot(\emptyset)$ for any $r > 0$. Therefore, the isolated singularity of $\sin z/z$ at $z = 0$ is a removable singularity.

A removable singularity at a point w is easily curable by defining $f(w) = \lim_{z \to w} f(z)$. In the above example, it is sufficient to define $f(0) = \lim_{z \to 0} f(z) = 1$.

12.2.2 Poles

> **Theorem 12.2**
>
> Let $f(z)$ be analytic in the punctured disk $\mathbf{D}_r^\odot(w)$, with Laurent series and component parts as shown in equation (12.1). Let $N \geq 1$ be the smallest integer such that the function $g(z) = f(z)(z-w)^N$ is analytic in $\mathbf{D}_r(w)$. Then, only a finite number of the coefficients of the series $f_2(z)$ are non-zero and, in particular: (1) $a_{-N} \neq 0$ and (2) for $k \geq 1$, $a_{-(N+k)} = 0$.

Proof. The assumptions of the theorem combined with Definition 12.4 mean that $f(z)$ has a pole of order N at w. Using the component parts in equation (12.1), we have

$$g(z) = f(z)(z-w)^N = [f_1(z) + f_2(z)](z-w)^N = f_1(z)(z-w)^N + f_2(z)(z-w)^N.$$

Regarding the coefficients of $f_2(z)$, we first eliminate two cases:

Case 1. Assume that $a_n = 0$ for all coefficients of $f_2(z)$. That means $f(z)$ has (at most) a removable singularity at w, so that $f(z) = f_1(z)$ is analytic in $\mathbf{D}_r(w)$. Therefore, contrary to assumption, we can set $N = 0$ and have $g(z)$ analytic because $g(z) = f(z)(z-w)^N = f(z)(z-w)^0 = f(z)$.

Case 2. Assume that $a_n \neq 0$ for an infinite number of coefficients of $f_2(z)$. Then, there exists an integer $k \geq 1$ such that the coefficient $a_{-(N+k)}$ of $f_2(z)$ is non-zero. Therefore, the Laurent series for $g(z)$ includes the term $a_{-(N+k)}(z-w)^{-k}$ which is unbounded as $z \to w$. Accordingly, contrary to assumption, $g(z)$ is not analytic in $\mathbf{D}_r(w)$.

Thus, based on our assumption that $f(z)$ has a pole at w, only a finite number of the coefficients of $f_2(z)$ are nonzero. Now let k be the largest integer such that the coefficient $a_{-(N+k)}$ of $f_2(z)$ is non-zero. Our proof will be complete if we show that $k = 0$.

Assume $k \geq 1$. As in *Case 2*, above, this means the Laurent series for $g(z)$ includes the term $a_{-(N+k)}(z-w)^{-k}$ which is unbounded as $z \to w$. Accordingly, contrary to assumption, $g(z)$ is not analytic in $\mathbf{D}_r(w)$.

Finally, assume $k \leq -1$. That means $a_{-N} = 0$. If we let $M = N - 1$ and $g(z) = f(z)(z-w)^M$, then

$$
\begin{aligned}
g(z) &= f_1(z)(z-w)^M + f_2(z)(z-w)^M \\
&= (z-w)^M \left[\sum_{n=0}^{\infty} a_n(z-w)^n + \sum_{n=-1}^{-M} a_n(z-w)^n \right] \\
&= \sum_{n=0}^{\infty} a_n(z-w)^{n+M} + \sum_{n=-1}^{-M} a_n(z-w)^{n+M} \\
&= \sum_{n=0}^{\infty} a_{n-M}(z-w)^n.
\end{aligned}
$$

Thus, $g(z)$ resolves to a standard power series, with no negative power terms in the Laurent series. Except for the first M terms, the coefficients are the same as $f_1(z)$, so the radius of convergence is the same as $f_1(z)$. Therefore, $g(z)$ is analytic in $\mathbf{D}_r(w)$, which is contrary to our assumption that N was the smallest integer making $g(z)$ analytic in $\mathbf{D}_r(w)$. Hence, we must have $k = 0$, as required. $\qquad \square$

Under the assumptions of Theorem 12.2, recall Definition 11.2. For a pole, the partial sum consisting of the N negative power terms of the Laurent series is the *principal part* of $f(z)$ at w.

Definition 12.6

*Let $f(z)$ be analytic in the domain Ω, except at a finite number of isolated singularities $w_1, w_2, ... w_n$. If all such isolated singularities are poles of $f(z)$, then the function $f(z)$ is **meromorphic** in Ω.*

There is a close relationship between the poles of a function $f(z)$ and the zeros of the reciprocal function $1/f(z)$, as shown in the following theorem. (See Chapter 10 for more on the zeros of analytic functions).

Theorem 12.3

Let $f(z)$ be analytic in the punctured disk $\mathbf{D}_r^{\circlearrowleft}(w)$, with a pole of order N at w. Then the function $1/f(z)$ is analytic in a neighborhood of w with a zero of order N at w.

Proof.[37] Let $g(z) = f(z)(z-w)^N$, and assume $f(z)$ is in the form of equation (12.1). It follows from Theorem 12.2 that: (1) $g(z)$ is analytic in $\mathbf{D}_r(w)$, and (2) the a_{-N} coefficient of $f_2(z)$ is nonzero. But the a_{-N} coefficient is equal to the a_0 coefficient of the power series for $g(z)$ and therefore $g(w)$ is nonzero.

Now define $h(z) = 1/g(z)$. Then, $h(w) \neq 0$ and $h(z)$ is analytic in a neighborhood of w. With $1/f(z) = (z-w)^N h(z)$, we also have that $1/f(z)$ is analytic in a neighborhood of w, and $1/f(z)$ has a zero of order N at w. $\square$

Theorem 12.4

Let $f(z)$ be analytic in the punctured disk $\mathbf{D}_r^{\circlearrowleft}(w)$, with a pole of order N at w. Then, for any $M > 0$ there exists an ϵ, with $0 < \epsilon < r$, such that $|f(z)| \geq M$ for $z \in \mathbf{D}_\epsilon^{\circlearrowleft}(w)$.

Proof.[38] Fix $M > 0$. The Laurent series for $f(z)$ is

$$
\begin{aligned}
f(z) &= \sum_{n=-N}^{\infty} a_n (z-w)^n \\
&= \frac{a_{-N}}{(z-w)^N} + \cdots + a_0 + a_1(z-w)^1 + a_2(z-w)^2 + \cdots \\
&= \frac{a_{-N}}{(z-w)^N} \left(1 + \left[\frac{1}{a_{-N}} \cdot \sum_{k=1}^{\infty} a_{k-N}(z-w)^k \right] \right),
\end{aligned}
$$

where $a_{-N} \neq 0$ by Theorem 12.2.

Choose ϵ small enough such that: (1) $\epsilon^N < |a_{-N}|/2M$, and (2) the absolute value of the amount in square brackets is less than $1/2$ for $|z - w| < \epsilon$. The last is clearly possible because the sum is a slightly modified version of the uniformly convergent power series for the $f_1(z)$ component of $f(z)$. With only a finite number of coefficients of the sum in brackets different than $f_1(z)$, you can apply Theorem 9.1 to see that the sum has the same radius of convergence as $f_1(z)$.

We then have, for all $|z - w| < \epsilon$

$$|f(z)| \geq \frac{|a_{-N}|}{\epsilon^N} \cdot \frac{1}{2} > M, \quad \text{as required.} \qquad \square$$

Using Theorem 12.4, we can *tentatively* give a different definition for a pole.

Definition 12.7

*Let $f(z)$ be analytic in a punctured disk $\mathbf{D}_r^{\odot}(w)$. The point w is called a **pole** of $f(z)$ if and only if $\lim_{z \to w} |f(z)| = \infty$.*

This alternative definition first requires us to show (as we do below) that the same limit does not apply to an essential singularity.

12.2.3 Essential Singularities

By Definition 12.5, an isolated singularity is an essential singularity if it is neither a removable singularity nor a pole. Returning to our function $f(z)$, analytic in a punctured disk $\mathbf{D}_r^{\odot}(w)$, consider the component parts of the Laurent series for $f(z)$ as shown in equation (12.1).

We have shown that if $a_n = 0$ for all coefficients of $f_2(z)$, then the isolated singularity is a removable singularity, and if $a_n \neq 0$ for only a finite number of the coefficients of $f_2(z)$, then the isolated singularity is a pole. Therefore, an essential singularity must have $a_n \neq 0$ for an infinite number of the coefficients of $f_2(z)$.

Now consider $\lim_{z \to w} f(z)$. For a removable singularity, we have $f(z) = f_1(z)$, which is an ordinary power series, so that $\lim_{z \to w} f(z) = a_0$. For a pole, we showed in Theorem 12.4 that $\lim_{z \to w} |f(z)| = \infty$. We promised above we would show $\lim_{z \to w} |f(z)| \neq \infty$ for $f(z)$ at an essential singularity. We prove that in the following theorem. We will show for an essential singularity that *no limit of any kind* exists as $z \to w$; in fact, in any neighborhood of w, no matter how small, there is an $f(z)$ that comes arbitrarily close to every complex number.

Theorem 12.5: Casorati-Weierstrass Theorem

Let $f(z)$ be analytic in the punctured disk $\mathbf{D}_r^{\odot}(w)$, with an essential singularity at w. Let c be any arbitrary complex number. And let $\epsilon > 0$ and $\delta > 0$ be any two arbitrarily small real numbers (neither dependent on the other). Then there exists some $z \in \mathbf{D}_\delta(w)$ such that $|f(z) - c| < \epsilon$.

Proof. [39] Assume the theorem is false for a given c and ϵ, so that $|f(z) - c| \geq \epsilon$ for all $z \in \mathbf{D}_\delta(w)$.

Let $g(z) = 1/(f(z) - c)$. Then $g(z)$ is analytic in $\mathbf{D}_\delta^{\odot}(w)$ because $f(z)$ is analytic in $\mathbf{D}_\delta^{\odot}(w)$ and $(f(z) - c) \neq 0$. Also, $|g(z)|$ is bounded in $\mathbf{D}_\delta(w)$ by $1/\epsilon$. By Theorem 12.1, $g(z)$ has a removable singularity at w and is therefore analytic in $\mathbf{D}_\delta(w)$.

Now consider the power series expansion $g(z) = \sum_{n=0}^{\infty} a_n (z-w)^n$. Let the integer N be the index of the first coefficient a_n such that $a_n \neq 0$. Using the same coefficients, let $h(z) = \sum_{n=N}^{\infty} a_n (z - w)^{(n-N)}$. Clearly, $h(z)$ is analytic in $\mathbf{D}_\delta(w)$, with $g(z) = (z - w)^N h(z)$ and $h(w) = a_N \neq 0$.

We have $f(z) - c = 1/g(z) = (z - w)^{-N}/h(z)$. Because $h(w) \neq 0$, we have $1/h(z)$ analytic in a neighborhood of w. Therefore, $f(z)$ either has a removable singularity at w (if $N = 0$) or a pole of order N at w (if $N > 0$). But the theorem assumes an essential singularity at w, so this contradiction proves the theorem. $\qquad \square$

We present next the classic example of an essential singularity. Let $f(z) = e^{1/z}$, so that

$$f(z) = e^{1/z} = \sum_{n=0}^{\infty} \frac{(1/z)^n}{n!} = \sum_{n=0}^{\infty} \frac{z^{-n}}{n!} = 1 + \sum_{n=1}^{\infty} \frac{z^{-n}}{n!}.$$

We have a Laurent series with $a_0 = 1$ and $a_n = 0$ for $n \geq 1$, giving

$$= f_1(z) + f_2(z) = \sum_{n=0}^{0} 1 z^n + \sum_{n=-1}^{-\infty} \frac{1}{|n|!} z^n = 1 + \sum_{n=-1}^{-\infty} \frac{1}{|n|!} z^n.$$

All coefficients of $f_2(z)$ are non-zero, so the isolated singularity at 0 is neither a removable singularity nor a pole. It is therefore an essential singularity.

Now think about the value of $e^{1/z}$ as $z \to 0$. Let $k \in \mathbb{N}$ and define

$$z_+ = \frac{1}{k} \qquad z_- = \frac{1}{-k} \qquad z_i = \frac{i}{k} = \frac{1}{-ik}.$$

In those definitions, as $k \to \infty$, z approaches 0 from the positive real axis, the negative real axis and the positive imaginary axis, respectively. We have

$$\lim_{k \to \infty} e^{1/z_+} = \lim_{k \to \infty} e^k \to \infty$$

$$\lim_{k \to \infty} e^{1/z_-} = \lim_{k \to \infty} e^{-k} \to 0$$

$$\lim_{k \to \infty} e^{1/z_i} = \lim_{k \to \infty} e^{-ik} \quad \text{(oscillates, but bounded).}$$

12.3 Analytic Functions at Infinity

It has been convenient to wait until now to discuss the behavior of analytic functions at infinity. We first needed the results from the above classification of isolated singularities.

In what follows[40], we assume that $f(z)$ is analytic in an annular region, with: (1) the negative terms of the Laurent series analytic in $|z| > R$, and (2) the positive terms of the Laurent series analytic in all of $\mathbb{C}$. If necessary, we make a change of variable so that the Laurent series is centered at the origin. Starting with our usual $f(z) = f_1(z) + f_2(z)$ approach, we separate out the a_0 term and use different variables for the positive and negative coefficients, giving

$$f(z) = f_1(z) + f_2(z) = \sum_{n=1}^{\infty} a_n z^n + a_0 + \sum_{n=-1}^{-\infty} b_n z^n. \tag{12.2}$$

By assumption, $f_1(z)$ is entire and $f_2(z)$ is analytic in $|z| > R$. Informally, you might think of $f(z)$ as being analytic in the punctured neighborhood of the "point at infinity" (see Section 1.10 for a discussion of the extended complex plane). Our goal here is to better understand the behavior of $f(z)$ at the point at infinity.

Let $w = z^{-1}$ and define $g(w) = f(w^{-1}) = f(z)$, so that

$$g(w) = \sum_{n=1}^{\infty} a_n w^{-n} + a_0 + \sum_{n=-1}^{-\infty} b_n w^{-n}$$

$$= \sum_{n=1}^{\infty} b_{-n} w^n + a_0 + \sum_{n=-1}^{-\infty} a_{-n} w^n. \tag{12.3}$$

Now consider equation (12.3), which is a standard Laurent series for $g(w)$. The behavior of $f(z)$ at the point at infinity is determined by the behavior of $f(w^{-1}) = g(w)$ at $w = 0$. The first sum converges for $|1/w| > R$ and thus for $|w| < 1/R$. We look to the second sum to understand the singularity of $g(w)$ at $w = 0$. We can conclude:

- $f(z)$ has an essential singularity at ∞ if an infinite number of a_n coefficients are non-zero;
- $f(z)$ has a pole of order N at ∞ if $a_N \neq 0$ for some $N \geq 1$ and $a_n = 0$ for $n > N$;
- $f(z)$ is analytic at ∞ if all $a_n = 0$ for $n \geq 1$, in which case a_0 is taken as the value of $f(z)$ at ∞.

Returning now to equation (12.2), we can summarize the results just above by concluding that the behavior of $f(z)$ at the point at infinity is based on the *positive coefficients* of the Laurent series for $f(z)$. For example:

- Every rational function with the degree of the denominator greater than or equal to the degree of the numerator is analytic at ∞.
- Every rational function with the degree of the denominator less than the degree of the numerator has a pole at ∞.
- Every entire transcendental function (such as e^z, $\sin z$ and $\cos z$) has an essential singularity at ∞.

12.4   Supplemental Material

12.4.1   Exercises

Exercises 12.1

Locate all isolated singularities of the listed functions and indicate the type (removable, pole or essential). If a pole, state the order of the pole.

(a) $\mathrm{Log}\left(1 - \dfrac{1}{z}\right)$,

(b) $\tan z$,

(c) $\dfrac{(z - 2)}{(z^2 - 1)^2}$,

(d) $z^N \sin\left(\dfrac{1}{z}\right)$ for any fixed $N \in \mathbb{N}$,

(e) $\dfrac{z}{e^z - 1}$.

Remark

Answers to exercises are in Appendix A.

Chapter 13

The Residue Calculus

The Residue Theorem can be thought of as an extension of Cauchy's Integral Theorem. Given a domain Ω, a closed contour $\gamma \subset \Omega$ and a function $f(z)$ analytic in Ω, Cauchy's Integral Theorem tells us that $\int_\gamma f(z)\,dz = 0$. What if $f(z)$ has a finite number of isolated singularities in Ω? In that case, the Residue Theorem provides a formula for the value of $\int_\gamma f(z)\,dz$.

In most cases, γ will be a positively oriented simple closed contour. Based on that simplifying assumption, we will develop our first version of the Residue Theorem. Then, we will consider the more general case, where γ is not assumed to be simple. The general case requires a concept we have not previously considered, the *winding number*.

In this chapter, we begin with a discussion of winding numbers and then move to the simpler case of the Residue Theorem. After that, we present the general case. Finally, we give several examples that show the usefulness of the Residue Theorem.

13.1　Winding Number

Assume a closed contour γ and a point $w \notin \gamma$. In this section, we are interested in determining how many times γ winds around w.

We start with the simplest case. Consider the integral

$$\int_C \frac{1}{z-w}\,dz,$$

where the contour C traverses n times around a circle centered at w of radius R. We parameterize our contour by $\phi(t) = w + Re^{int}$ for $0 \le t \le 2\pi$, $R > 0$ and $n \in \mathbb{Z}$. A positive value of n means a traversal in the positive direction, while a negative value means a traversal in the negative direction. We have

$$\int_C \frac{1}{z-w}\,dz = \int_0^{2\pi} \frac{\phi'(t)}{(w+Re^{int})-w}\,dt = \int_0^{2\pi} \frac{inRe^{int}}{Re^{int}}\,dt = in\int_0^{2\pi} dt = 2\pi in. \tag{13.1}$$

Dividing the result by $2\pi i$, the number n gives you the number of times the contour winds around w in the positive or negative direction. This motivates the following definition.

> **Definition 13.1**
> *For the closed contour γ and the point $w \notin \gamma$, the following expression*
>
> $$\mathbf{W}(\gamma, w) = \frac{1}{2\pi i} \int_\gamma \frac{1}{z-w}\,dz \tag{13.2}$$
>
> *is called the **winding number** of γ around w.*

We have shown above that equation (13.2) provides the expected result when a contour traverses a circle centered at w. It remains to justify the result for the general closed contour. We first discuss a topological matter.

Let γ be a closed contour, so that γ is closed and bounded. Now let $\Gamma = \mathbb{C} \backslash \gamma$. Then Γ is open and consists of two or more disjoint open domains, $\Gamma = \Gamma_1 \cup \Gamma_2 \cup \ldots \cup \Gamma_m$, which we will call the connected components of the complement of γ. All but one of the connected components are bounded, and together make up the interior of γ. Exactly one of the connected components is unbounded and makes up the exterior of γ.

We can now establish some important facts regarding $\mathbf{W}(\gamma, w)$.

Lemma 13.1

Let γ be a closed contour and assume the point $w \notin \gamma$.

    (a) The winding number $\mathbf{W}(\gamma, w)$ is an integer.

    (b) If w_1 and w_2 belong to the same connected component of the complement of γ, then $\mathbf{W}(\gamma, w_1) = \mathbf{W}(\gamma, w_2)$.

    (c) If w is in the exterior of γ, then $\mathbf{W}(\gamma, w) = 0$.

Proof (a). For the reasons explained in footnote 21 of Theorem 7.4, we may assume that γ is a smooth path. Let γ be parameterized by $\omega(t) : 0 \le t \le 1$, and define

$$g(t) = \int_0^t \frac{\omega'(s)}{\omega(s) - w} \, ds,$$

so that $g(0) = 0$ and

$$g'(t) = \frac{\omega'(t)}{\omega(t) - w} \qquad 0 \le t \le 1.$$

As seen in the next equation, our goal is to evaluate $g(1)$, because

$$g(1) = \int_0^1 \frac{\omega'(s)}{\omega(s) - w} \, ds = \int_\gamma \frac{1}{z - w} \, dz = 2\pi i \, \mathbf{W}(\gamma, w), \tag{13.3}$$

where we have applied equation (5.1) and Definition 13.1. Next, consider

$$\frac{d}{dt} \left(e^{-g(t)} (\omega(t) - w) \right) = e^{-g(t)} \omega'(t) - g'(t) e^{-g(t)} (\omega(t) - w)$$

$$= e^{-g(t)} \left[\omega'(t) - \frac{\omega'(t)}{(\omega(t) - w)} (\omega(t) - w) \right]$$

$$= 0,$$

which means $e^{-g(t)} (\omega(t) - w)$ is a constant. Putting all of the above together

$$e^{-g(t)} (\omega(t) - w) = e^{-g(0)} (\omega(0) - w) = 1 \cdot (\omega(0) - w) = e^{-g(1)} (\omega(1) - w).$$

But $\omega(0) = \omega(1)$ (because γ is closed) and thus $e^{-g(1)} = 1$, which is only possible if $g(1) = 2\pi i n$ for some integer n. Returning to equation (13.3), we see that $\mathbf{W}(\gamma, w)$ must be an integer, as required. $\quad\square$

Proof (b). Call our connected component Γ_j. For $z \in \Gamma_j$, we have $z \notin \gamma$ and $\mathbf{W}(\gamma, z)$ is a continuous function of z. But from (a) we have that $\mathbf{W}(\gamma, z)$ is an integer and therefore must be constant. It follows that $\mathbf{W}(\gamma, w_1) = \mathbf{W}(\gamma, w_2)$. $\qquad\square$

Proof (c). Checking the formula for $\mathbf{W}(\gamma, w)$, it is immediately clear that $\lim\limits_{|w|\to\infty} \mathbf{W}(\gamma, w) = 0$. From (b), it follows that $\mathbf{W}(\gamma, w) = 0$ for all w in the exterior of γ. $\qquad\square$

Remark

We still need to show that the winding number $\mathbf{W}(\gamma, w)$ gives the expected results for the general closed contour. One highly technical approach is to show that any such closed contour can be continuously deformed into a "circle contour", like above, that traverses the circle the expected number of times. Such a proof can be found in other textbooks[41], but is beyond the scope of this book. Our approach will be a bit more informal.

Theorem 13.1

Let γ be a closed contour and assume the point $w \notin \gamma$. Then, the winding number $\mathbf{W}(\gamma, w)$ calculates the number of times γ winds around w. That number is positive if γ winds around w in the positive direction and negative if γ winds around w in the negative direction. Note that $\mathbf{W}(\gamma, w)$ computes a net amount after taking into account both positive and negative traversals.

Proof. We develop this proof in several steps.

Step 1: Assume $w = 0$. By making a change of variable in equation (13.2), we can reduce the formula in Definition 13.1 to the case $\mathbf{W}(\gamma, 0)$ (i.e., $w = 0$). We will use that simplification in what follows.

Step 2: Polygon. Assume our contour γ is parameterized by $\omega(t) : 0 \le t \le 1$. We subdivide the interval $[0, 1]$ into n equal-width subintervals $0 = x_0 < x_1 < x_2 < ... < x_n = 1$, so that $\omega(x_0) = z_0, \omega(x_1) = z_1, \cdots, \omega(x_n) = z_n$ are $n + 1$ oriented points along the contour γ. Connecting those points by straight line segments creates an n-sided polygon we will call P_n. As n increases, P_n becomes a closer and closer fit to γ. As we showed in Theorem 7.4, for large enough n, the integral over P_n can be made arbitrarily close in value to the integral over γ. Thus, for n sufficiently large, it suffices to consider our contour γ to be the polygon P_n.

Step 3: Quadrants. Ordinarily, the fours quadrants of $\mathbb{C}$ are open sets that exclude the real and imaginary axis. For reasons that will become clearer below, here we define the second quadrant to *include* the negative real axis, $Re(z) < 0, Im(z) \ge 0$, and the third quadrant to *exclude* the negative real axis, $Re(z) < 0, Im(z) < 0$.

Step 4: Polygonal Sides. Let $\delta = \min(|z| : z \in \gamma)$, so that $\gamma \cap \mathbf{D}_\delta(0) = \emptyset$. Choose N large enough so that, for $n > N$, all polygonal sides of P_n have length less than δ. Simple trigonometry tells us that no such polygonal side of P_n can reside in more than two quadrants. In particular, the only polygonal sides of P_n that can cross over the negative real axis are sides that begin in the second quadrant and end in the third quadrant, or begin in the third quadrant and end in the second.

Step 5: The Integral. For our winding number integral, using $w = 0$ and P_n in place of γ, we therefore have

$$\int_{P_n} \frac{1}{z} dz = \sum_{n=1}^{n} \int_{z_{n-1}}^{z_n} \frac{1}{z} dz$$

$$= \sum_{n=1}^{n} \big[\log |z_n| + i \arg(z_n) \big] - \big[\log |z_{n-1}| + i \arg(z_{n-1}) \big]$$

The log terms telescope to 0 because $\log |z_0| = \log |z_n|$, giving

$$= i \sum_{n=1}^{n} \arg(z_n) - \arg(z_{n-1}).$$

Apparently, our integral resolves to the total change in the argument of each polygon side as we traverse P_n. This is very promising because we would expect a 2π change in the argument for each time the contour winds around 0, which is our desired result.

Unfortunately, it is not quite that easy. We have the little matter of $\arg(z)$ being multi-valued. And if we stay with the principal branch, $\text{Arg}(z)$, there is a 2π jump discontinuity as we cross the negative real axis. We solve this problem by using a "continuous argument function".

Step 6: Continuous Argument Function. We will denote the kth branch of the argument function by $\arg_k(z) \in (2\pi k - \pi, 2\pi k + \pi]$, so that the principal branch $\text{Arg}(z) = \arg_0(z)$.

To make our special version of the argument function continuous along our traversal of P_n, we begin at z_0 with the principal branch $\arg_0(z_0) = \text{Arg}(z_0)$. Each time a polygonal side crosses the negative real axis, we adjust the branch as follows.

Assume the current branch is $\arg_k(z)$. If during our traversal of a polygonal side there is a positive crossing of the negative real axis (from the second quadrant to the third), then when our traversal crosses into the third quadrant we increase the branch of the argument function by one to $\arg_{k+1}(z)$. Similarly, when there is a negative crossing of the negative real axis (from the third quadrant to the second), we decrease the branch of the argument function by one to $\arg_{k-1}(z)$. This ensures that our special version of the argument function is continuous at all points along the traversal of P_n.

At the end of our traversal of P_n at z_n, we will have $\arg_k(z_n)$ for some $k \in \mathbb{Z}$. It is not difficult to see that the resulting k will tell us precisely the number of times P_n has wound around the origin. The traversal was in the positive direction for k positive and in the negative direction for k negative. Hence, noting that $\omega(0) = z_0 = z_n = \omega(1)$, we have $i \big[\arg_k(z_0) - \arg_0(z_0) \big] = 2\pi i k$, giving our desired result:

$$\mathbf{W}(\gamma, 0) = \frac{1}{2\pi i} \int_\gamma \frac{1}{z - 0} dz = \lim_{n \to \infty} \frac{1}{2\pi i} \int_{P_n} \frac{1}{z} dz = \frac{1}{2\pi i} \cdot i \big[\arg_k(z_0) - \arg_0(z_0) \big] = k. \qquad \square$$

13.2   The Residue Theorem - Simple Closed Contour

Let $f(z)$ be analytic in a punctured disk $\mathbf{D}_r^{\odot}(w)$, with an isolated singularity at w. Let $\mathbf{C} \subset \mathbf{D}_r^{\odot}(w)$ be a positively oriented simple closed contour, so that w is in the interior of $\mathbf{C}$. Expand $f(z)$ into its Laurent series for $\mathbf{D}_r^{\odot}(w)$. Now consider equation (11.2) from Theorem 11.1, which we repeat here:

$$a_n = \frac{1}{2\pi i} \int_{\mathbf{C}} \frac{f(z)}{(z - w)^{n+1}} dz \quad \text{for } n < 0.$$

Setting $n = -1$, we have

$$a_{-1} = \frac{1}{2\pi i} \int_C f(z) \, dz.$$

This makes sense when you consider that every term of a Laurent series (except the $n = -1$ term) has a primitive. Thus, the integral over C for all terms except $n = -1$ resolves to zero by application of Theorem 5.4 (because the punctured disk is a region). For the $n = -1$ term, we have

$$\frac{1}{2\pi i} \int_C a_{-1} (z - w)^{-1} \, dz = \frac{a_{-1}}{2\pi i} \int_C \frac{1}{(z - w)} \, dz = \frac{a_{-1}}{2\pi i} \cdot 2\pi i = a_{-1}.$$

The coefficient a_{-1} of the Laurent series is called the *residue* of $f(z)$ at w. We formalize this result in the following definition.

Definition 13.2

Let $f(z)$ be analytic in the punctured disk $\mathbf{D}_R^{\odot}(w)$, with an isolated singularity at w, let $C \subset \mathbf{D}_R^{\odot}(w)$ be any positively oriented simple closed contour, and let $f(z)$ be given by the following Laurent series expansion in $\mathbf{D}_R^{\odot}(w)$

$$\sum_{n=-\infty}^{\infty} a_n (z - w)^n.$$

*Then, the **residue** of $f(z)$ at w is the coefficient a_{-1} of the Laurent series, denoted by*

$$\mathbf{Res}\,(f(z), w) = a_{-1} = \frac{1}{2\pi i} \int_C f(z) \, dz.$$

Remark

With the above definition, we are now in a position to state our first version of the Residue Theorem. In this version, we assume that C is a positively oriented simple closed contour.

Theorem 13.2: Residue Theorem (First Version)

Let Ω be a domain and let $\mathcal{A} = \{w_1, w_2, \cdots w_n\}$ be a finite set of points with $\mathcal{A} \subset \Omega$. Let $f(z)$ be analytic in $\Omega \setminus \mathcal{A}$, with the points in $\mathcal{A}$ being isolated singularities of $f(z)$.

Let $C \subset \Omega$ be a positively oriented simple closed contour, let C° be the interior of C, and assume $\mathcal{A} \subset C^{\circ}$. For all $w_k \in \mathcal{A}$ and their open disks $\mathbf{D}_r(w_k)$, choose r small enough such that $\mathbf{D}_r(w_k) \subset C^{\circ}$, $\mathbf{D}_r(w_k) \cap C = \emptyset$ and $\mathbf{D}_r(w_1) \cap \mathbf{D}_r(w_2) \cap \cdots \cap \mathbf{D}_r(w_n) = \emptyset$. Then

$$\int_C f(z) \, dz = \sum_{k=1}^{n} \int_{C_k} f(z) \, dz = 2\pi i \sum_{k=1}^{n} \mathbf{Res}\,(f(z), w_k),$$

where $C_k \subset \mathbf{D}_r^{\odot}(w_k)$ is any positively oriented simple closed contour.

Proof. The result is immediate by applying Theorem 7.6 and Definition 13.2. □

13.3   The Residue Theorem - Any Closed Contour

With our first version of the Residue Theorem as a warm-up, we can now move to the general case. We start with a lemma that will make our final Residue Theorem proof easier to follow.

Lemma 13.2

Let Ω be a domain with $w \in \Omega$, and let $f(z)$ be analytic in $\Omega \backslash w$. Choose r small enough so that $\mathbf{D}_r(w) \subset \Omega$. Now let

$$f(z) = \sum_{n=-\infty}^{\infty} a_n (z-w)^n \qquad \text{and} \qquad h(z) = \sum_{n=-1}^{-\infty} a_n (z-w)^n.$$

where on the left we have the Laurent series expansion of $f(z)$ at $\mathbf{D}_r^{\odot}(w)$, and on the right we have the principal part of that Laurent series expansion.
   Then, $g(z) = f(z) - h(z)$ is analytic in Ω.

Proof. As defined, $h(z)$ is analytic in $\mathbb{C} \backslash w$, so that $g(z)$ is analytic in $\Omega \backslash w$. It remains only to show that w is a removable singularity of $g(z)$. Using Theorem 12.1(d), we only need to note that

$$\lim_{z \to w} (z-w)g(z) = \lim_{z \to w} (z-w) \sum_{n=0}^{\infty} a_n (z-w)^n = 0.$$ $\square$

Theorem 13.3: Residue Theorem (Final Version)

Let Ω be a domain and let $\mathcal{A} = \{w_1, w_2, \cdots w_n\}$ be a finite set of points with $\mathcal{A} \subset \Omega$. Let $f(z)$ be analytic in $\Omega \backslash \mathcal{A}$, with the points in $\mathcal{A}$ being isolated singularities of $f(z)$. Finally, let $\mathbf{C} \subset \Omega$ be a closed contour. Then

$$\int_{\mathbf{C}} f(z)\,dz = 2\pi i \sum_{k=1}^{n} \left[\mathbf{Res}\left(f(z), w_k \right) \cdot \mathbf{W}(\mathbf{C}, w_k) \right].$$

Proof. For all $w_k \in \mathcal{A}$ and their open disks $\mathbf{D}_r(w_k)$, choose r small enough such that $\mathbf{D}_r(w_k) \subset \Omega$, $\mathbf{D}_r(w_k) \cap \mathbf{C} = \emptyset$ and $\mathbf{D}_r(w_1) \cap \mathbf{D}_r(w_2) \cap \cdots \cap \mathbf{D}_r(w_n) = \emptyset$.

Following the approach in Lemma 13.2, for each w_k define $h_k(z) = \sum_{n=-1}^{-\infty} a_n^{(k)} (z-w)^n$ to be the principal part of the Laurent series expansion of $f(z)$ at $\mathbf{D}_r^{\odot}(w_k)$.

Now define $g(z) = f(z) - \sum_{k=1}^{n} h_k(z)$. By Lemma 13.2, $g(z)$ is analytic in Ω. We therefore have

$$0 = \int_{\mathbf{C}} g(z)\,dz = \int_{\mathbf{C}} \left[f(z) - \sum_{k=1}^{n} h_k(z) \right] dz$$

$$= \int_{\mathbf{C}} f(z)\,dz - \sum_{k=1}^{n} \int_{\mathbf{C}} h_k(z)\,dz$$

$$= \int_{\mathbf{C}} f(z)\,dz - \sum_{k=1}^{n} \int_{\mathbf{C}} \sum_{n=-1}^{-\infty} a_n^{(k)} (z-w)^n\,dz$$

$$= \int_{\mathbf{C}} f(z)\,dz - \sum_{k=1}^{n} \sum_{n=-1}^{-\infty} a_n^{(k)} \int_{\mathbf{C}} (z-w)^n\,dz.$$

The right integral evaluates to zero for all n except $n = -1$, so that

$$0 = \int_{\mathbf{C}} f(z)\,dz - \sum_{k=1}^{n} a_{-1}^{(k)} \int_{\mathbf{C}} \frac{1}{z-w}\,dz.$$

But $a_{-1}^{(k)}$ is just $\mathbf{Res}\,(f(z), w_k)$ and the right integral is just $[2\pi i \cdot \mathbf{W}(\mathbf{C}, w_k)]$. Thus,

$$\int_{\mathbf{C}} f(z)\,dz = 2\pi i \sum_{k=1}^{n} \left[\mathbf{Res}\,(f(z), w_k) \cdot \mathbf{W}(\mathbf{C}, w_k)\right].$$ $\square$

Remark

Of course, one or more of the isolated singularities in Theorem 13.3 may be in the exterior of $\mathbf{C}$, in which case its winding number will be zero and will not contribute to the value of the integral.

Why can we assume there are only finitely many isolated singularities? By assumption, our closed contour is of finite length and our domain is simply connected. Because $D = \mathbf{C} \cup \mathbf{C}^\circ$ is compact, we can apply the logic of Exercise 10.1(a) to see that D can have only a finite number of isolated singularities.

Note that we did not assume that $\mathbf{C}$ was positively oriented (or simple). In this final version of the Residue Theorem, the winding number $\mathbf{W}(\mathbf{C}, w_k)$ makes the necessary adjustments for both orientation and for non-simple closed contours.

13.4   Calculating Residues

In this section, we consider five common cases and demonstrate how to calculate residues.

Lemma 13.3: Simple Pole

Assume the conditions of Definition 13.2 and assume that $f(z)$ has a simple pole at w. Then

$$\mathbf{Res}\,(f(z), w) = \lim_{z \to w}(z-w)f(z).$$

Proof. Let $g(z) = (z-w)f(z)$. By Theorem 12.2, $g(z)$ is analytic in $\mathbf{D}_R^\odot(w)$. Let $\sum_{n=0}^{\infty} b_n(z-w)^n$ be the power series expansion for $g(z)$, so that the b_0 coefficient in the power series is equal to the a_{-1} coefficient in the Laurent series for $f(z)$. Thus,

$$\lim_{z \to w}(z-w)f(z) = \lim_{z \to w} g(z) = b_0 = a_{-1} = \mathbf{Res}\,(f(z), w).$$ $\square$

Remark

The above method of calculating residues at simple poles is used constantly and important to remember.

Lemma 13.4: Double Pole

Assume the conditions of Definition 13.2 and assume that $f(z)$ has a pole of order 2 at w. Then

$$\textbf{Res}\,(f(z), w) = \lim_{z \to w} \frac{d}{dz}\left[(z-w)^2 f(z)\right].$$

Proof. Let $g(z) = (z-w)^2 f(z)$. By Theorem 12.2, $g(z)$ is analytic in $\mathbf{D}_R^{\ominus}(w)$. Let $\sum_{n=0}^{\infty} b_n (z-w)^n$ be the power series expansion for $g(z)$, so that the b_1 coefficient in the power series is equal to the a_{-1} coefficient in the Laurent series for $f(z)$. Thus,

$$g(z) = b_0(z-w)^0 + b_1(z-w)^1 + \sum_{n=2}^{\infty} b_n(z-w)^n$$

$$= a_{-2}(z-w)^0 + a_{-1}(z-w)^1 + \sum_{n=2}^{\infty} b_n(z-w)^n$$

$$g'(z) = 0 + a_{-1} + \sum_{n=2}^{\infty} n \cdot b_n \cdot (z-w)^{n-1}$$

$$\lim_{z \to w} g'(z) = 0 + a_{-1} + 0 = a_{-1}.$$

Therefore

$$\lim_{z \to w} \frac{d}{dz}\left[(z-w)^2 f(z)\right] = \lim_{z \to w} g'(z) = b_1 = a_{-1} = \textbf{Res}\,(f(z), w). \qquad \square$$

Remark

In the next lemma, we generalize the above approach for a pole of order n.

Lemma 13.5: Pole of Order N

Assume the conditions of Definition 13.2 and assume that $f(z)$ has a pole of order N at w. Then

$$\textbf{Res}\,(f(z), w) = \lim_{z \to w} \frac{1}{(N-1)!}\left(\frac{d}{dz}\right)^{N-1}\left[(z-w)^N f(z)\right].$$

Proof. Let $g(z) = (z-w)^N f(z)$. By Theorem 12.2, $g(z)$ is analytic in $\mathbf{D}_R^{\ominus}(w)$. Let $\sum_{n=0}^{\infty} b_n(z-w)^n$ be the power series expansion for $g(z)$, so that the b_{N-1} coefficient in the power series is equal to the a_{-1} coefficient in the Laurent series for $f(z)$.

We can then read off the formula for b_{N-1} from Theorem 9.4, noting that, in the power series for $g(z)$: (1) the derivative $g^{(N-1)}(z)$ zeros out all of the terms with $n < (N-1)$, and (2) setting $z = w$ zeros out all of the terms with $n > (N-1)$. $\qquad \square$

Lemma 13.6: Simple Zero in Denominator (Case 1)

Let $f(z)$ and $g(z)$ be analytic in $\mathbf{D}_R(w)$ and let $g(z)$ have a simple zero at w. Then

$$\textbf{Res}\left[\frac{f(z)}{g(z)}, w\right] = \frac{f(w)}{g'(w)}.$$

Proof. First assume the zero of $g(z)$ at w is not removed by $f(z)$, so that f/g has a simple pole at w. Then, by Lemma 13.3, we have

$$\mathbf{Res}\left[\frac{f(z)}{g(z)}, w\right] = \lim_{z \to w}(z-w)\frac{f(z)}{g(z)} = \lim_{z \to w}\frac{f(z)}{\frac{(g(z)-0)}{(z-w)}} = \lim_{z \to w}\frac{f(z)}{\frac{(g(z)-g(w))}{(z-w)}} = \frac{f(w)}{g'(w)}.$$

Now assume the zero of $g(z)$ at w is removed by $f(z)$, so that $f(z)$ has a zero at w of at least order one. Then f/g is analytic in the disk with a residue of 0. Because $g(z)$ has a simple zero at w, we know $g'(w) \neq 0$ by application of Theorems 10.1 and 9.2. That means $f(w)/g'(w) = 0$ and the above formula for the residue still applies. $\square$

Lemma 13.7: Simple Zero in Denominator (Case 2)

Let $g(z)$ be analytic in $\mathbf{D}_R(w)$, with a simple zero at w. Then

$$\mathbf{Res}\left[\frac{1}{g(z)}, w\right] = \frac{1}{g'(w)}.$$

Proof. Using Lemma 13.6, set $f(z) = 1$ and the result is immediate. $\square$

13.5 Using Residues to Evaluate Real Integrals

One of the early goals of complex function theory was to develop new methods of evaluating definite real integrals that have no known primitive. In many cases, the Residue Theorem is well-suited to that task.

We will demonstrate a typical approach: (1) restate the integrand as a complex-valued function, (2) carefully select a simple closed contour $\boldsymbol{C}$ by combining the desired part of the real axis $\boldsymbol{L}$ plus a connected contour $\boldsymbol{\gamma}$ (usually a semicircle or three sides of a rectangle) in the upper or lower half plane, (3) use the Residue Theorem to compute the complex integral over the closed contour $\boldsymbol{C}$, (4) compute the value of the complex integral over the (open) contour $\boldsymbol{\gamma}$ (it often evaluates to zero), and (5) what remains is the computed value of the real integral over $\boldsymbol{L}$.

We begin with a discussion of the *Cauchy principal value* of an integral. That special form of integral is often needed when using the Residue Theorem to calculate a real integral.

13.5.1 Cauchy Principal Value

Suppose the real variable function $f(x)$ is continuous in $\mathbb{R}$. The improper integral of $f(x)$ over the interval $(-\infty, \infty)$ is defined as

$$\int_{-\infty}^{\infty} f(x)\, dx = \lim_{R_1 \to \infty}\int_{-R_1}^{0} f(x)\, dx + \lim_{R_2 \to \infty}\int_{0}^{R_2} f(x)\, dx.$$

If both limits exist, the integral is said to converge to the sum of those limits. If *either* of the limits diverges, then the full integral diverges.

A different approach is to obtain the *Cauchy principal value* of the integral (denoted P.V.), as follows

$$P.V. \int_{-\infty}^{\infty} f(x)\, dx = \lim_{R \to \infty}\int_{-R}^{R} f(x)\, dx.$$

Clearly, if the integral converges under the normal rules of evaluation, then the Cauchy principal value exists and converges to the same value. However, as shown in the following example, the Cauchy principal value may exist even where the integral (under normal rules) diverges.

$$P.V. \int_{-\infty}^{\infty} x\,dx = \lim_{R\to\infty} \int_{-R}^{R} x\,dx = \lim_{R\to\infty} \left[R^2/2 - (-R^2)/2 \right] = 0$$

$$\int_{-\infty}^{\infty} x\,dx = \lim_{R_1\to\infty} \int_{-R_1}^{0} x\,dx + \lim_{R_2\to\infty} \int_{0}^{R_2} x\,dx = -\infty + \infty.$$

In effect, the difference is the order of summation. In the P.V. case, we are pairing positive and negative values of x *before* taking them to the limit. This seems like a satisfactory result, because it obtains a value that is consistent with our expectation regarding the total (net) area under the curve when we graph the function $f(x) = x$. However, it is *not* right to say that one result is "correct" and the other is incorrect. For that reason, you should always indicate by P.V. that you are using the Cauchy principal value.

The Cauchy principal value is not just used for limits at infinity. Suppose that $f(x)$ is continuous in $\mathbb{R} \backslash x_1$. Then the Cauchy principal value is defined as

$$P.V. \int_{-\infty}^{\infty} f(x)\,dx = \lim_{\substack{R\to\infty \\ \epsilon\to 0}} \left[\int_{-R}^{x_1-\epsilon} f(x)\,dx + \int_{x_1+\epsilon}^{R} f(x)\,dx \right]$$

or, equally, for $a < x_1 < b$

$$P.V. \int_{a}^{b} f(x)\,dx = \lim_{\epsilon\to 0} \left[\int_{a}^{x_1-\epsilon} f(x)\,dx + \int_{x_1+\epsilon}^{b} f(x)\,dx \right].$$

For example, without using the Cauchy principal value, we have

$$\int_{-1}^{1} \frac{1}{x}\,dx = \left[\lim_{\epsilon\to 0} \int_{-1}^{-\epsilon} \frac{1}{x}\,dx \right] + \left[\lim_{\epsilon\to 0} \int_{\epsilon}^{1} \frac{1}{x}\,dx \right]$$

$$= \left[\lim_{\epsilon\to 0} \int_{1}^{\epsilon} \frac{1}{u}\,du \right] + \left[\lim_{\epsilon\to 0} \int_{\epsilon}^{1} \frac{1}{x}\,dx \right] \qquad \text{we use } -u = x, -du = dx$$

$$= \left[\lim_{\epsilon\to 0} (\log \epsilon - \log 1) \right] + \left[\lim_{\epsilon\to 0} (\log 1 - \log \epsilon) \right],$$

where each side diverges.

If we use the Cauchy principal value and thus combine the integral values before taking the limit

$$P.V. \int_{-1}^{1} \frac{1}{x}\,dx = \lim_{\epsilon\to 0} \left[\int_{-1}^{-\epsilon} \frac{1}{x}\,dx + \int_{\epsilon}^{1} \frac{1}{x}\,dx \right]$$

$$= \lim_{\epsilon\to 0} \left[(\log \epsilon - \log 1) + (\log 1 - \log \epsilon) \right]$$

$$= 0.$$

> **Remark**
>
> Recall that in real variable calculus, an *even function* is one where $f(x) = f(-x)$. Now consider the real integral $\int_{-\infty}^{\infty} f(x)\,dx$. If $f(x)$ is an even function, there can be no need for the Cauchy principal value because there is no need to pair positive and negative terms to obtain convergence. Similar reasoning applies to non-negative functions.

13.5.2 A Bounding Condition Allowing Use of the Residue Theorem

Given a real integral $\int_{-\infty}^{\infty} f(x)\,dx$, the next theorem shows a bounding condition for the complex function $f(z)$ which allows us to use the Residue Theorem (combined with a semicircle in the upper half complex plane) to compute the real integral.

Theorem 13.4

Let $\mathbb{H}$ be the open upper half plane ($Im(z) > 0$) and let $\overline{\mathbb{H}}$ be the closed upper half plane ($Im(z) \geq 0$). Let Ω be a domain with $\overline{\mathbb{H}} \subset \Omega$. Let $\mathcal{A} = z_1, z_2, \cdots z_n$ be a finite set of isolated points, with $\mathcal{A} \subset \mathbb{H}$ and $R > \max(|z_1|, |z_2|, \cdots |z_n|)$. Let $f(z)$ be analytic in $\Omega \setminus \mathcal{A}$.

Let $\cap_R \subset \overline{\mathbb{H}}$ be a semicircle parameterized by $\omega(t) = Re^{it}, 0 \leq t \leq \pi$ and let L_R be a line segment on the real axis parameterized by $\omega(t) = t, -R < t < R$.

Define $\boldsymbol{C}_R = \cap_R + L_R$, so that $\boldsymbol{C}_R$ is a positively oriented simple closed contour with $\mathcal{A}$ in its interior. Assume there is a $\sigma > 1$ and an $M > 0$ such that, for sufficiently large $|z|$

$$|f(z)| < \frac{M}{|z|^\sigma}.$$

Then

$$\lim_{R \to \infty} \int_{\cap_R} f(z)\,dz = 0 \quad \text{and} \quad P.V. \int_{-\infty}^{\infty} f(x)\,dx = 2\pi i \sum_{k=1}^{n} \mathbf{Res}\,(f(z), z_k).$$

Proof. For $\cap_R$ we have for sufficiently large $|z|$

$$\left| \int_{\cap_R} f(z)\,dz \right| \leq \int_{\cap_R} |f(z)||\,dz| \leq \int_{\cap_R} \frac{M}{|z|^\sigma} |\,dz| \leq \int_0^\pi \frac{M}{R^\sigma} R\,d\theta = \frac{M\pi}{R^{\sigma-1}}.$$

With $\sigma > 1$, we have shown $\boxed{\lim_{R \to \infty} \int_{\cap_R} f(z)\,dz = 0}$.

Because $\boldsymbol{C}_R = \cap_R + L_R$ is a positively oriented simple closed contour, by the first version of the Residue Theorem (Theorem 13.2), we have

$$\int_{\cap_R} f(z)\,dz + \int_{L_R} f(z)\,dz = 2\pi i \sum_{k=1}^{n} \mathbf{Res}\,(f(z), z_k)$$

$$\lim_{R \to \infty} \int_{\cap_R} f(z)\,dz + \lim_{R \to \infty} \int_{L_R} f(z)\,dz = 2\pi i \sum_{k=1}^{n} \mathbf{Res}\,(f(z), z_k)$$

$$0 + \lim_{R \to \infty} \int_{-R}^{R} f(x)\,dx = \boxed{P.V. \int_{-\infty}^{\infty} f(x)\,dx = 2\pi i \sum_{k=1}^{n} \mathbf{Res}\,(f(z), z_k)}. \qquad \square$$

In our next lemma, we use the bounding condition of Theorem 13.4 to compute a real integral.

Lemma 13.8

$$\int_{-\infty}^{\infty} \frac{1}{(1 + x^2)^2}\,dx = \frac{\pi}{2}.$$

Proof. We begin by setting:

$$f(z) = \frac{1}{(1+z^2)^2} = \frac{1}{(z+i)^2 \cdot (z-i)^2}.$$

We see that $f(z)$ has poles of order 2 at i and $-i$, and no other singularities. Computing the residue of $f(z)$ at i, we apply Lemma 13.4 and have

$$\mathbf{Res}\,(f(z),i) = \lim_{z \to i} \frac{d}{dz}\left[(z-i)^2 f(z)\right] = \lim_{z \to i} \frac{d}{dz}\left[(z+i)^{-2}\right] = \lim_{z \to i} \frac{-2}{(z+i)^3} = \frac{-2}{(2i)^3} = \frac{1}{4i}.$$

Setting $M = 1$ and $\sigma = 4$, $f(z)$ meets the requirements of Theorem 13.4 for all $|z| > 1$. Because i is the only singularity in the upper half plane, we can therefore apply Theorem 13.4 and have

$$P.V. \int_{-\infty}^{\infty} \frac{1}{(1+x^2)^2}\,dx = 2\pi i\,\mathbf{Res}\,(f(z),i) = 2\pi i \cdot \frac{1}{4i} = \frac{\pi}{2}.$$

Note that $f(x)$ is an even function. Thus, our integral converges under normal rules, without need for the Cauchy principal value. $\qquad\square$

13.5.3 A Singularity on the Real Axis

Lemma 13.9

$P.V. \int_{-\infty}^{\infty} \frac{e^{ix}}{x}\,dx = \pi i.$ *From our first result, we also have* $\int_{0}^{\infty} \frac{\sin x}{x}\,dx = \frac{\pi}{2}.$

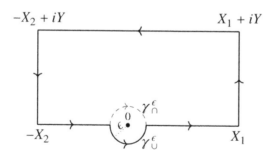

Figure 13.1: Pole on Real Axis

Proof. We will again use the Residue Theorem to help calculate our real integrals. The problem this time is that there is an isolated singularity at 0 on the real axis.

We begin by restating the integrand as a complex-valued function

$$f(z) = \frac{e^{iz}}{z} = \frac{1}{z} + \sum_{n=1}^{\infty} \frac{i^n z^{n-1}}{n!} = \frac{1}{z} + g(z). \tag{13.4}$$

Now see Figure 13.1, where we assume $X_1, X_2, Y > 0$ and $\epsilon > 0$ small. We have a positively oriented rectangle, except near 0 where we avoid the singularity by use of a very small semi-circle γ_U^ϵ

---

in the lower half plane. Call the closed contour $\boldsymbol{C}_\cup$. We also define the closed contour $\boldsymbol{C}_\cap$, which is identical to $\boldsymbol{C}_\cup$ except the semicircle $\gamma_\cap^\epsilon$ about the origin is in the upper half plane.

We see that $f(z)$ has an isolated singularity in the interior of $\boldsymbol{C}_\cup$, whereas $f(z)$ is analytic in and on $\boldsymbol{C}_\cap$. Using the Laurent series shown in (13.4), it is easily seen that

$$\int_{C_\cup} \frac{e^{iz}}{z}\, dz = 2\pi i\, \mathbf{Res}\,(f(z), 0) = 2\pi i \quad \text{and} \quad \int_{C_\cap} \frac{e^{iz}}{z}\, dz = 0.$$

To further evaluate our integrals, we stop to compute the value along each of the three rectangle sides that are not on the real axis. In directional order, beginning with the right vertical side, we will call those sides γ_1, γ_2 and γ_3. Our goal is to show that as $X_1, X_2, Y \to \infty$ the integral over each of the three sides $\to 0$.

Beginning with γ_1, parameterized by $\phi(t) = X_1 + it, 0 \le t \le Y$, we have

$$\left| \int_{\gamma_1} \frac{e^{iz}}{z}\, dz \right| = \left| \int_0^Y \frac{e^{i(\phi(t))}}{\phi(t)} \phi'(t)\, dt \right| = \left| \int_0^Y \frac{e^{iX_1 - t}}{X_1 + it} i\, dt \right| \le \int_0^Y \frac{e^{-t}}{X_1}\, dt \le \frac{1}{X_1},$$

which $\to 0$ as $X_1 \to \infty$. The same reasoning applies to the other vertical side γ_3.

For side γ_2, we parameterize in the reverse direction by $\phi(t) = t + iY, -X_2 \le t \le X_1$, and then adjust the sign of the integral, giving

$$\left| \int_{\gamma_2} \frac{e^{iz}}{z}\, dz \right| = \left| - \int_{-X_2}^{X_1} \frac{e^{i(\phi(t))}}{\phi(t)} \phi'(t)\, dt \right| = \left| \int_{-X_2}^{X_1} \frac{e^{it - Y}}{(t + iY)}\, dt \right| \le \int_{-X_2}^{X_1} \frac{e^{-Y}}{Y}\, dt = \frac{(X_1 + X_2)}{Y e^Y}.$$

For any fixed X_1 and X_2, no matter how large, the integral rapidly $\to 0$ as $Y \to \infty$. Thus, the integral over γ_2 eventually $\to 0$.

Next, we evaluate the integrals over our semicircles $\gamma_\cup^\epsilon$ and $\gamma_\cap^\epsilon$. The function $g(z)$ in equation (13.4) is entire and is bounded in the unit circle by $|g(z)| \le (e - 1)$. Thus, by the ML inequality, the integrals over the $g(z)$ term $\to 0$ as $\epsilon \to 0$. What remains is the known integral over z^{-1}. Because $\gamma_\cup^\epsilon$ runs counterclockwise, $\int_{\gamma_\cup^\epsilon} z^{-1}\, dz = \pi i$. Conversely, because $\gamma_\cap^\epsilon$ runs clockwise, $\int_{\gamma_\cap^\epsilon} z^{-1}\, dz = -\pi i$.

The integrals over γ_1, γ_2 and γ_3 all $\to 0$ for large X_1, X_2 and Y. For any fixed ϵ, we can therefore compute the value of the integral over the real axis (excluding the semicircle), as follows

$$\lim_{X_1, X_2 \to \infty} \left[\int_{-X_2}^{-\epsilon} \frac{e^{it}}{t}\, dt + \int_\epsilon^{X_1} \frac{e^{it}}{t}\, dt \right] = \int_{C_\cup} \frac{e^{iz}}{z}\, dz - \int_{\gamma_\cup^\epsilon} \frac{e^{iz}}{z}\, dz = 2\pi i - \int_{\gamma_\cup^\epsilon} \frac{e^{iz}}{z}\, dz = \pi i$$

$$\lim_{X_1, X_2 \to \infty} \left[\int_{-X_2}^{-\epsilon} \frac{e^{it}}{t}\, dt + \int_\epsilon^{X_1} \frac{e^{it}}{t}\, dt \right] = \int_{C_\cap} \frac{e^{iz}}{z}\, dz - \int_{\gamma_\cap^\epsilon} \frac{e^{iz}}{z}\, dz = 0 - \int_{\gamma_\cap^\epsilon} \frac{e^{iz}}{z}\, dz = \pi i.$$

We are now in a position to use the Cauchy principal value and obtain

$$P.V. \int_{-\infty}^\infty \frac{e^{ix}}{x}\, dx = P.V. \int_{-\infty}^\infty \left(\frac{\cos x}{x} + \frac{i \sin x}{x} \right) dx = \lim_{\substack{X_1, X_2 \to \infty \\ \epsilon \to 0}} \left[\int_{-X_2}^{-\epsilon} \frac{e^{it}}{t}\, dt + \int_\epsilon^{X_1} \frac{e^{it}}{t}\, dt \right] = \pi i.$$

Considering the real and imaginary parts, we have

$$P.V. \int_{-\infty}^\infty \frac{\cos x}{x}\, dx = 0 \quad \text{and} \quad P.V. \int_{-\infty}^\infty \frac{\sin x}{x}\, dx = \pi.$$

Because $\sin x / x$ is an even function, there is no need for the Cauchy principal value. Thus

$$\int_0^\infty \frac{\sin x}{x}\, dx = \frac{1}{2} \int_{-\infty}^\infty \frac{\sin x}{x}\, dx = \frac{\pi}{2}. \qquad \square$$

13.6 Supplemental Material

13.6.1 Exercises

Exercises 13.1

(a) *Using Lemma 13.3, calculate* **Res** $\left(\dfrac{\sin z}{z^2}, 0 \right)$.

(b) *Using Lemma 13.4, calculate* **Res** $\left(\dfrac{\cos z}{z^2}, 0 \right)$.

(c) *Using Lemma 13.6, calculate* **Res** $\left(\dfrac{z}{\text{Log} \, z}, 1 \right)$.

(d) *For* $a > 0$, *let* $f(z) = \dfrac{1}{(z^2 + a)}$. *Identify the isolated singularities of* $f(z)$. *Using Lemma 13.7, calculate the residue at those singularities.*

(e) *Using the Laurent series, calculate* **Res** $\left(\dfrac{e^z}{z^3}, 0 \right)$.

Remark

Answers to exercises are in Appendix A.

Chapter 14

The Argument Principle

We begin this chapter with a discussion of the logarithmic derivative of a complex function. Proofs using the logarithmic derivative are seen often, particularity in the field of analytic number theory.

Here, we use the logarithmic derivative to develop the *argument principle*. Inside a given contour, the argument principle counts the zeros of an analytic function. For a meromorphic function, it counts both the zeros and poles of the function.

14.1   The Logarithmic Derivative

Let $f(z)$ be a meromorphic function defined on a domain Ω. From our prior discussions of the complex logarithm, it is clear that $\log f(z)$ (for $f(z) \neq 0$) is multi-valued, with $\log f(z) = \log |f(z)| + i \arg(f(z))$. Applying the chain rule, the (single-valued) derivative of $\log f(z)$ (the "logarithmic derivative") is

$$\frac{d}{dz} \log f(z) = \frac{f'(z)}{f(z)} \quad z \neq 0.$$

Why is the logarithmic derivative single-valued? Recall that $i \arg(z) = i \operatorname{Arg}(z) + 2\pi i k$ where k is the branch of the logarithm. When we take the derivative, the $2\pi i k$ constant reduces to 0.

The lemma below is included to demonstrate use of the logarithmic derivative. We know that every non-zero complex number w can be written as $w = e^z$. We would like to extend that idea to non-zero holomorphic functions $f(z)$, with $f(z) = e^{g(z)}$ for some holomorphic function $g(z)$, so that $g(z)$ is one branch of $\log f(z)$.

Lemma 14.1

Let $f(z)$ be holomorphic and non-zero in the domain Ω. Then there exists a holomorphic function $g(z)$ on Ω such that

$$f(z) = e^{g(z)}.$$

Proof. [42] Fix $z_0 \in \Omega$, and let

$$g(z) = \int_\gamma \frac{f'(w)}{f(w)} \, dw + w_0,$$

where $\gamma \subset \Omega$ is a path connecting z_0 to z and w_0 is chosen so that $e^{w_0} = f(z_0)$.

Note that $g(z_0) = w_0$. Also, since f is non-zero and holomorphic, $g(z)$ is holomorphic with

$$g'(z) = \frac{f'(z)}{f(z)}.$$

With a derivative of zero, we next show $f(z)e^{-g(z)} = K$ for some constant K, so that $f(z) = Ke^{g(z)}$:

$$\frac{d}{dz}\left(f(z)e^{-g(z)}\right) = \frac{d}{dz}\left(\frac{f(z)}{e^{g(z)}}\right) = \frac{f'e^g - (e^g)'f}{(e^g)^2} = \frac{f'e^g - e^g g'f}{(e^g)^2} = \frac{f' - g'f}{e^g} = \frac{f' - \left(\frac{f'}{f}\right)f}{e^g} = \frac{f' - f'}{e^g} = 0,$$

With $f(z_0) = e^{w_0}$ and $g(z_0) = w_0$, we have $f(z_0)e^{-g(z_0)} = f(z_0)e^{-w_0} = 1$. That means $K = 1$ and we can conclude that $f(z) = e^{g(z)}$ for all $z \in \Omega$. $\qquad\square$

14.2   The Argument Principle

Assume $f(z)$ is meromorphic in the domain Ω, $\boldsymbol{C} \subset \Omega$ is a simple closed contour, and $f(z) \neq 0$ for $z \in \boldsymbol{C}$. Using the logarithmic derivative of $f(z)$, consider the integral

$$\int_{\boldsymbol{C}} \frac{f'(z)}{f(z)}\,dz = \int_{\boldsymbol{C}}\left[\frac{d}{dz}\log f(z)\right]dz = \int_{\boldsymbol{C}}\left[\frac{d}{dz}\log|f(z)|\right]dz + i\int_{\boldsymbol{C}}\left[\frac{d}{dz}\arg(f(z))\right]dz.$$

Here, $\log|f(z)|$ is just the real variable logarithm, where the value $|f(z)|$ is positive and continuous. If we parameterize the contour $\boldsymbol{C}$ by $\omega(t) = x(t) + iy(t), a \leq t \leq b$, then $\int_{\boldsymbol{C}} d\log|f(z)|$ resolves to $\log|f(\omega(b))| - \log|f(\omega(a))|$. Thus, the integral is 0 for any closed contour.

Therefore, at least in the case of a closed contour, the integral of the logarithmic derivative of a function equals $i\int_{\boldsymbol{C}} d\arg(f(z))$, which can be thought of as the change in $\arg(f(z))$ as z traverses $\boldsymbol{C}$. For this purpose, we use the "continuous argument function" described in Theorem 13.1.

To better understand the argument principle, consider the integral that results from a change of variable. Think of our current path $\boldsymbol{C}$ as a parameterization $z = \boldsymbol{C}(t)$. Let $w = f(z)$, so that $w = f(\boldsymbol{C}(t))$ is another contour. Then $dw = f'(z)\,dz$, giving the following equality

$$\frac{1}{2\pi i}\int_{\boldsymbol{C}}\frac{f'(z)}{f(z)}\,dz = \frac{1}{2\pi i}\int_{f(\boldsymbol{C})}\frac{dw}{w}. \tag{14.1}$$

By assumption, $\boldsymbol{C}$ does not go through any zeros of f, so $w = f(\boldsymbol{C}(t))$ is never zero and $1/w$ in the integral is not a problem. For $\boldsymbol{C}$ closed, we can apply Definition 13.1 and Theorem 13.1 and see that the right integral equals $\boldsymbol{W}(f(\boldsymbol{C}), 0)$; that is, the winding number of the closed path $f(\boldsymbol{C})$.

With the above as background, we are now in a position to present the argument principle. The important insight is that the zeros and poles of $f(z)$ all resolve to simple poles of the logarithmic derivative $f'(z)/f(z)$. With that, the proof is nothing more than a simple application of the Residue Theorem to the logarithmic derivative.

Theorem 14.1: Argument Principle

Let $f(z)$ be meromorphic in the domain Ω and let $\boldsymbol{C} \subset \Omega$ be a positively oriented simple closed contour. Let Λ be the interior of $\boldsymbol{C}$. Assume that $f(z)$ has no zeros or poles on $\boldsymbol{C}$. Then

$$\frac{1}{2\pi i}\int_{\boldsymbol{C}}\frac{f'(z)}{f(z)}\,dz = Z - P,$$

where, counting multiplicities, Z is the number of zeros and P is the number of poles of $f(z)$ in Λ.

Proof.[43] Our strategy is to show that: (1) each zero of order n of $f(z)$ produces a simple pole of $f'(z)/f(z)$ with residue n, and (2) each pole of order m of $f(z)$ produces a simple pole of $f'(z)/f(z)$ with residue $-m$.

The Zeros. Let $w \in \Lambda$ be a zero of order n of $f(z)$. Then, from Theorem 10.1 and Definition 10.2, there is a $g(z)$ with $g(w) \neq 0$ and with $f(z) = (z - w)^n g(z)$. Also, for some small $\epsilon > 0$, $g(z)$ is holomorphic in $\mathbf{D}_\epsilon(w)$. We have

$$f'(z) = n(z - w)^{n-1} g(z) + (z - w)^n g'(z)$$

so that

$$\frac{f'(z)}{f(z)} = \frac{n(z - w)^{n-1} g(z) + (z - w)^n g'(z)}{(z - w)^n g(z)} = \frac{n}{(z - w)} + \frac{g'(z)}{g(z)}. \tag{14.2}$$

Because $g(w) \neq 0$, we have that $g'(z)/g(z)$ is holomorphic in $\mathbf{D}_\epsilon(w)$. From equation (14.2), we can read off the a_{-1} coefficient of the Laurent series for $f'(z)/f(z)$ at w and can conclude that the residue of $f'(z)/f(z)$ at w is n.

The Poles. Let $w \in \Lambda$ be a pole of order m of $f(z)$. Then, from Theorem 12.2 and Definition 12.4, there is a $g(z)$ with $g(w) \neq 0$ and with $f(z) = (z - w)^{-m} g(z)$. Also, for some small $\epsilon > 0$, $g(z)$ is holomorphic in $\mathbf{D}_\epsilon(w)$. We have

$$f'(z) = -m(z - w)^{-m-1} g(z) + (z - w)^{-m} g'(z)$$

so that

$$\frac{f'(z)}{f(z)} = \frac{-m(z - w)^{-m-1} g(z) + (z - w)^{-m} g'(z)}{(z - w)^{-m} g(z)} = \frac{-m}{(z - w)} + \frac{g'(z)}{g(z)}. \tag{14.3}$$

Because $g(w) \neq 0$, we have that $g'(z)/g(z)$ is holomorphic in $\mathbf{D}_\epsilon(w)$. From equation (14.3), we can read off the a_{-1} coefficient of the Laurent series for $f'(z)/f(z)$ at w and can conclude that the residue of $f'(z)/f(z)$ at w is $-m$.

Combining. Combining the above results, we see that $f'(z)/f(z)$ has simple poles at each of the zeros and poles of $f(z)$. At each such simple pole, the residue is equal to: (1) n if at a zero of order n of $f(z)$, or (2) $-m$ if at a pole of order m of $f(z)$. Applying Theorem 13.2, we have our result. □

Remark

Compare the results of Theorem 14.1 with equation (14.1). The count (with multiplicities) of the zeros minus the poles of $f(z)$ inside $\boldsymbol{C}$ is exactly equal to $\mathbf{W}(f(\boldsymbol{C}), 0)$ – the winding number of the closed contour $f(\boldsymbol{C})$ about the origin.

Exercise Answers

A.1 Chapter 1 - Answers to Exercises 1.1

Proof (a). Applying Theorem 1.1(b): $|z| = |1 + z - 1| \le |1| + |z - 1| = 1 + |1 - z|$. $\qquad\square$

Proof (b). Using the same reasoning as Theorem 1.1(a): $|z - w|^2 = |z + (-w)|^2 = |z|^2 - 2Re(z\overline{w}) + |w|^2$. Combine that with $|z + w|^2 = |z|^2 + 2Re(z\overline{w}) + |w|^2$ from Theorem 1.1(a) and the result follows. $\qquad\square$

Proof (c). The assertion is trivially true for $n = 1$ and is true for $n = 2$ by Theorem 1.1(b). Our proof will be by induction. We assume the inequality is true for $n = k$ and show it is true for $n = k + 1$. Let $A = \sum_{i=1}^{k} z_i$ and let $B = \sum_{i=1}^{k} |z_i| = |B|$. Our inductive assumption is that $|A| \le B = |B|$. We need to show that $|A + z_{k+1}| \le |B| + |z_{k+1}|$.

We have by Theorem 1.1(b) that $|A + z_{k+1}| \le |A| + |z_{k+1}|$. And we also have by assumption that $|A| + |z_{k+1}| \le |B| + |z_{k+1}|$. Combining, we have $|A + z_{k+1}| \le |A| + |z_{k+1}| \le |B| + |z_{k+1}|$. $\qquad\square$

Proof (d). We have:

$$\frac{e^z - 1}{z} = \frac{\left(\sum_{k=0}^{\infty} \frac{z^k}{k!}\right) - 1}{z} = \frac{\sum_{k=1}^{\infty} \frac{z^k}{k!}}{z} = \sum_{k=1}^{\infty} \left(\frac{z^{k-1}}{k!}\right) = 1 + \sum_{k=2}^{\infty} \left(\frac{z^{k-1}}{k!}\right).$$

Now fix ϵ and use Theorem 1.1(d) and Exercise 1.1(c):

$$\left|\frac{e^z - 1}{z}\right| = \frac{|e^z - 1|}{|z|} = \left|1 + \sum_{k=2}^{\infty} \left(\frac{z^{k-1}}{k!}\right)\right|$$

$$= \left|1 - \left(-\sum_{k=2}^{\infty} \left(\frac{z^{k-1}}{k!}\right)\right)\right|$$

$$\ge |1| - \left|-\sum_{k=2}^{\infty} \left(\frac{z^{k-1}}{k!}\right)\right| = 1 - \left|\sum_{k=2}^{\infty} \left(\frac{z^{k-1}}{k!}\right)\right| \quad \text{(By Theorem 1.1(d))}$$

$$\ge 1 - \left|\sum_{k=2}^{\infty} \frac{|z^{k-1}|}{k!}\right| \quad \text{(By Exercise 1.1(c))}$$

$$\ge 1 - \left|\sum_{k=2}^{\infty} \frac{\epsilon}{k!}\right| \quad \text{(Because } |z^{k-1}| \le |z| \le \epsilon < 1\text{)}$$

$$= 1 - \epsilon \sum_{k=2}^{\infty} \frac{1}{k!} = 1 - \epsilon(e - 2) \ge (1 - \epsilon).$$

Thus: $|e^z - 1| \ge |z|(1 - \epsilon)$. $\qquad\square$

Corollary A.1. *For $\{z \in \mathbb{C} : |z| \le 1/2\}$, $|e^z - 1| \ge |z|/2$.*

A.2 Chapter 4 - Answers to Exercises 4.1

Proof (a). Fix $\epsilon > 0$. Because f is continuous, for every $z \in G$ there exists a $\delta(z) > 0$ such that if $w \in \mathbf{D}_{\delta(z)}(z) \cap G$ then $|f(z) - f(w)| < \epsilon/2$. For each $z \in G$, define the open disk $\mathbf{D}_{\delta(z)/2}(z)$ and let

$$K = \bigcup_{z \in G} \mathbf{D}_{\delta(z)/2}(z).$$

Then K is an open cover of G. By Theorem 2.8, for some $N \in \mathbb{N}$, K has a finite subcover S, with the disks making up S centered at a set of N points $\{z_j\}_{j=1}^{N} = J_N \subset G$. Define δ_0 as the minimum radius of the N disks $\mathbf{D}_{\delta(z_j)/2}(z_j)$ making up S.

Now fix $w_1 \in G$. Then $w_1 \in \mathbf{D}_{\delta(z_j)/2}(z_j)$ for some $z_j \in J_N$, so that $|w_1 - z_j| < \delta(z_j)/2$. Next, choose any w_2 such that $|w_1 - w_2| < \delta_0$ and therefore $|w_1 - w_2| < \delta(z_j)/2$. Combining, for our selected z_j, we see that $w_2 \in \mathbf{D}_{\delta(z_j)}(z_j)$:

$$
\begin{aligned}
|w_2 - z_j| = |(w_2 - w_1) + (w_1 - z_j)| \\
\leq |(w_2 - w_1)| + |(w_1 - z_j)| \\
< \delta(z_j)/2 + \delta(z_j)/2 \\
< \delta(z_j).
\end{aligned}
$$

For our fixed ϵ, we can choose $\delta = \delta_0$ to show uniform convergence. In particular, for any $w_1, w_2 \in G$ with $|w_1 - w_2| < \delta_0$, there exists a $z_j \in J_N$ with both $w_1, w_2 \in \mathbf{D}_{\delta(z_j)}(z_j)$, giving

$$|f(w_1) - f(w_2)| \leq |f(w_1) - f(z_j)| + |f(w_2) - f(z_j)| < \epsilon/2 + \epsilon/2 = \epsilon. \qquad \square$$

Proof (b) - Version 1. For $f(z) = \bar{z}$, the difference quotient becomes

$$\frac{f(z + \Delta z) - f(z)}{\Delta z} = \frac{\overline{(z + \Delta z)} - \bar{z}}{\Delta z} = \frac{\overline{\Delta z}}{\Delta z}.$$

If $\Delta z = \epsilon$ is real, then the difference quotient is 1, whereas if $\Delta z = i\epsilon$ is imaginary, then the difference quotient is -1. Thus the difference quotients do not have a limit as $\Delta z \to 0$. $\qquad \square$

Proof (b) - Version 2. For $z = x + iy$, let $u(x, y) = x$ and $v(x, y) = -y$, so that $f(z) = u(x, y) + iv(x, y)$. The first order partial derivatives of $u(x, y)$ and $v(x, y)$ are

$$
\frac{\partial u}{\partial x}(x, y) = 1 \qquad \frac{\partial u}{\partial y}(x, y) = 0
$$
$$
\frac{\partial v}{\partial x}(x, y) = 0 \qquad \frac{\partial v}{\partial y}(x, y) = -1,
$$

and the Cauchy-Riemann equations require

$$1 = \frac{\partial u}{\partial x}(x, y) = \frac{\partial v}{\partial y}(x, y) = -1.$$

With the Cauchy-Riemann equations satisfied nowhere, $f(z)$ cannot be holomorphic. $\qquad \square$

APPENDIX A. EXERCISE ANSWERS

Proof (c). Let $f(z) = z^n$ and fix z. For $n = 0$, $z^n = 0$ and therefore $(z^n)' = 0$, so the derivative formula nz^{n-1} applies. Now consider the case $n = 1$, where

$$f'(z) = \lim_{\Delta z \to 0} \frac{f(z + \Delta z) - f(z)}{\Delta z} = \lim_{\Delta z \to 0} \frac{\Delta z}{\Delta z} = 1 = nz^{n-1}.$$

Next, assume $n \geq 2$. We use the binomial theorem (noting that each binomial term is a constant and z is fixed)

$$
\begin{aligned}
f'(z) &= \lim_{\Delta z \to 0} \frac{f(z + \Delta z) - f(z)}{\Delta z} \\
&= \lim_{\Delta z \to 0} \frac{(z + \Delta z)^n - z^n}{\Delta z} \\
&= \lim_{\Delta z \to 0} \frac{\left[\binom{n}{0}z^n \Delta z^0 + \binom{n}{1}z^{n-1}\Delta z^1 + \binom{n}{2}z^{n-2}\Delta z^2 + \cdots + \binom{n}{n-1}z^1 \Delta z^{n-1} + \binom{n}{n}z^0 \Delta z^n\right] - z^n}{\Delta z} \\
&= \lim_{\Delta z \to 0} \frac{\left[z^n + \binom{n}{1}z^{n-1}\Delta z^1 + \binom{n}{2}z^{n-2}\Delta z^2 + \cdots + \binom{n}{n-1}z^1 \Delta z^{n-1} + \binom{n}{n}z^0 \Delta z^n\right] - z^n}{\Delta z} \\
&= nz^{n-1} + \lim_{\Delta z \to 0} \Delta z \left[\binom{n}{2}z^{n-2}\Delta z^1 + \cdots + \binom{n}{n-1}z^1 \Delta z^{n-2} + \binom{n}{n}z^0 \Delta z^{n-1}\right] \\
&= nz^{n-1}.
\end{aligned}
$$

Finally, for $n \leq -1$, we use the quotient rule

$$\left(\frac{1}{g(z)}\right)' = \frac{-g'(z)}{g(z)^2} \quad \text{for } g(z) \neq 0.$$

Letting $r = -n$ so that $f(z) = z^n = 1/z^r$ and $f'(z) = (1/z^r)'$, we have

$$\left(\frac{1}{z^r}\right)' = \frac{-(z^r)'}{(z^r)^2} = \frac{-rz^{r-1}}{z^{2r}} = -rz^{r-1-2r} = -rz^{(-r-1)}.$$

Substituting back n for r, we have $f'(z) = nz^{n-1}$. It remains only to note that for $n \leq 0$, the derivative formula requires $z \neq 0$. $\qquad \square$

Proof (d). Clearly $g(z)$ is continuous in Ω. Fix $z_0 \in \Omega$. The continuity of $g(z)$ gives

$$\lim_{\Delta z \to 0} g(z_0 + \Delta z) = g(z_0) \quad \text{so that} \quad \lim_{\Delta z \to 0} \frac{1}{f(z_0 + \Delta z)} = \frac{1}{f(z_0)}.$$

Because $f(z)$ is holomorphic in Ω, we also have

$$\lim_{\Delta z \to 0} \frac{f(z_0 + \Delta z) - f(z_0)}{\Delta z} = f'(z_0).$$

Combining the two gives

$$g'(z_0) = \lim_{\Delta z \to 0} \frac{g(z_0 + \Delta z) - g(z_0)}{\Delta z} = \lim_{\Delta z \to 0} \frac{\frac{1}{f(z_0 + \Delta z)} - \frac{1}{f(z_0)}}{\Delta z}$$

$$= \lim_{\Delta z \to 0} \frac{\frac{f(z_0)}{f(z_0)f(z_0 + \Delta z)} - \frac{f(z_0 + \Delta z)}{f(z_0 + \Delta z)f(z_0)}}{\Delta z}$$

$$= \lim_{\Delta z \to 0} \left(\frac{1}{f(z_0)f(z_0 + \Delta z)} \right) \left(\frac{f(z_0) - f(z_0 + \Delta z)}{\Delta z} \right)$$

$$= -\frac{1}{f(z_0)} \lim_{\Delta z \to 0} \left[\left(\frac{1}{f(z_0 + \Delta z)} \right) \left(\frac{f(z_0 + \Delta z) - f(z_0)}{\Delta z} \right) \right]$$

$$= -\frac{1}{f(z_0)^2} \cdot f'(z_0).$$

Thus, $g(z)$ has a complex derivative at each point $z_0 \in \Omega$ and is therefore holomorphic in Ω. $\quad\square$

A.3   Chapter 5 - Answers to Exercises 5.1

Proof. For the path L, we have:

$$\int_L f(z)\,dz = \int_0^1 f(\omega(t))\omega'(t)\,dt = \int_0^1 (1 - t + it)^2 (i - 1)\,dt$$

$$= \int_0^1 (2t^2 - 1)\,dt + i \int_0^1 (2t^2 - 4t + 1)\,dt$$

$$= (2t^3/3 - t)\big|_0^1 + i\left((2t^3/3 - 2t^2 + t)\big|_0^1\right) = \frac{2}{3} - 1 + i\left(\frac{2}{3} - 2 + 1\right) = -\frac{1}{3} - \frac{i}{3}.$$

For the path $\boldsymbol{C}$, we have:

$$\int_C f(z)\,dz = \int_0^{\pi/2} f(\phi(t))\phi'(t)\,dt = \int_0^{\pi/2} (e^{it})^2 (ie^{it})\,dt = \int_0^{\pi/2} ie^{3it}\,dt$$

$$= \left(\frac{i}{3i}\right)e^{3it}\bigg|_0^{\pi/2} = \left(\frac{1}{3}e^{i(3\pi/2)}\right) - \left(\frac{1}{3}e^0\right) = \left[\frac{1}{3} \cdot -i\right] - \frac{1}{3} = -\frac{1}{3} - \frac{i}{3}.$$

To verify, we use Exercise 4.1(c) and let $F(z) = z^3/3$, so that $F'(z) = z^2$. Thus, $f(z)$ has a primitive for all $z \in \mathbb{C}$. By the Fundamental Theorem of Calculus (Theorem 5.4), the above two integrals are equal to

$$F(i) - F(1) = \frac{i^3}{3} - \frac{1^3}{3} = -\frac{1}{3} - \frac{i}{3}. \qquad\square$$

A.4   Chapter 6 - Answers to Exercises 6.1

Proof (a)(1). let $a_n = \sqrt{\frac{2}{n+1}}$ so that $x_n = (-1)^n a_n$. Because a_n is monotone decreasing and $a_n \to 0$, we can use the Alternating Series Test (a well-known real variable theorem not proved here) to see that the sum $\sum_{n=1}^{\infty} x_n$ converges.

Next, consider the partial products, and note that each term of the partial product is positive. It will be convenient to start our sequence at $n = 3$. We begin with partial products ending in an even numbered subscript

$$P_{2n} = \prod_{k=3}^{2n} (1 + x_k) = \prod_{k=3}^{2n} (1 + (-1)^k a_k)$$
$$= \prod_{j=2}^{n} (1 - a_{2j-1})(1 + a_{2j})$$

Now using that a_j is monotone decreasing so that $a_{2j} \leq a_{2j-1}$

$$\leq \prod_{j=2}^{n} (1 - a_{2j-1})(1 + a_{2j-1})$$
$$= \prod_{j=2}^{n} (1 - [a_{2j-1}]^2) = \prod_{j=2}^{n} \left(1 - \frac{1}{j}\right) = \prod_{j=2}^{n} \left(\frac{j-1}{j}\right) = \frac{1}{n}.$$

For odd numbered subscripts, note that $(1 + z_{2n+1}) = (1 - a_{2n+1}) < 1$, so that

$$P_{2n+1} = (1 - a_{2n+1})P_{2n} \leq P_{2n} \leq \frac{1}{n}.$$

Thus, $\lim_{n \to \infty} P_n = 0$. By definition, that means the infinite product $\prod_{n=3}^{\infty} (1 + x_n)$ diverges to zero. $\quad\square$

Proof (a)(2). By combining x_{2j-1} and x_{2j}, we have

$$\sum_{n=1}^{\infty} x_n = \sum_{j=1}^{\infty} \left(x_{2j-1} + x_{2j}\right) = \sum_{j=1}^{\infty} \frac{1}{j}.$$

We show in Exercise 6.1(b)(1) that the last sum diverges.

Looking next at the infinite product, we have

$$= \prod_{n=1}^{\infty} (1 + x_n) = \prod_{j=1}^{\infty} \left[(1 + x_{2j-1})(1 + x_{2j})\right]$$
$$= \prod_{j=1}^{\infty} \left[\left(1 + \frac{1}{\sqrt{j}}\right)\left(1 - \frac{1}{\sqrt{j}} + \frac{1}{j}\right)\right] = \prod_{j=1}^{\infty} \left(1 + \frac{1}{j^{3/2}}\right).$$

By Lemma 6.1, the final product on the RHS (just above) converges if $\sum_{n=1}^{\infty} 1/n^{3/2}$ converges. The sum is equal to $\zeta(3/2)$, which converges by Theorem 6.12(c). $\quad\square$

Proof (b)(1). For $z_n = 1/n$, note that the series over z_n is equal to $\zeta(1)$, which by Theorem 6.12(a) diverges.

Looking next at the infinite product, we have

$$P_N = \prod_{n=1}^{N} (1 + z_n) = \prod_{n=1}^{N} \left(1 + \frac{1}{n}\right) = \prod_{n=1}^{N} \left(\frac{n+1}{n}\right) = N + 1,$$

so that $P_N \to +\infty$ and the product also diverges. $\quad\square$

Proof (b)(2). For $z_n = -1/n$, we have

$$\sum_{n=1}^{\infty} z_n = \sum_{n=1}^{\infty} \frac{-1}{n} = -\sum_{n=1}^{\infty} \frac{1}{n}$$

We can therefore use the results just above and conclude the sum diverges $\to -\infty$.

Looking next at the infinite product, we begin our index at $n = 2$ to avoid a zero term.

$$P_N = \prod_{n=2}^{N} (1 + z_n) = \prod_{n=2}^{N} \left(1 - \frac{1}{n}\right) = \prod_{n=2}^{N} \left(\frac{n-1}{n}\right) = \frac{1}{N}.$$

so that $P_N \to 0$ and the product diverges to 0.

A simple application of Lemma 6.2 shows that Lemma 6.1 applies any time that all terms of z_n are negative. □

Proof (b)(3). For $z_n = -1/n^2$, note that the series over z_n is equal to $-\zeta(2)$, which by Theorem 6.12(b) converges.

Looking next at the infinite product, we have

$$P_N = \prod_{n=2}^{N} \left(1 - \frac{1}{n^2}\right) = \prod_{n=2}^{N} \left(\frac{(n-1)(n+1)}{n^2}\right)$$

$$= \frac{1 \cdot 3}{2 \cdot 2} \cdot \frac{2 \cdot 4}{3 \cdot 3} \cdot \frac{3 \cdot 5}{4 \cdot 4} \cdots \frac{(N-2) \cdot N}{(N-1) \cdot (N-1)} \cdot \frac{(N-1) \cdot (N+1)}{N \cdot N}$$

All terms cancel except the first half of the first term and the last half of the last term, giving

$$= \frac{1}{2}\left(\frac{N+1}{N}\right).$$

Thus, $\lim_{n\to\infty} P_N = \frac{1}{2}$, showing that the infinite product converges. □

Proof (c)(1). Taking the absolute value of the terms, we have $\sum_{n=1}^{\infty} |(-1)^{n+1}/n| = \sum_{n=1}^{\infty} 1/n$. The latter series is equal to $\zeta(1)$, which diverges by Theorem 6.12(a). □

Proof (c)(2). We begin with the Taylor Series for the logarithm

$$\log(1 + x) = \sum_{n=1}^{\infty} \frac{(-1)^{n+1}}{n} x^n \quad \text{for } -1 < x \leq 1.$$

Letting $x = 1$, we see that our alternating series is equal to $\log(2)$. □

Proof (c)(3). We reorder our alternating series as follows

$$= \left(1 - \frac{1}{2}\right) - \frac{1}{4} + \left(\frac{1}{3} - \frac{1}{6}\right) - \frac{1}{8} + \left(\frac{1}{5} - \frac{1}{10}\right) - \frac{1}{12} \cdots$$

$$= \frac{1}{2} - \frac{1}{4} + \frac{1}{6} - \frac{1}{8} + \frac{1}{10} \cdots = \frac{1}{2}\left(1 - \frac{1}{2} + \frac{1}{3} - \frac{1}{4} + \frac{1}{5} \cdots\right) = \frac{\log(2)}{2}.$$
□

Proof (d). We are assuming that the sum $\sum_{n=1}^{\infty} z_n$ converges absolutely. Therefore, the product $\prod_{n=1}^{\infty}(1 + z_n)$ converges absolutely by Theorem 6.8(a), converges by Theorem 6.8(b), and satisfies the Cauchy criteria by Theorem 6.6. This allows us to choose an N such that, for all $n > N$, we have $z_n > -1$ and thus $|1 + z_n| = (1 + z_n)$, giving

$$\prod_{n=1}^{\infty} |1 + z_n| = \prod_{n=1}^{N} |1 + z_n| + \prod_{n=N+1}^{\infty} (1 + z_n).$$

On the RHS, the first product is finite, and the second product satisfies the Cauchy criterion. Therefore, the LHS product converges, as required. $\qquad \square$

A.5   Chapter 9 - Answers to Exercises 9.1

Proof (a). We develop our function into a power series centered at $z = 1$, as follows:

$$f(z) = \frac{2z + 3}{z + 1} = \frac{2(z + 1) + 1}{z + 1} = 2 + \frac{1}{(z - 1) + 2} = 2 + \frac{1}{2} \left[\frac{1}{1 - \left(\frac{(1-z)}{2} \right)} \right]$$

$$= 2 + \frac{1}{2} \sum_{n=0}^{\infty} \left(\frac{1 - z}{2} \right)^n = 2 + \frac{1}{2} \sum_{n=0}^{\infty} \left(\frac{-1}{2} \right)^n (z - 1)^n = 2 + \sum_{n=0}^{\infty} a_n (z - 1)^n \text{ for } a_n = \frac{1}{2} \cdot \left(\frac{-1}{2} \right)^n.$$

Thus, by Theorem 9.1, the radius of convergence R is

$$R = \frac{1}{\limsup_{n \to \infty} |a_n|^{1/n}} = \frac{1}{\limsup_{n \to \infty} |1/2|^{1/n} \cdot |(1/2)^n|^{1/n}} = \frac{1}{1/2} = 2. \qquad \square$$

Proof (b). From Theorem 9.1, the radius of convergence R of a power series is obtained by the formula

$$\frac{1}{R} = \limsup_{n \to \infty} |a_n|^{1/n}.$$

It follows immediately by the definition of lim sup that the value of R is unchanged if the first N members of the sequence $\{a_n\}$ are modified. $\qquad \square$

Proof (c). We can assume $c = 0$. Let $R' = \lim_{n \to \infty} |a_n / a_{n+1}|$. First assume $|z| < r < R'$, so that there exists an N such that for $n \geq N$ we have $r < |a_n / a_{n+1}|$. Fix $B = |a_N| r^N$ and assume $n \geq N$, giving

$$|a_{N+1}| r^{N+1} = |a_{N+1}| \cdot r \cdot r^N < |a_{N+1}| \cdot |a_n / a_{n+1}| \cdot r^N = |a_N| r^N = B.$$

In similar fashion, $|a_{N+k+1}| r^{N+k+1} \leq |a_{N+k}| r^{N+k}$ for all $k \in \mathbb{N}$ so that $|a_n r^n| \leq B$ for $n \geq N$. Therefore

$$|a_n z^n| = |a_n r^n| \frac{|z^n|}{r^n} \leq B \frac{|z^n|}{r^n}.$$

Using $|z|/r < 1$, we see that the tails of both the following series converge

$$\sum_{n=N}^{\infty} |a_n z^n| \leq \sum_{n=N}^{\infty} B \frac{|z^n|}{r^n},$$

so that our power series converges for $|z| < r$. But $r < R'$ was arbitrarily chosen, so the power series must converge for $|z| < R'$, which is only possible if $R' \leq R$.

Now assume $|z| > r > R'$, so that there exists an N such that for $n \geq N$ we have $r > |a_n/a_{n+1}|$. Applying reasoning similar to above, we have $|a_n r^n| \geq B = |a_N r^N|$ for $n \geq N$. Using $|z| > r$

$$|a_n z^n| = |a_n r^n| \frac{|z^n|}{r^n} \geq B \frac{|z^n|}{r^n}$$

$$\lim_{n \to \infty} |a_n z^n| \geq \lim_{n \to \infty} B \frac{|z^n|}{r^n} \to \infty.$$

That means the power series diverges for $|z| > r$. But $r > R'$ was arbitrarily chosen, so the power series must diverge for $|z| > R'$, which is only possible if $R' \geq R$. We have shown $R \leq R' \leq R$. Thus $R' = R$, as required. $\qquad \square$

Proof (d).

(i) $\quad a_n/a_{n+1} = (n+1)^2/n^2 = 1 + 2/n + 1/n^2 \quad$ so that $\quad \lim_{n \to \infty} |(n+1)^2/n^2| = 1$;

(ii) $\quad a_n/a_{n+1} = (n+1)/n \quad$ so that $\quad \lim_{n \to \infty} |(n+1)/n| = 1$;

(iii) $\quad a_n/a_{n+1} = 1/1 \quad$ so that $\quad \lim_{n \to \infty} |1/1| = 1$;

(iv) $\quad a_n/a_{n+1} = n/(n+1) \quad$ so that $\quad \lim_{n \to \infty} |n/(n+1)| = 1$;

(v) $\quad a_n/a_{n+1} = n \quad$ so that $\quad \lim_{n \to \infty} |n| = \infty.$ $\qquad \square$

A.6 Chapter 10 - Answers to Exercises 10.1

Proof (a). If $f(z)$ has an infinite number of zeros in G, those zeros form an infinite sequence $\{z_n\} \subset G$. Because G is compact, by Theorem 2.7 the sequence $\{z_n\}$ has a convergent subsequence $\{z_{n_m}\}$ whose limit is some $p \in G$. Applying Theorems 10.2 and 10.3, this is only possible if $f(z)$ is constant in Ω, contrary to assumption. $\qquad \square$

Proof (b). Define $h(z) = f(z) - f(z_0)$. Then, $h(z)$ is holomorphic in Ω, with $h(z_0) = 0$. By Theorem 10.2, $h(z_0)$ is an isolated zero, so there is an $\epsilon > 0$ such that $h(w) \neq 0$ for $w \in \mathbf{D}_\epsilon^\odot(z_0)$. But that means $f(w) - f(z_0) \neq 0$ (and therefore $f(w) \neq f(z_0)$) for $w \in \mathbf{D}_\epsilon^\odot(z_0)$. $\qquad \square$

Proof (c). Define $h(z) = f(z) - f(z_0)$. Then, $h(z)$ is holomorphic in Ω, with $h(z_0) = 0$. The terms of the power series for $f(z)$ and $h(z)$ at z_0 are identical, except for the a_0 terms. Thus, they have the same radius of convergence at z_0. Call it $R > 0$. By proof (a), the closed disk $\overline{\mathbf{D}}_{R/2}(z_0) \subset \Omega$ has a finite number of zeros of $h(z)$ (including z_0). Call them $z_0, z_1, \cdots z_n$. Let $\epsilon = \min_{k=1}^{n} |z_0 - z_k|$. Then we have $h(w) \neq 0$ for $w \in \mathbf{D}_\epsilon^\odot(z_0)$ giving our result for the reasons explained in (b). $\qquad \square$

Proof (d). By Theorem 10.2, the zeros of $f(z)$ are isolated. Thus, by Theorem 2.5 we can encircle each such zero by a disk with rational coordinates and radius that encloses no other zero of $f(z)$. Together, all such disks are a subset of a countable set by Corollary 2.4 and therefore countable. $\qquad \square$

A.7   Chapter 11 - Answers to Exercises 11.1

Proof (a). We begin by restating $f(z)$ is a more useful form

$$\boxed{f(z)} = \frac{1}{(z-1)(z-2)} = \frac{(z-1)-(z-2)}{(z-1)(z-2)} = \frac{(z-1)}{(z-2)(z-1)} - \frac{(z-2)}{(z-1)(z-2)} \boxed{= \frac{1}{z-2} - \frac{1}{z-1}}.$$

For $z \in \Omega_1$, we have $|z| < 1$ and $|z/2| < 1$, allowing use of a geometric series

$$\boxed{-\frac{1}{z-1}} = \frac{1}{1-z} \boxed{= \sum_{k=0}^{\infty} z^k} \tag{A.1}$$

$$\boxed{\frac{1}{z-2}} = \frac{-1}{2-z} = \left(\frac{1/2}{1/2}\right) \cdot \frac{-1}{2-z} = \frac{1}{2} \cdot \frac{-1}{1-(z/2)} \boxed{= -\sum_{k=0}^{\infty} \frac{z^k}{2^{k+1}}}. \tag{A.2}$$

Combining equations (A.1) and (A.2), we have our power series

$$f(z) = \sum_{k=0}^{\infty} z^k - \sum_{k=0}^{\infty} \frac{z^k}{2^{k+1}} = \sum_{k=0}^{\infty} \left[1 - 2^{(-k-1)}\right] z^k \quad |z| < 1. \qquad \square$$

Proof (b). For $z \in \Omega_2$, we have $|1/z| < 1$ and $|z/2| < 1$, allowing use of a geometric series

$$\boxed{-\frac{1}{z-1}} = \left(\frac{1/z}{1/z}\right) \frac{-1}{z-1} = \frac{1}{z} \cdot \frac{-1}{1-(1/z)} \boxed{= -\sum_{k=0}^{\infty} \frac{1}{z^{(k+1)}}}. \tag{A.3}$$

Combining equations (A.2) and (A.3), we have our Laurent series

$$f(z) = -\sum_{k=0}^{\infty} \frac{1}{z^{(k+1)}} - \sum_{k=0}^{\infty} \frac{z^k}{2^{k+1}} = -\sum_{k=1}^{\infty} \frac{1}{z^k} - \sum_{k=0}^{\infty} \frac{z^k}{2^{k+1}} = -\sum_{k=-1}^{-\infty} z^k - \sum_{k=0}^{\infty} \frac{z^k}{2^{k+1}} \quad 1 < |z| < 2. \qquad \square$$

Proof (c). For $z \in \Omega_3$, we have $|1/z| < 1$ and $|2/z| < 1$, allowing use of a geometric series

$$\boxed{\frac{1}{z-2}} = \left(\frac{1/z}{1/z}\right) \frac{1}{z-2} = \frac{1}{z} \cdot \frac{1}{1-(2/z)} \boxed{= \sum_{k=0}^{\infty} \frac{2^k}{z^{(k+1)}}}. \tag{A.4}$$

Combining equations (A.3) and (A.4), we have our Laurent series

$$f(z) = \sum_{k=0}^{\infty} \frac{2^k}{z^{(k+1)}} - \sum_{k=0}^{\infty} \frac{1}{z^{(k+1)}} = \sum_{k=1}^{\infty} \frac{2^{(k-1)}-1}{z^k} = \sum_{k=-1}^{-\infty} \left[2^{(-k-1)}-1\right] z^k \quad 2 < |z| < \infty. \qquad \square$$

Proof (d). We restate $g(z)$:

$$\boxed{g(z)} = \frac{(1-iz)}{(1+iz)} = \frac{i}{i} \cdot \frac{(1-iz)}{(1+iz)} = \frac{i+z}{i-z} = -\frac{(i+z)}{z-i} = -\frac{(z-i+2i)}{z-i} \boxed{= -1 - 2i(z-i)^{-1}}.$$

Our restatement of $g(z)$ is just a Laurent series centered at i, whose only non-zero terms are $a_0 = -1$ and $a_{-1} = -2i$. $\qquad \square$

A.8 Chapter 12 - Answers to Exercises 12.1

Proof (a). From Definition 1.3, $\mathrm{Log}(w)$ is the principal value of the complex logarithm. And from Theorem 4.9, $\mathrm{Log}(w)$ is holomorphic in the slit plane $\mathbb{C}\backslash(-\infty, 0]$. If we let $w = [1 - 1/z]$, then w is in the slit plane if and only if $z \in [0, 1]$. Thus, $\mathrm{Log}(w)$ is holomorphic on $\mathbb{C}\backslash[0, 1]$. That means $\mathrm{Log}(w)$, and therefore $\mathrm{Log}(1 - 1/z)$, has no isolated singularities. $\qquad\square$

Proof (b). We start with $\tan z = \frac{\sin z}{\cos z}$. Because $\cos z$ has simple zeros at $\pi/2 + k\pi$ for $k \in \mathbb{N}$, its reciprocal has simple poles at those points. None of those poles are canceled by $\sin z$ because $\sin z$ is non-zero at all such points. Therefore, $\tan z$ has the same simple poles as $1/\cos z$. $\qquad\square$

Proof (c). We immediately see the potential poles at $z = 1$ and $z = -1$. To test the pole at $z = 1$, define $g(z) = (z - 2)/(z + 1)^2$, so that $f(z) = g(z)/(z - 1)^2$. Because $g(z)$ is holomorphic and non-zero in a neighborhood of 1, we can disregard it in assessing the pole at 1. We are left with $1/(z - 1)^2$, which is easily seen to be a pole of order 2. In similar fashion, we define $h(z) = (z - 2)/(z - 1)^2$, holomorphic and non-zero in a neighborhood of -1. Then, $f(z) = h(z)/(z + 1)^2$, giving a pole of order 2 at -1. $\qquad\square$

Proof (d). The function is clearly holomorphic on $\mathbb{C}\backslash\{0\}$, with an isolated singularity at 0. Using the standard Taylor series for $\sin z$, we have

$$f(z) = z^N \sin\left(\frac{1}{z}\right) = z^N \sum_{k=0}^{\infty} \frac{(-1)^k}{(2k + 1)!}\left(\frac{1}{z}\right)^{2k+1} = \sum_{k=0}^{\infty} \frac{(-1)^k}{(2k + 1)!}\left(\frac{1}{z}\right)^{(2k+1-N)}$$

Now let $M = [(N - 1)/2]$, where the notation $[(N - 1)/2]$ means the integral part of $(N - 1)/2$.

$$= \sum_{k=0}^{M} \frac{(-1)^k}{(2k + 1)!}\left(\frac{1}{z}\right)^{(2k+1-N)} + \sum_{k=(M+1)}^{\infty} \frac{(-1)^k}{(2k + 1)!}\left(\frac{1}{z}\right)^{(2k+1-N)}$$

$$= \sum_{k=0}^{M} \frac{(-1)^k}{(2k + 1)!}z^{(N-2k-1)} + \sum_{k=(M+1)}^{\infty} \frac{(-1)^k}{(2k + 1)!}z^{(N-2k-1)} \qquad (A.5)$$

In equation (A.5), the finite number of terms in the left sum include only non-negative coefficients of z, while the infinite number of terms in the right sum include only negative coefficients of z. With an infinite number of negative coefficients, $z = 0$ is an essential singularity. $\qquad\square$

Proof (e). There is a potential singularity at $z = 0$ because $e^0 - 1 = 0$. However, we have

$$\lim_{z\to 0} \frac{z}{e^z - 1} = \lim_{z\to 0} \frac{z}{\sum_{n=1}^{\infty} \frac{z^n}{n!}} = \lim_{z\to 0} \frac{1}{\sum_{n=1}^{\infty} \frac{z^{n-1}}{n!}} = \lim_{z\to 0} \frac{1}{1 + \sum_{n=2}^{\infty} \frac{z^{n-1}}{n!}} = 1.$$

Thus, the singularity is a removable singularity and the function is an entire function. $\qquad\square$

A.9 Chapter 13 - Answers to Exercises 13.1

Proof (a). In Section 12.2.1, we showed that $\sin z/z$ has a removable singularity at $z = 0$. Thus $\sin z/z^2$ has a simple pole at $z = 0$. Using Lemma 13.3, we have

$$\mathbf{Res}\left(\frac{\sin z}{z^2}, 0\right) = \lim_{z\to 0}(z - 0)\frac{\sin z}{z^2} = \lim_{z\to 0} \frac{\sin z}{z} = 1. \qquad\square$$

Proof (b). In this case, $\cos 0 \neq 0$, so there is no removable singularity at $z = 0$. Thus, we have a double pole. Using Lemma 13.4, we have

$$\mathbf{Res}\left(\frac{\cos z}{z^2}, 0\right) = \lim_{z \to 0} \frac{d}{dz}\left[(z - 0)^2 \cdot \frac{\cos z}{z^2}\right] = \lim_{z \to 0} \frac{d}{dz}\cos z = \lim_{z \to 0}(-\sin z) = 0. \qquad \square$$

Proof (c). In this case, $\mathrm{Log}\, 1 = 0$ so we have a simple pole at $z = 1$. Let $f(z) = z$ and $g(z) = \mathrm{Log}\, z$. Using Lemma 13.6, we have

$$\mathbf{Res}\left(\frac{z}{\mathrm{Log}\, z}, 1\right) = \mathbf{Res}\left(\frac{f(z)}{g(z)}, 1\right) = \left.\frac{f(z)}{g'(z)}\right|_{z=1} = \left.\frac{z}{1/z}\right|_{z=1} = 1. \qquad \square$$

Proof (d). We have $f(z) = \dfrac{1}{(z^2 + a)}$ for $a > 0$. Thus, we have simple zeros at $z = \pm i\sqrt{a}$. Let $f(z) = z^2 + a$. Using Lemma 13.7, we have

$$\mathbf{Res}\left(\frac{1}{(z^2 + a)}, \pm i\sqrt{a}\right) = \mathbf{Res}\left(\frac{1}{f(z)}, \pm i\sqrt{a}\right) = \left.\frac{1}{f'(z)}\right|_{z=\pm i\sqrt{a}} = \left.\frac{1}{2z}\right|_{z=\pm i\sqrt{a}} = \frac{1}{\pm 2i\sqrt{a}}. \qquad \square$$

Proof (e). We develop the Laurent series for e^z/z^3:

$$\frac{e^z}{z^3} = \frac{\sum_{n=0}^{\infty}\frac{z^n}{n!}}{z^3} = \sum_{n=0}^{\infty}\frac{z^{n-3}}{n!} = \frac{z^{-3}}{0!} + \frac{z^{-2}}{1!} + \frac{z^{-1}}{2!} + \sum_{n=3}^{\infty}\frac{z^{n-3}}{n!}.$$

Reading off the coefficient of the z^{-1} term, we have $\mathbf{Res}\left(\dfrac{e^z}{z^3}, 0\right) = \dfrac{1}{2!}$. $\qquad \square$

Notes

[1] We follow Stein/Shakarchi [14, pp. 86-89] for the approach and figure.

[2] This proof uses ideas from Ahlfors [1, pp. 10-11] and Rudin [13, pp. 15-16].

[3] The point ∞ is generally disregarded in this definition.

[4] We rely here on the Archimedean property of $\mathbb{R}$, which essentially states that there is no largest natural number and no smallest reciprocal of a natural number. As an interesting side note, the property is incorrectly attributed to Archimedes – it was already found in Euclid, *Elements*, Book V, Def. 4.

[5] Follows a proof from the web site of Professor (Emeritus) James A. Morrow, Department of Mathematics, University of Washington: sites.math.washington.edu/~morrow/334_16/heine-borel.pdf.

[6] Note that we are *not* claiming that a finite number of our $\{D_j\}$ cover $\{G_\alpha\}$, but only that a finite number cover the compact set Ω.

[7] This clever proof follows an approach from Knopp [9, p. 19].

[8] We follow an approach from Ahlfors [1, pp. 56-57].

[9] We follow an approach from Knopp [9, pp. 15-17].

[10] We follow an approach from Knopp [9, pp. 17-18].

[11] We follow an approach from Stein/Shakarchi [14, pp. 37-39].

[12] We follow an approach from Gamelin [8, pp. 46-47].

[13] We follow an approach from Gamelin [8, pp. 47-48].

[14] We follow an approach from Stein/Shakarchi [14, pp. 22-23]; see also Remmert [11, pp. 184-185].

[15] We follow an approach from Brown/Churchill [3, pp. 142, 146-149].

[16] We follow an approach from Ahlfors [1, pp. 191-192].

[17] We follow an approach from Ash/Novinger [2, pp. 138-139].

[18] Both proofs (a) and (b) follow an approach from Knopp [9, pp. 73-76].

[19] We follow an approach from Stein/Shakarchi [14, pp. 34-36].

[20] We follow an approach from Knopp [9, pp. 49-54].

[21] Recall that our contour C consists of a finite number of smooth paths joined together. As explained in the *Remark* on page 51, we can (and will) assume that C is a single smooth path. It is just a matter of "paperwork" to apply this proof to each individual smooth path that together make up C. Then, applying Theorem 5.2(b), and noting that the finite number of endpoints of the smooth paths have measure zero, we can combine those results to complete our proof for C.

[22] We follow an approach from Knopp [9, pp. 56-57].

[23] We follow an approach from Stein/Shakarchi [14, pp. 37-39].

[24] We follow an approach from Knopp [9, pp. 62-64].

[25] We follow an approach from Conway [4, pp. 83-84]; see also Gamelin [8, p. 115] for the binomial expansion.

[26] We follow an approach from Brown/Churchill [3, pp. 175-178]; see also Knopp [9, pp. 84-85].

[27] Both proofs (a) and (b) follow an approach from Conway [4, p. 31].

[28] Proofs (a) thru (d) are based on ideas from Ahlfors [1, pp. 38-40], Conway [4, pp. 35-37], Remmert [11, pp. 123-124] and Stein/Shakarchi [14, pp. 16-18].

[29] We follow an approach from Knopp [9, p. 81].

[30] We follow an approach from Knopp [9, pp. 79-81].

[31] We follow an approach from Knopp [9, p. 90].

[32] We follow an approach from Gamelin [8, p. 156].

[33] In this section, we follow ideas from Knopp [9, pp. 92-106].

[34] This proof uses ideas from Knopp [9, pp. 117-121], Ahlfors [1, pp. 184-186], Gamelin [8, pp. 165-168] and Brown/Churchill [3, pp. 197-202].

[35] We follow an approach from https://en.wikipedia.org/wiki/Removable_singularity.

[36] We follow an approach from Gamelin [8, p. 172].

[37] We follow an approach from Gamelin [8, p. 173].

[38] We follow an approach from Knopp [9, p. 124].

[39] We follow an approach from Gamelin [8, p. 175]; see also Conway [4, pp. 109-110].

[40] We follow an approach from Knopp [9, pp. 126-128].

[41] See, for example, Freitag/Busam [6, pp. 235-238].

[42] We follow an approach from Stein/Shakarchi [14, pp. 100-101].

[43] We follow an approach from Stein/Shakarchi [14, pp. 89-91]; see also Gamelin [8, pp. 224-226].

Bibliography

[1] Lars V. Ahlfors: *Complex Analysis*, Third Edition, McGraw-Hill, Inc., 1979.

[2] R. B. Ash and W.P. Novinger: *Complex Variables*, Second Edition, 2004.

[3] James W. Brown and Ruel V. Churchill: *Complex Variables and Applications*, Eighth Edition, McGraw-Hill, Inc., 2009.

[4] John B. Conway: *Functions of One Complex Variable I*, Second Edition, Springer, 1978.

[5] John Derbyshire: *Prime Obsession*, Joseph Henry Press, 2003.

[6] Eberhard Freitag and Rolf Busam: *Complex Analysis, 2nd Edition*, Springer-Verlag, 2009.

[7] H.M. Edwards: *Riemann Zeta Function*, Dover 2001 republication, Academic Press, Inc., 1974.

[8] Theodore W. Gamelin: *Complex Analysis*, Springer-Verlag, 2001.

[9] Konrad Knopp: *Theory of Functions: Part I*, First American Edition, Dover Publications, 1945.

[10] Terrence P. Murphy: *A Study of Bernhard Riemann's 1859 Paper*, First Edition, Paramount Ridge Press, 2020.

[11] Reinhold Remmert: *Theory of Complex Functions*, Springer-Verlag, 1989.

[12] B. Riemann: *Ueber die Anzahl der Primzahlen unter einer gegebenen Grösse* [*On the Number of Primes Less Than a Given Magnitude*] (Monatsberichte der Berliner Akademie, November 1859, 671-680) Translated by David R. Wilkins.

[13] Walter Rudin: *Principles of Mathematical Analysis, Third Edition*, McGraw-Hill, Inc., 1976.

[14] Elias M. Stein and Rami Shakarchi: *Princeton Lectures in Analysis II - Complex Analysis*, Princeton University Press, 2003.

Index

A

absolute value 2
accumulation point 106
analytic 101
analytic continuation 108
Analytic Continuation (Intersecting Sets) 108
Analytic Continuation (Subset) 108
argument 7
Argument Principle 142

B

Bolzano-Weierstrass Theorem 21
boundary 16
boundary point 15
bounded 20
branch 8

C

cardinal number 14
Casorati-Weierstrass Theorem 124
Cauchy sequence 61
Cauchy's Inequality 93
Cauchy's Integral Formula 88
Cauchy's Integral Formula for Derivatives 92
Cauchy's Integral Theorem 81
Cauchy-Riemann equations 41
Cauchy-Riemann Equations (part 1) 40
Cauchy-Riemann Equations (part 2) 41
Cauchy-Schwarz Inequality 11
circle 16
clockwise (orientation) 25
closed 15
closed contour 27
closed disk 16
closed domain 28
closed path 25
closed polygon 29
closed region 28
closure 16
coefficients 97
compact 21
complement 15
complex conjugate 2

complex derivative 36
complex differentiable 36
complex number 1
connected 27
continuity along a path 36
continuity from the interior 36
continuous 35
contour 27
contour integrals 47
converge 61
converge absolutely 67
convergent 63
converges 64
converges to zero 64
converges uniformly 71
countable 14
counterclockwise (orientation) 25

D

diameter 20
digon 29
disconnected 27
disk of convergence 99
diverge 61
divergent 63
diverges 64
diverges to zero 64
domain 28
domain of convergence 70
double pole 120

E

elements 13
empty set 13
entire 37
equivalence relationship 14
essential singularity 120
Estimation Lemma 53
exponential function 4–6
extended complex plane 9
exterior point 15

F

finite 14
function 14
function series 70
Fundamental Theorem of Calculus 53

G

geometric series 72–73
Goursat's Theorem 77

H

harmonic conjugate 43
harmonic function 43
Heine-Borel Theorem 22
holomorphic 37

I

Identity Theorem 107
imaginary part 1
Inequality Lemma 52
infinite 14
infinite product 64
infinite series 63
interior 16
interior point 15
isolated point 15, 106
isolated singularity 119

J

joined 25

L

Laplace's equation 43
Laurent series 113
Laurent Series Expansion 114
length 27, 52
limit point 15
Liouville's Theorem 93

M

mapping 14
Maximum Modulus Principle 94
meromorphic 123
Minimum Modulus Principle 96
ML inequality 53

N

negative (orientation) 25
neighborhood 15
nth partial product 64

nth partial sum 63

O

one-to-one 14
open 16
open covering 22
open disk 16
order (of a zero) 106
orientation 25, 27

P

parameterization 25
partial neighborhood 36
path 25
path connected 28
path neighborhood 36
piecewise continuous 36
point at infinity 9
polar coordinates 6
polar form 6
pole 120, 124
pole of order n 120
polygon 29
positive (orientation) 25
power function 8
Power Series 98
power series 97
primitive 53
principal branch 8
principal part 117
principal value 7, 8
punctured disk 119

R

radius of convergence 99
real part 1
reflexive 14
region 28
removable singularity 120
residue 131
Residue Theorem (Final Version) 132
Residue Theorem (First Version) 131
reversed path 26

S

sequence 15
series 63
set 13
simple closed contour 27
simple closed path 25

simple closed polygon 29
simple contour 27
simple path 25
simple pole 120
simply connected 28
smooth 25
sum 63
symmetric 14

T
Theorems (Named)
   Analytic Continuation (Intersecting Sets) . . . 108
   Analytic Continuation (Subset) 108
   Argument Principle 142
   Bolzano-Weierstrass Theorem 21
   Casorati-Weierstrass Theorem 124
   Cauchy's Inequality 93
   Cauchy's Integral Formula 88
   Cauchy's Integral Formula for Derivatives . . . 92
   Cauchy's Integral Theorem 81
   Cauchy-Riemann Equations (part 1) 40
   Cauchy-Riemann Equations (part 2) 41
   Cauchy-Schwarz Inequality 11
   Fundamental Theorem of Calculus 53
   Goursat's Theorem 77
   Heine-Borel Theorem 22
   Identity Theorem 107
   Laurent Series Expansion 114
   Liouville's Theorem 93
   Maximum Modulus Principle 94
   Minimum Modulus Principle 96
   Power Series 98
   Residue Theorem (Final Version) 132
   Residue Theorem (First Version) 131
   Triangle Inequality 3
   Weierstrass M-test 71
transitive 14
Triangle Inequality 3

U
unbounded 20
uncountable 14
uniformly continuous 36

W
Weierstrass M-test 71
winding number 127

Z
zero 105
zero of multiplicity n 106
zero of order n 106
Zeta function 73

Made in the USA
Las Vegas, NV
14 May 2023